T.4
WORKSHOP
TECHNOLOGY

For Mechanical Engineering Technicians

by the same author

General Course Workshop Processes and Materials

Workshop Processes for Mechanical Engineering Technicians
(in two volumes)

T.3 Workshop Technology for Mechanical Engineering Technicians

also of interest

Materials for the Engineering Technician
R. A. Higgins B Sc (Birm.), F I M

Engineering Drawing and Materials for Mechanical Engineering Technicians
(in four volumes)

H. Ord M I E D, M I Plant E, A R Ae S

T.4
WORKSHOP
TECHNOLOGY

For Mechanical Engineering Technicians

R. T. Pritchard

C Eng, M I Prod E, Full Tech. Cert. C G L I
Teacher's Cert. in Metalwork

Lecturer in Mechanical Engineering,
Garretts Green Technical College, Birmingham.
Examiner for the City and Guilds of London Institute,
The Union of Educational Institutions, and
The Welsh Joint Education Committee.

The English Universities Press Limited

ISBN 0 340 05311 9 (boards edition)
      0 340 11532 7 (paperback edition)

First printed 1970
Reprinted (with corrections) 1972

The English Universities Press Limited
St Paul's House Warwick Lane London EC4P 4AH

Printed and bound in Great Britain by
Richard Clay (The Chaucer Press) Ltd, Bungay, Suffolk

General Editor's Foreword

The Technical College Series covers a wide range of technician and craft courses, and includes books designed to cover subjects in National Certificate and Diploma courses and City and Guilds Technician and Craft syllabuses. This important sector of technical education has been the subject of very considerable changes over the past few years. The more recent of these have been the result of the establishment of the Training Boards, under the Industrial Training Act. Although the Boards have no direct responsibility for education, their activities in ensuring proper training in industry have had a marked influence on the complementary courses which Technical Colleges must provide. For example, the introduction of the module system of training for craftsmen by the Engineering Industry Training Board led directly to the City and Guilds 500 series of courses.

The Haslegrave Committee on Technician Courses and Examinations reported late in 1969, and made recommendations for far-reaching administrative changes, which will undoubtedly eventually result in new syllabuses and examination requirements.

It should, perhaps, be emphasised that these changes are being made not for their own sake, but to meet the needs of industry and the young men and women who are seeking to equip themselves for a career in industry. And industry and technology are changing at an unprecedented rate, so that technical education must be more concerned with fundamental principles than with techniques.

Many of the books in the Technical College Series are now standard works, having stood the test of time over a long period of years. Such books are reviewed from time to time and new editions published to keep them up to date, both in respect of new technological developments and changing examination requirements. For instance, these books have had to be rewritten in the metric system, using SI units. To keep pace with the rapid changes taking place both in courses and in technology, new works are constantly being added to the list. The Publishers are fully aware of the part that well-written up-to-date textbooks can play in supplementing teaching, and it is their intention that the Technical College Series shall continue to made a substantial contribution to the development of technical education.

E. G. STERLAND

Author's Preface

In this, the fourth volume of the Technician Series, I have attempted to outline the basic principles and techniques in common use in many of our manufacturing industries. So rapid is both the advance and introduction of new technological processes, calculated not only to improve product quality but also to reduce manufacturing costs, that it is becoming increasingly difficult to keep abreast with these new developments.

It is even more difficult, and perhaps impossible, to give them adequate coverage in a volume of this size, and so the aim of this volume has been to present them in an interesting and simple manner, proceeding at all times from the simple principles on which the new processes are based. In other words, it is hoped that the interest of the T4 student will be captured, and that he will turn to more detailed descriptions of the processes in which he is interested, of which there is no better source than the excellent descriptive material supplied by the people who really know what they are about; namely the practical engineers or manufacturers of the equipment and machinery which make the newer techniques possible.

Finally, I have been much encouraged by the many letters of appreciation received from readers of the three previous volumes. I hope that they will receive as much pleasure and encouragement from this, the final volume of the series, and once again I am indebted to Brian G. Staples, MA, FLA, for his continued help and advice in checking the manuscript and reading the proofs.

R. T. PRITCHARD
Sutton Coldfield

SI Units

SI units have been used throughout this volume. To assist the student, the following list gives the six basic units of the Système International D'Unités (International System of Units).

Unit	Abbreviation
Length—the metre	m
Mass—the kilogram	kg
Time—the second	s
Electric current—the ampere	A
Luminous intensity—the candela	cd
Temperature—the kelvin	K

These six units permit a rationalised coherent system, or a constant related system. For example, velocity is the ratio of the two basic units—length and time,

$$\text{hence velocity} = \text{metre} \div \text{second}$$
$$\text{or (m/s)}$$

Similarly, the unit of acceleration is (m/s^2).

Multiples and submultiples of the basic units are shown in the following table, and preferred multiples and submultiples are those separated by a factor of the form 10^{3n}, where n is an integer.

	Prefix	Symbol
10^{12}	terra	T
10^{9}	giga	G
10^{6}	mega	M
10^{3}	kilo	k
10^{2}	hecto	h
10^{1}	deca	da
10^{-1}	deci	d
10^{-2}	centi	c
10^{-3}	milli	m
10^{-6}	micro	μ
10^{-9}	nano	n
10^{-12}	pico	p
10^{-15}	femto	f
10^{-18}	atto	a

Contents

1

CASTING TECHNIQUES

1.1 The importance of the casting process

The manufacture of an engineering component by the relatively simple technique of filling a cavity with liquid metal represents the most basic production method available to engineers.

There is perhaps a tendency among engineers to regard a casting as a fairly rough or approximate product, needing a considerable amount of further finishing or machining before it can be made part of an assembly. It may be thought, too, that casting is a slow, laborious and expensive process, necessitating a high proportion of skilled personnel.

Such opinions are misplaced in the light of modern casting techniques, and it is the aim of this chapter to show the principles and accruing advantages of modern methods of casting.

Clearly these new techniques must remove the faults and disadvantages found in the more conventional methods of casting, and it may be worth while to take a broad look at the casting processes available for engineering manufacture.

1.2. Casting processes

Fig. 1.1 shows in diagrammatic form the main casting processes in use. We see at once that two main principles are employed to ensure that the liquid metal completely fills the cavity:

(i) gravity;
(ii) pressure.

Note too that the resultant casting may be further identified by the material used for the mould, thus producing the following types of castings:

(i) sand;
(ii) shell;
(iii) die.

Hence a casting produced by pouring liquid metal into a sand mould is known as a gravity sand casting; a casting produced by pouring metal

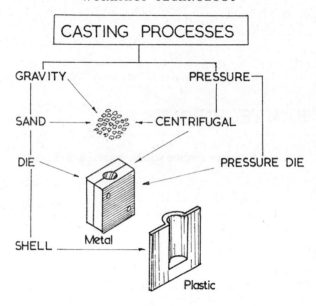

FIG. 1.1.—CASTING PROCESSES

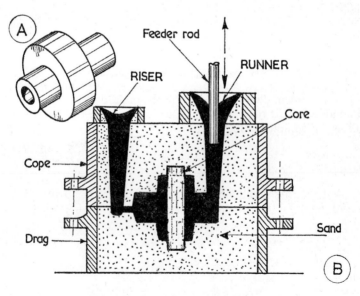

FIG. 1.2.—SAND CASTING WITH CORE

into metal dies is known as a gravity die casting; and if pressure is used to force liquid metal into metal dies the result is known as a pressure die casting.

1.3. Limitations of gravity sand casting

In order to appreciate the limitations of gravity sand casting we may consider in a simple manner the casting shown in Fig. 1.2A, and the section through the mould shown in Fig. 1.2B. Clearly the volume of metal required greatly exceeds the actual amount needed to make the casting, and this means that the cost of bringing the metal to its liquid state (always an expensive item) is excessive.

This additional metal in the form of runners and risers is, however, an essential part of the gravity-sand-casting process, for its weight helps to ensure that the cavity within the mould is completely filled. At the same time it produces a reservoir of liquid metal to compensate for the shrinkage which must take place as the outer layers of the casting solidify.

1.3.1. Solidification shrinkage

The change in size or reduction in volume which accompanies the solidification of the casting results in a reduction of all linear dimensions, and the pattern is accordingly made bigger to compensate for the solidification shrinkage. Of greater importance, however, are the adverse effects of shrinkage on the structure of the metal during the solidification process. Fig. 1.3 makes clear the effect of shrinkage on the structure of a casting.

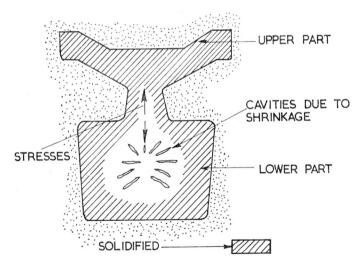

FIG. 1.3.—EFFECT OF UNEVEN COOLING RATES

The metal in contact with the sand forming the cavity face has solidified, shrinking in the process. This shrinkage tends to draw the metal from the inner or central portion, which is still in the liquid state. If the design of the casting is similar to that in the example shown in Fig. 1.3 there is a serious tendency for the upper part to solidify before the lower, and this means that the inner structure of the lower part is liable to contain internal cavities caused by loss of metal to the outer surfaces, as well as being subjected to severe stressing because of the considerable forces exerted by the shrinkage during cooling.

The use of a feeder rod (as shown in Fig. 1.2) pumped up and down in a large-diameter feeding bush helps to feed metal into the mould and thus reduce the risk of an unsound casting.

1.3.2. Finish and accuracy

It is certain that a considerable amount of machining will be required on all gravity sand castings. This is mainly because of the tendency of the molten metal to pick up particles of sand from the mould; much care is needed when taking first cuts on cast-iron castings produced in sand moulds. If we remember, too, that the mould, on which so much care and skill has been exercised, is destroyed in order to remove the finished casting, it is clear that some variation may exist from casting to casting. Yet for the production of large-sized castings in cast iron or steel the gravity-sand-casting process has no equal. With the use of suitable cores and the dry-sand moulding technique (that is to say baking the mould to give greater strength and rigidity, instead of using damp sand for the smaller-sized castings as in green-sand moulding) complicated castings are readily produced which would be impossible to make by any other method.

If we refer back to Fig. 1.2 we see that a large volume of sand is needed to make each mould, and this sand needs to be stored, handled and renewed. At the same time the process of sand moulding is one that requires a high ratio of skilled personnel. Thus the production of medium-sized components by the gravity-sand-casting process must of necessity be fairly expensive, taking up a large area of space, employing a high degree of skill, yet producing castings which need considerable machining allowance.

These disadvantages have led to the introduction of shell moulding.

1.4. Shell moulding

Shell moulding replaces the bulky sand mould with a relatively thin shell. The metal is poured into the cavity between two shells held firmly together, as shown in Fig. 1.4. Note the very small amount of material in the shell moulds. Clearly it is a simple matter to handle, store or stack these shell moulds, using the minimum of space, thus allowing stock-piling in order to ensure continuity of production. This means that the actual manufacture of the shell moulds needs to be simplified if they are to be supplied at an economical rate in the numbers required.

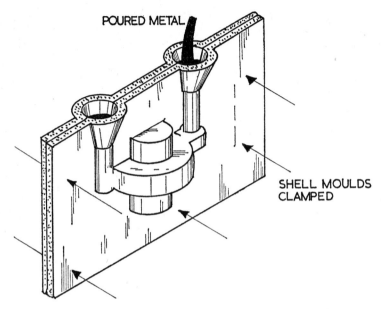

POURED METAL

SHELL MOULDS
CLAMPED

FIG. 1.4.—PRINCIPLE OF SHELL MOULDING

1.4.1. The shell-moulding technique

In order to explain the shell-moulding technique we will consider shell moulding the component used as an example of gravity sand casting in Fig. 1.2. We may divide the shell-moulding process into the following sections:

   (i) making the pattern plate;
   (ii) making the shell (investment);
   (iii) joining the shells and pouring the metal.

The pattern plate

Fig. 1.5 shows the pattern plate for the component to be shell moulded. The pattern plate must be metal, and mild steel is a popular choice. Note that the half-pattern is attached to the pattern plate, and the pattern also incorporates a runner and riser as shown in the diagram. Clearly the manufacture of the pattern and its assembly to the pattern plate represent a skilled technique, with due allowance needing to be made for metal shrinkage. The patterns need a small angle, more commonly known as draft, to ensure ready stripping of the shell from the pattern plate.

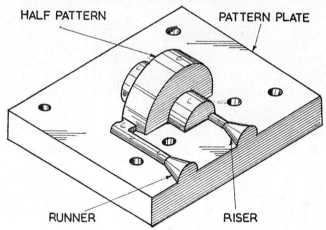

FIG. 1.5.—METAL PATTERN PLATE FOR SHELL MOULDING

Making the shell

In order to make the shell a dump box is used. A simple dump box is illustrated in section in Fig. 1.6A; the technique is known as **pattern investment.** The pattern plate is heated to between 300° and 600° C

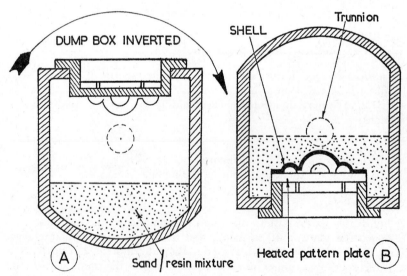

FIG. 1.6.—USE OF DUMP BOX FOR SHELL MOULDING

according to the thickness of shell required. The heated pattern plate is inserted in the dump box and clamped in position with an asbestos pad insulating the heated pattern plate and preventing loss of heat to the dump box.

It may be seen on reference to the diagram that the bottom part of the dump box contains a mixture of sand and plastic. Rotation of the dump box on trunnions reverses the position of the heated pattern plate. This is shown in Fig. 1.6B, and it will be seen that the sand–resin mixture completely covers the pattern plate. The heated pattern plate softens the resin part of the mixture, forming a thin shell around the pattern. After a certain period of time, ranging from 10 to 20 seconds, the dump box is inverted, and the pattern plate together with the adhering shell is removed and placed in an oven for final heating or curing.

This technique produces a fairly rigid shell, light in weight and readily stored for subsequent use, with only about 5% of the volume of sand needed for the equivalent casting using the gravity-sand-casting process.

The shell-making cycle is repeated; thus we see that relatively unskilled personnel are required to produce the shell moulds, with much saving of material bulk and floor space.

Pouring the metal

The two shells to make the complete mould are firmly held together using clamps, bolts, tapes or glue; additional support may be obtained by supporting the shells in suitable frames, or by packing around them with sand. Because of the high permeability of the shells, that is to say their ability to allow the free passage of gases through their structure, there is a complete absence of casting faults such as scabbing, blowholes or buckles, and sound, well-finished castings result.

The heat lost from the cooling metal burns away the resin in the mixture, and on solidification of the casting the remaining sand is easily broken away.

1.4.2. Advantages of shell moulding

Apart from the saving of floor space, and the considerable reduction in the volume of sand required to be handled and stored, the accuracy and finish produced by the shell-moulding process greatly exceed those possible with the green-sand casting process.

With regard to accuracy, the machining allowance can be reduced, resulting in a saving of metal costs; in some cases the clean, smooth surface of the casting allows an immediate grinding operation. The excellent finish permits the reproduction of fine detail on the casting, and the high permeability of the sand–resin mixture allows relatively thin sections to be cast with reasonable ease.

A typical example of a thin-walled component in grey cast iron is given in Fig. 1.7A, where we see a section through a typical motor-cycle engine cylinder. Clearly this type of casting presents difficult problems when cast by the green-sand moulding process. At B we see an example of a component passed straight for finish grinding from the shell-moulding process.

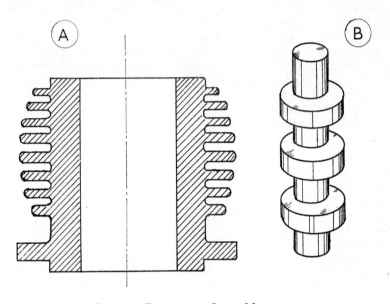

FIG. I.7.—EXAMPLES OF SHELL MOULDING

Most metals are readily cast using the shell-moulding process, and the technique lends itself admirably to the quantity production of medium-sized castings such as are required in the manufacture and assembly of motor cars. The process is readily automated, with a considerable reduction in the ratio of skilled personnel normally expected in the casting of precision components. For batch production, however, that is to say for the turning out of relatively small numbers of components at infrequent intervals, it is doubtful whether the shell-moulding technique has any advantage over gravity sand casting.

1.5. Gravity die casting

If metal is poured into steel or cast-iron moulds or dies, with gravitational force used to ensure that the cavity within the dies is completely filled, the process is known as gravity die casting. This is a useful technique for the manufacture of medium-sized components in aluminium alloys, the resultant castings possessing finish and accuracy superior to what is possible with sand moulds. At the same time the metal dies are permanent, allowing high production rates, although much depends on their design and efficiency.

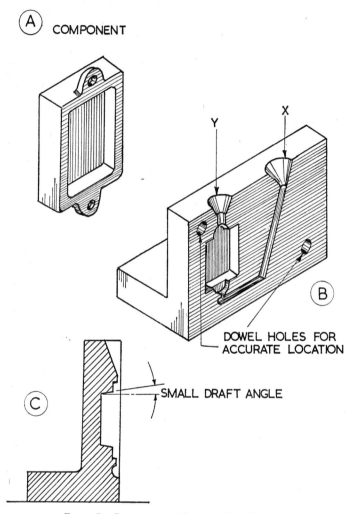

(A) COMPONENT

X

Y

(B)

DOWEL HOLES FOR ACCURATE LOCATION

(C)

SMALL DRAFT ANGLE

FIG. 1.8.—PRINCIPLE OF GRAVITY DIE CASTING

1.5.1. Principle of gravity die casting

In order to show the principle underlying the application of gravity die casting we will consider the manufacture of the aluminium-alloy component shown in Fig. 1.8A. This is a simple cover plate, and the pictorial view makes clear the appearance of the finished casting. As in all casting techniques two half-dies are needed, Fig. 1.8B shows one half-die. Note the runner, shown as X in the diagram, and the riser, shown as Y. This arrangement is quite suitable if the aluminium alloy is of the free-running type, while the more sluggish-running alloys may

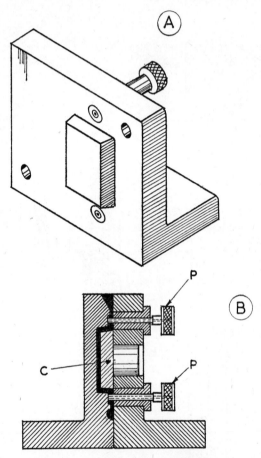

FIG. 1.9.—DIES FOR GRAVITY DIE CASTING

require two runners to promote heavy feeding. The sectional view at C makes clear the importance of the small draft angle and small radius to promote easy removal of the casting.

A view of the opposite die is shown in Fig. 1.9A, while at B we see a sectional view of the two dies in the closed position, with the poured metal shown in black.

Note the two steel core pins, shown as P in the diagram; these pins must be withdrawn before the casting is removed. The core C provides the hollow part of the casting. Ejector pins may be fitted to facilitate removal of the casting, and it may be appreciated at this stage that the design and manufacture of the dies calls for a high degree of skill and experience.

1.5.2. Air venting

Where sharp edges are required on the casting it is necessary to ensure that provision exists for the escape of air from within the cavity enclosed by the dies. Fig. 1.10A shows the effect produced when the molten metal meets a sharp corner from which the air cannot escape. We see from the diagram that a small radius is formed at the metal edge. This effect is prevented by using an insert leaving about 0·13 mm gap, thus allowing escape of air through this narrow vent as shown in Fig. 1.10B.

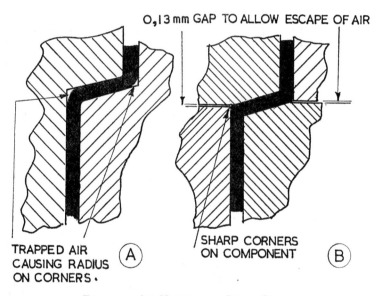

FIG. 1.10.—AIR VENTING FOR SHARP CORNERS

1.5.3. Advantages of gravity die casting

The gravity-die-casting process occupies an intermediate position between sand or shell moulding and pressure die casting. It is suitable for all types of aluminium alloys, and complicated castings of medium size are readily produced, using collapsible metal cores or oven-baked sand cores.

The surfaces of the casting are clean and free from sand inclusions, with detail clearly defined. Output rates are high, with no problems of space, storage or handling such as are encountered with sand moulding.

Much care, however, is needed in the design and manufacture of the gravity dies, and due regard must be paid to the running qualities of the particular alloy used.

1.6. Pressure die casting

As the name suggests, pressure die casting involves the application of an external force to fill the cavity between two closed metal dies. A simple example of pressure die casting is provided by the Cothias process, whereby a plunger is used to force liquid metal into the cavity. This technique is simply illustrated in Fig. 1.11, where it may be seen that

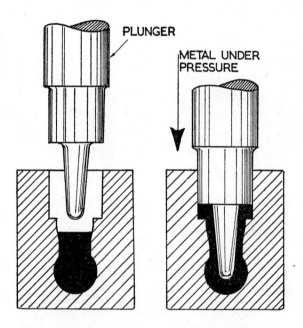

PLUNGER

METAL UNDER PRESSURE

Fig. 1.11.—Cothias Pressure Die-Casting Principle

the metal core or plunger enters the die under pressure, thus forcing the metal tightly against the cavity walls, producing a well-defined casting of dense structure. Expensive die-casting machines are not needed for this simple application of pressure die casting, and the technique finds ready application in the manufacture of small ornaments or statuary in antimonial lead.

1.6.1. Advantages of the pressure-die-casting process

Fig. 1.12 shows a car door handle produced as a pressure die casting. This component will serve as an example of the advantages offered by the pressure-die-casting process, as outlined below.

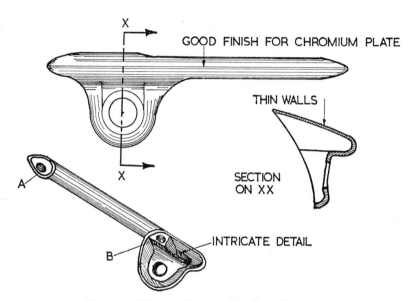

GOOD FINISH FOR CHROMIUM PLATE

THIN WALLS

SECTION ON X X

INTRICATE DETAIL

FIG. 1.12.—TYPICAL PRESSURE DIE-CAST COMPONENT

Wall thickness

One of the most important advantages of pressure die casting is that the wall thickness can be a bare minimum. This is clearly seen by reference to Fig. 1.12, where the end elevation shows a section of the car door handle. The high pressures used in forcing the liquid metal into the die aperture ensure complete filling of the cavity, and this means that considerable metal economy is achieved. If we consider the numbers of car door handles produced we will realise that the saving of only a few grams on each handle adds up to a considerable total of metal saved in the course of a year's production.

Dimensional accuracy

The use of highly polished dies ensures a high degree of accuracy in the pressure die castings. In many cases the degree of accuracy is such that further machining operations are eliminated. For example, the car door handle illustrated in Fig. 1.12 needs only the tapping of the two holes indicated as A and B; no further machining operations are required.

There is little doubt that for the production of intricate components in aluminium- or zinc-based alloys, necessitating the minimum of machining, the pressure-die-casting process has no equal. Holes of less than 1·5 mm diameter can be produced, and in certain cases screw threads may also be incorporated on the casting.

Surface finish

The high quality of the surface finish is also instrumental in eliminating further machining operations. The pressure exerted on the liquid metal. together with the rapid chilling of the metal as it comes into contact with the cavity walls, tends to promote a fine or dense grain structure. Thus the surface is ideal for chromium plating, the car door handle being a typical component finished in this way.

Casting strength

The dense grain associated with pressure and rapid cooling ensures a strong, reliable casting. Slow cooling always promotes a coarse, weak grain, with the possibility of voids or cavities as the metal contracts on solidification.

The high pressures maintained during the pressure-die-casting process ensure that shrinkage is countered by the effect of the sustained pressure on the metal during solidification.

Production rates

The pressure-die-casting process lends itself readily to an automated sequence of casting cycles. Provided an adequate supply of liquid metal is available the whole casting cycle can be incorporated into a single machine, with consequently high output rates. For example, small castings in zinc-based alloy weighing less than 20 grams can be produced on a suitable machine at a rate of up to 600 per hour, and even fairly large castings are produced at the rate of several per minute.

1.6.2. Disadvantages of pressure die casting

The disadvantages of pressure die casting are few, and may be summarised as follows:

(i) high initial cost of machine and dies;
(ii) restriction on metals available;
(iii) restriction on size and intricacy of casting.

Cost of machine and dies

Both the casting machines and dies are expensive pieces of equipment. Fig. 1.13 shows a transmission case produced as a pressure die casting in aluminium-based alloy, the mass of the case being about 10 kg. Yet the dies required for this casting have a mass of approximately 3 000 kg, representing a very high standard of precision machining at a correspondingly high cost.

PRESSURE DIE CAST AUTOMOBILE TRANSMISSION CASE IN ALUMINIUM ALLOY.

FIG. 1.13.—LARGE PRESSURE DIE CASTING IN ALUMINIUM ALLOY

Clearly if the pressure-die-casting process is to be used to advantage, a large number of components needs to be produced in a short time in order that the initial high cost of the dies can be offset.

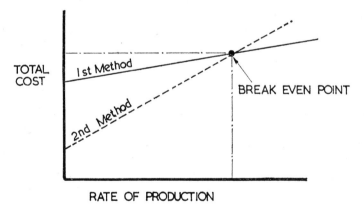

FIG. 1.14.—THE 'BREAK-EVEN' GRAPH

If it is required to determine the number of components that warrants the application of the pressure-die-casting process, when compared to an alternative method of manufacture, use may be made of the 'break-even' graph. Fig. 1.14 shows the principle involved. The vertical axis represents the cost of the initial equipment, and the horizontal axis the number of components produced. The broken line indicates an alternative method of manufacture; with this alternative, while the initial cost of the equipment is much less than the pressure-die-casting process, the manufacturing cost of the component is much higher, as indicated by the steeper slope of the broken line.

The meeting point of the two lines indicates the number of components for which the total production cost is identical; above this number the pressure-die-casting process is a more economical method of manufacture.

1.7. Metals for pressure die casting

The precision nature of the dies used in pressure die casting precludes the use of the high-melting-point metals such as cast iron and steel. This means that the process is limited to those metals or alloys having relatively low melting points. The tendency over the last few decades has been to restrict the number of metals used in pressure die casting, with the result that the following alloys now dominate the industry:

    (i) zinc-based alloys;
    (ii) aluminium-based alloys;
    (iii) magnesium-based alloys.

1.7.1. Zinc-based alloys

It is an essential condition of all zinc-based alloys that only high-purity zinc is used. The presence of minute quantities of tin, cadmium or lead in a zinc-based alloy leads to severe brittleness in a pressure die casting; this condition is further hastened if the casting is exposed to damp conditions.

Once again the tendency at the present time is to restrict the number of zinc-based alloys used in pressure die casting, keeping very strict control over the zinc purity and the alloying elements.

In general two zinc-based alloys are now in wide use, each carrying the trade name Mazak (a term derived from the initials of magnesium, aluminium, zinc and 'kopper').

The compositions and main properties of these two alloys are given below:

| Alloy | Percentages | | | UTS N/mm^2 | Percentage elongation on 50 mm |
	Aluminium	Copper	Magnesium		
Mazak 3	4·0	—	0·05	280	13
Mazak 5	4·0	1·0	0·05	340	8·5

TABLE 1.1. Zinc-based pressure-die-casting alloys.

It can be seen that Mazak 5 is a stronger and harder alloy than Mazak 3, possessing a higher UTS and lower ductility, and is used for components subject to some degree of stressing under service conditions. Mazak 3 can be considered as a general all-purpose alloy having good dimensional stability. Both alloys are readily plated with chromium or stove enamelled.

1.7.2. Aluminium-based alloys

Because of the wide use of aluminium alloys in the aircraft industry, where the properties of alloys or metals are of paramount importance with respect to safety, strict specifications are in force as laid down in BS 1470–1477 and BS 1490. Fig. 1.15 shows a simplified version of the system by which all aluminium alloys are readily identified or specified.

The alloys used for pressure die casting carry the prefix LM. The following table gives two typical aluminium alloys in use.

Specification	Percentages		UTS N/mm^2	Percentage elongation on 50 mm
	Copper	Silicon		
LM24-M	4·0	9·5	280	3
LM6-M	—	13	310	3·5

TABLE 1.2. Aluminium-based pressure-die-casting alloys

In addition to the alloying elements of silicon and copper, the alloys shown in the table may also possess small amounts of zinc, iron and magnesium, but the amount of these elements must not exceed a stated maximum.

The high-silicon alloy LM6 has exceptional fluidity and a low shrinkage value, and finds extensive use for the pressure die casting of fairly intricate components requiring a good resistance to corrosion.

1.7.3. Magnesium-based alloys

Increasing use is now being made of magnesium-based alloys for the pressure die casting of components requiring a favourable strength–weight ratio. Typical examples of such components are provided by castings of intricate shape found in portable typewriters, tape recorders and precision instruments such as cameras and binoculars.

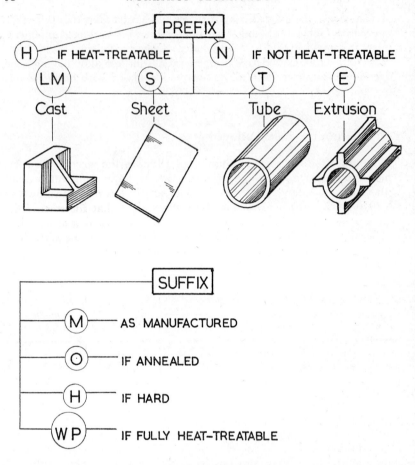

PREFIX

(H) IF HEAT-TREATABLE   (N) IF NOT HEAT-TREATABLE

(LM)   (S)   (T)   (E)

Cast   Sheet   Tube   Extrusion

SUFFIX

(M) ——— AS MANUFACTURED

(O) ——— IF ANNEALED

(H) ——— IF HARD

(WP) ——— IF FULLY HEAT-TREATABLE

SPECIFIC ALLOYS ARE GIVEN NUMBERS   1, 2, 3, 4, 5, etc.

Examples

LM 24M
Casting in No 24 alloy as manufactured

NE6
Extruded section in
No 6 alloy non-heat-treatable

FIG. 1.15.—SPECIFICATIONS FOR ALUMINIUM-BASE ALLOYS

A typical magnesium-based alloy is given below:

Specification	Percentages		UTS N/mm^2	Percentage elongation on 50 mm
	Zinc	Magnesium		
L123 (BS 2970)	1·0 (max.)	99	155	1·5

TABLE 1.3. Magnesium-based pressure-die-casting alloy.

The above alloy machines extremely well, at about twice the speed suitable for aluminium alloys and over ten times that for steel. The tools need to have a keen edge, heavy cuts must be taken, and all swarf must be removed as soon as possible to minimise fire risk, as the material is subject to burning if excessive heat is generated through the friction of the cutting action.

1.8. Die-casting machines

The basic requirements of a die-casting machine may be listed as follows:

(i) a reservoir of molten metal;
(ii) a means of injecting metal from the reservoir into the die under pressure;
(iii) a suitable metal die having a negative impression of the casting required;
(iv) a means of ejecting the solidified casting from the die.

Fig. 1.16 shows a simple arrangement of one of the first die-casting machines, introduced about 1850, probably for the manufacture of printers' type using an alloy of lead and antimony.

Downward movement of the piston through a hand-operated lever system forces liquid metal through the channel into the die, the cut-off valve seals the metal port during the pressure stroke, and seals the nozzle during the upward movement of the piston or plunger.

As may be expected, great strides have taken place in the development of die-casting machines over the 115 years that have elapsed since the introduction of the simple machine shown in Fig. 1.16, but the tendency has been to limit the design of die-casting machines to **two** main types:

(i) hot-chamber machines;
(ii) cold-chamber machines.

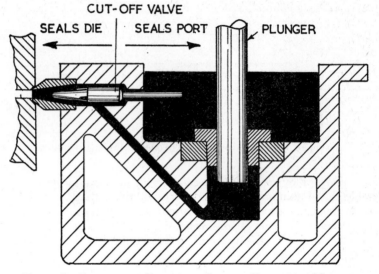

FIG. 1.16.—PRINCIPLE OF EARLY-TYPE PRESSURE DIE-CASTING MACHINE

1.8.1. Hot-chamber principle

This principle is extensively used for pressure die casting in zinc, tin and lead based alloys, all of which have relatively low melting points.

Reference to Fig. 1.17 shows that basically the principle differs little from that of the primitive machine illustrated in Fig. 1.16. The purpose or function of the main elements may be described as follows.

Melting pot

Made from high-grade heat-resisting alloy, the melting pot may be integral with the machine, or a separate unit. Heated by low-pressure town gas, propane or any suitable gas, the metal is kept at just above its melting point; the melting pot must be replenished from time to time with suitable ingots.

Gooseneck

This is the channel by which the liquid metal leaves the melting pot; it then enters the fixed platen or die via the nozzle. It is essential that both gooseneck and nozzle are heated to ensure that the liquid metal runs back down the gooseneck at the return stroke of the plunger. This process is assisted by the vacuum created by the stroke.

Plunger

The plunger operates within a sleeve, the whole unit being capable of rapid removal for changing to a different bore size or for replacement.

The means of actuation may be pneumatic or hydraulic; that is to say air or oil under pressure may be used. Modern machines make use of the technique of slow advancement of the plunger or dual-phase injection.

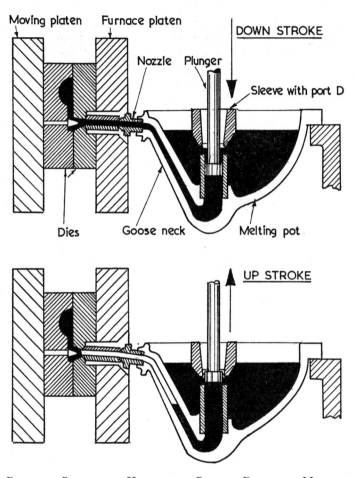

FIG. 1.17.—PRINCIPLE OF HOT-CHAMBER PRESSURE DIE-CASTING MACHINE

The slow initial speed or descent of the plunger causes relatively slow rising of the metal within the gooseneck, thus avoiding air turbulence which would lead to porosity in the casting. With the gooseneck full the stroke velocity is considerably increased, ensuring rapid filling of the die, very necessary for thin-sectioned castings.

Note the port D in the sleeve. This is uncovered by the plunger at the top of the stroke, allowing metal to enter the sleeve. On the downward stroke the port is covered; thus the pressure exerted by the plunger is transferred to the metal within the sleeve.

1.8.2. Cold-chamber principle

The higher melting points of aluminium alloys, together with their ability to become contaminated with iron, preclude the use of hot-chamber machines, in which the molten aluminium alloy must of necessity be in continual contact with the sleeve and gooseneck. Fig. 1.18 shows that the liquid aluminium alloy is ladled directly into the injection cylinder or sleeve.

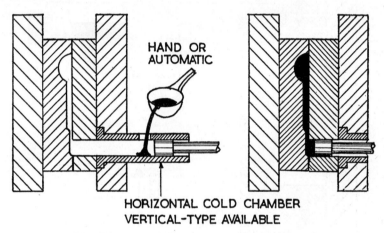

FIG. 1.18.—PRINCIPLE OF COLD-CHAMBER PRESSURE DIE-CASTING MACHINE

On completion of ladling the plunger moves forward, thus forcing the metal into the die, and as the aluminium alloy has only brief contact with the sleeve contamination with iron is prevented, with a sound casting resulting.

Many machines may now be switched to either hot- or cold-chamber operation with the adoption of interchangeable injection units; thus both zinc- and aluminium-based castings can be produced. The hot-chamber principle is adopted for the zinc-based castings, and the cold-chamber principle for the aluminium-based castings.

1.9. Platens and dies

We have seen that pressure is utilised to force the liquid metal into the negative cavity produced when the dies are in the closed position. This pressure varies according to the mass of the casting produced. For example, if the ejected pressure die casting has a mass of about 12 kg the maximum pressure on the metal is in the region of 15 MN/m². Assuming, then, that the casting has a projected area of 65 cm², the force tending to thrust the die members apart amounts to approximately 109·5 kN.

Clearly very rigid support is needed for the dies, together with a powerful clamping force to resist the pressure of the injected metal.

1.10. The clamping unit

The clamping unit forms an integral part of the die-casting machine, and the principle is simply illustrated in Fig. 1.19. The platens are of ample proportions; note that the fixed or furnace platen is provided with two injection positions, one at centre and one below centre, and the gooseneck nozzle engages the fixed die opening through the holes shown. The moving platen is equipped with heavy bronze bearing bushes, bearing on four high-tensile-steel ground bars of ample proportions.

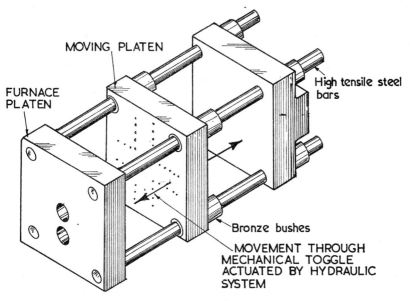

FIG. 1.19.—FIXED AND MOVING PLATENS

Movement of the sliding platen is effected with hydraulic pressure or with a toggle system, and the locking force on the dies can, on the larger machines, exceed a value of 1·1 MN.

To avoid damage to the dies many machines are equipped with a sensing device which prevents application of the full locking force should any obstruction remain between the die faces. Additional safety precautions include interlocking devices which ensure that no movement of

B

the platen is possible when the safety door is open, and that metal injection cannot take place unless the full locking force is applied. A further device consists of the use of a safety tray. This tray actuates a microswitch immediately the ejected pressure die casting falls on to it. Should the casting be only partially formed, or fail to be ejected from the dies, non-operation of the microswitch arrests further operation of the machine, thus allowing the operator to investigate and clear the fault.

1.11. The dies

As might be expected, the dies are in two halves, one fixed to the furnace platen and the other to the moving platen. These dies are expensive pieces of equipment, representing a very high standard of precision engineering. Both dies are subject to continued thermal shock, that is to say expansion and contraction of the cavity faces each time a casting is produced. The slightest scratch or indentation is likely to lead to premature cracking, and a very high degree of polish is required on all the cavity faces if a long and useful life is to be obtained.

The standard technique of pressure die casting is to keep one die stationary; this die is attached to the furnace platen. The other die is attached to the moving platen of the clamp unit, and the disposition of the cavity between the two dies is such that the solidified casting tends to remain in the moving die.

This simple principle is illustrated in Fig. 1.20. Note that the fixed die is completely unmachined. The cavity is in the moving die; thus

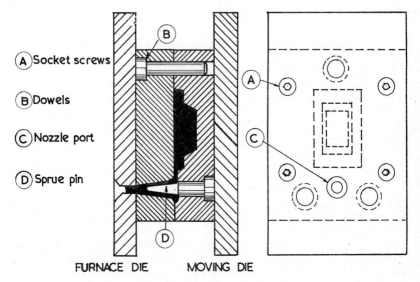

FIG. 1.20.—DIES USED IN PRESSURE DIE CASTING

it is certain that the solidified casting remains in this die as the moving platen comes away on completion of the injection and solidification of the metal. Note also the sprue pin to promote an even flow of metal.

To ensure that the casting remains in the moving die it is customary to provide generous draft angles on the cavity faces of the fixed member, and to reduce the draft or taper on the moving die.

1.11.1. Ejection

Efficient ejection of the casting from the moving die is essential if a pressure die-casting machine is to produce castings at high output rates. The principle is simply illustrated at Fig. 1.21, where it can be seen

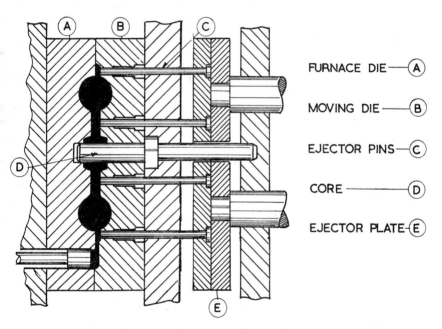

FURNACE DIE —Ⓐ

MOVING DIE —Ⓑ

EJECTOR PINS—Ⓒ

CORE —Ⓓ

EJECTOR PLATE-Ⓔ

FIG. 1.21.—PRINCIPLE OF CASTING EJECTION

that ejector pins are fitted. Opening of the dies allows the ejector plate to make contact with the pins, moving them forward and thus ejecting the casting. Clearly an intricate casting demands a complicated pair of die blocks, for provision may have to be made for withdrawable cores or inserts in the moving die block in addition to ejector pins, and the design of such dies calls for a high degree of skill and experience.

1.12. Die steels

The choice of a particular die steel from which to make both the fixed and moving dies depends mainly on the alloys to be cast and the component production number or length of run. As previously stated, pressure-die-casting dies are subject to considerable thermal shock owing to the continued expansion and contraction of the cavity surfaces during the injection and solidifying cycles. Clearly a better-quality steel is required for long runs in aluminium alloy, while short runs in lead- or tin-based alloys are quite possible using a lower-quality steel.

1.12.1. Plain carbon steel

Suitable for tin- or lead-based alloys, or short runs in zinc-based alloys. No heat treatment is necessary. A typical composition would be as follows:

	%
Carbon	0·45
Manganese	0·6

1.12.2. Chrome-molybdenum alloy steel

A general-purpose die steel, very suitable for long runs in zinc-based alloy. Die-block blanks are available in the heat-treated form (200–300 Brinell), although if maximum die life is required the dies may be subject to a further heat-treatment process, the Brinell value being increased to 350.
Typical composition:

	%
Chromium	0·8
Manganese	0·75
Silicon	0·5
Carbon	0·3
Molybdenum	0·125

1.12.3. Chrome-vanadium steel

Used for long runs in aluminium- or magnesium-based alloys, this die steel has exceptional resistance to arduous conditions, including erosion.
Typical composition:

	%
Chromium	5·0
Molybdenum	1·35
Vanadium	1·1
Silicon	1·05
Carbon	0·4

The above are only a few of the die steels available, and in all cases it is essential that the heat treatments specified by the makers are rigidly adhered to.

1.13. Examples of pressure die castings

The following examples are chosen to give some indication of the versatility of the pressure-die-casting process.

In each case an outline of the pressure-die-casting machine is shown, together with some details regarding platen size, piston diameter and die-locking force.

1.13.1. Zinc-based alloy, multi-cavity die, hot-chamber machine

Fig. 1.22A shows a familiar object, namely a wooden table leg equipped with a metal tip. At B we see the pressure die casting having a central sprue with six zinc-alloy tips radially spaced. Note the gates through

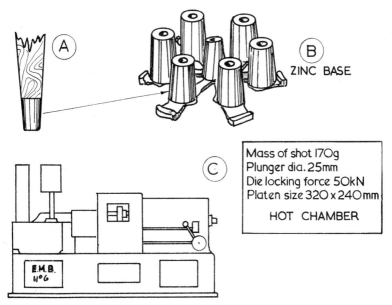

Mass of shot 170g
Plunger dia. 25mm
Die locking force 50kN
Platen size 320 x 240mm

HOT CHAMBER

FIG. 1.22.—EXAMPLE OF ZINC-BASE MULTI-CAVITY PRESSURE DIE CASTING

which the metal is injected into each cavity, and the lugs at the periphery of the casting. These lugs assist in the retention of the casting in the moving die member, and also provide additional metal for the ejection of the castings using ejector pins. At c we see a simplified outline of the hot-chamber pressure-die-casting machine used to produce the table-leg tips.

1.13.2. Zinc-based alloy, single-cavity die, hot-chamber machine

Fig. 1.23A shows a fairly large pressure die-casting in zinc-based alloy. Of intricate design, it is to be chromium plated, and as it forms part of a rear light for a motor car large numbers are required. This is a typical example of the sort of component for which the pressure-die-casting

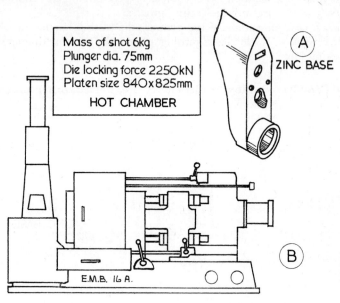

FIG. 1.23.—EXAMPLE OF SINGLE-CAVITY PRESSURE DIE CASTING

process is ideal. The amount of further machining is minimal; the surface finish is excellent and quite suitable for chromium plating, while output figures are high, the casting cycle taking only about 12 seconds or less.

The outline of the pressure-die-casting machine is shown at *B*; note the ample proportions of the platens and the high value of the die-locking force.

1.13.3. Aluminium-based alloy, single-cavity die, cold-chamber machine

The component shown in Fig. 1.24A is a gear-change housing mounted on the steering column of a motor car. Produced in aluminium alloy, this is another example of an intricate component manufactured at high production rates, requiring little or no subsequent machining.

The cold-chamber pressure-die-casting machine used for the production of this casting is shown in simple outline at B. Note the absence of

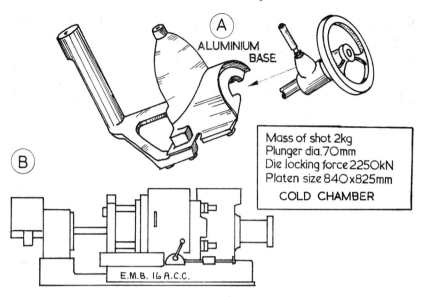

Mass of shot 2kg
Plunger dia.70mm
Die locking force 2250kN
Platen size 840x825mm
COLD CHAMBER

FIG. 1.24.—EXAMPLE OF ALUMINIUM-BASE SINGLE-CAVITY PRESSURE DIE CASTING
IN ALUMINIUM-ALLOY

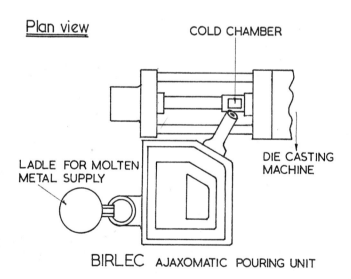

FIG. 1.25.—AUTOMATIC POURING UNIT

the melting unit, which has been replaced by an injection cylinder. Production rates may be increased by replacing the conventional hand-ladle method of feeding with an automatic pouring unit. A typical unit is simply illustrated in plan view in Fig. 1.25. This unit is capable of delivering molten aluminium alloy at the rate of 1 kg per second, the total amounts being adjustable between 0·25 kg and 10 kg. With timing dials correctly set the device automatically supplies a measured quantity of metal to the injection cylinder, the metal leaving the unit at a point well below the surface, ensuring complete freedom from contamination of the aluminium alloy.

Summary

The production of engineering components in required shapes by the direct filling of cavities with liquid metal is still a major engineering technique. With the ever-increasing implementation of new developments in engineering manufacture it is inevitable that new processes tend to replace the older techniques, resulting in a more uniform product at higher rates of production.

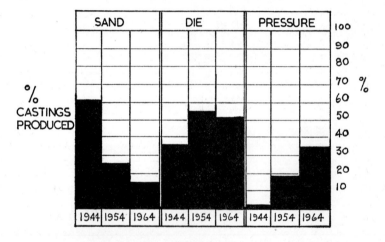

PRODUCTION OF ALUMINIUM ALLOY CASTINGS

FIG. 1.26.—GRAPH TO SHOW CHANGES IN CASTING TECHNIQUES

The simple graph illustrated in Fig. 1.26 shows clearly the trend in the production of aluminium castings over the last three decades. The time-honoured process of sand casting is on the decline, making way for the pressure-die-casting process, and it is certain that further advances will be made by the latter.

The importance of a casting technique capable of producing well-defined castings at high production rates cannot be overstated. For the well-established manufacturing technique of transfer-machining, that is to say the automatic indexing of castings to fixed tooling stations, a prime requisite is the supply of precise castings of uniform dimensions as cast, allowing immediate location without prior machining of datum faces or reference planes. This is the province of the pressure-die-casting process, especially for the manufacture of components from the low-melting-point range of alloys, namely zinc-, aluminium- and magnesium-based.

We have seen that pressure-die-casting machines fall into two main types, cold-chamber and hot-chamber machines, the tendency of aluminium alloys to contamination necessitating the use of the cold chamber, where the molten alloy is in momentary contact only with the filling chamber.

We have seen, too, that the tendency is to restrict the alloys available for the pressure-die-casting process, and keep extreme control over the purity of the metals used.

At the same time, sight must not be lost of the fact that conventional sand casting has no equal when heavy castings are needed in the ferrous metals such as cast iron or steel. For example, the pressure-die-casting machines themselves need heavy castings in grey cast iron, and this need can be met only by conventional sand casting.

For medium-size castings in ferrous metals the shell-moulding technique offers considerable saving in the volume of mould material needed, together with corresponding saving in storage space and handling facilities. Castings produced in this way possess a better finish, free from sand inclusions, the high permeability of the sand–resin shell allowing thin sections to be cast with comparative ease.

Finally, the gravity-die-casting technique can be considered as a compromise between gravity sand casting and pressure die casting. The permanent nature of the dies allows a good production rate, and the use of removable cores and inserts makes possible the casting of relatively intricate components.

Yet it must not be thought that the increasing application of the pressure-die-casting process or the shell-moulding process tends to remove or reduce the level of craft skill or the need for high-quality technicians. Pattern plates for shell-moulding, dies for gravity die or pressure die casting, all represent a very high standard of engineering design and manufacture, while the actual operation of both gravity and pressure die-casting techniques demands a rare standard of skill from the personnel responsible for the production of castings.

The competent mechanical engineering technician who possesses a basic knowledge and appreciation of the principles underlying the newer casting techniques is an important factor in satisfying the ever-increasing demand for precision castings to meet the needs of manufacture.

EXERCISE 1

1 For a ferrous casting, outline the principles and advantages of the shell-moulding casting technique.

2 Explain the technique adopted to ensure that a gravity die casting possesses sharp edges. Name four metals or alloys suitable for gravity die casting.

3 With simple diagrams outline the hot-chamber method of pressure die casting. Name two metals or alloys suitable for this process.

4 Explain why all aluminium alloys are pressure die cast using the cold-chamber principle. With a neat diagram illustrate this principle.

5 Outline the advantages offered by the pressure-die-casting process. Name the main casting metals in use, and describe any device designed to avoid damage to machine or dies occasioned by non-ejection of the casting.

6 Explain why pressure die castings are eminently suitable for the machining technique known as 'transfer machining'.

7 Describe briefly suitable die steels for the following conditions:

    (i) short runs in tin- or lead-based alloys;
    (ii) long runs in zinc-based alloy;
    (iii) long runs in aluminium-based alloy.

8 With typical applications of your own choice, illustrate an example of a pressure die casting in each of the following alloys:

    (i) zinc-based;
    (ii) aluminium-based.

9 Explain briefly the main characteristics indicated by the following:

    (i) LM24-M;
    (ii) T6-WP;
    (iii) NE6.

10 With a neat diagram, illustrate the technique adopted to obtain ejection of a pressure die casting.

2

HEAT-TREATMENT
FURNACES AND PROCESSES

2.1. The importance of furnaces and heat treatments

The purpose of any heat-treatment process is to modify or change the structure of a metal, thus making it more amenable to a manufacturing technique, or making the finished component better able to stand up to service conditions.

The same basic principle applies to all heat-treatment processes, namely heating the component to a given temperature, ensuring that the component has uniform absorption of heat, soaking and cooling at a specified rate according to particular requirements. Furnaces are used to bring the component to the required temperature, and if we keep in mind that heat is an expensive commodity, difficult to control or confine, then clearly the skilled operation of efficient furnaces offers considerable prospects of savings in money and time.

2.2. Heating principles

Basically, the primary purpose of any furnace consists in raising the temperature of the parts requiring heat treatment to a specified level, and holding it within the permissible limits. Any heat which is not used

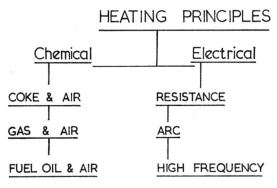

Fig. 2.1.—Principles of Furnace Heating

to raise the temperature of the parts, that is to say heat which raises the temperature of the furnace walls, or heat which is lost through convection or radiation, represents waste and increases the cost of the process.

Ideally, a really efficient furnace would absorb no heat itself, but would bring the component rapidly and uniformly to the required temperature.

The type of furnace used for any particular heat-treatment process depends on the heating principle adopted, and Fig. 2.1 shows in simple diagrammatic form the main heating principles in use. We see that the two main headings are:

  (i) chemical;
  (ii) electrical.

2.3. Gas-fired furnaces

Unlike coke, which poses severe problems in terms of storage, handling and removal of ash or combustion-waste products, gas represents a relatively cheap and efficient fuel. The gas once widely used for heat-treatment furnaces was known as 'town' gas, and the constancy of its heating or calorific value rendered it very suitable for accurate temperature control, although increasing use is now being made of liquid petroleum gas (LPG), and natural gas.

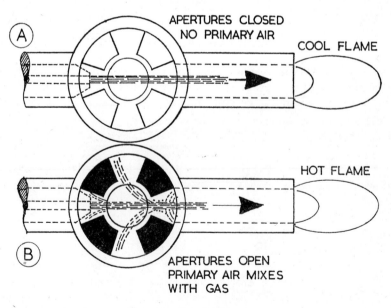

FIG. 2.2.—GAS–AIR BURNER

2.3.1. Principles of gas–air combustion

In order to obtain the maximum amount of heat from a given volume of gas it is necessary to employ a suitable burner, and the most widely used type of burner operates on the well-known and familiar **bunsen** principle. Fig. 2.2 shows this in simple form. At A we see that **no** primary air enters the burner, owing to the fact that the gas ignites at the right-hand side or open end of the burner, combining with the oxygen in the atmosphere at this point. Air which is burned at the open end of the burner is called secondary air, and a cool yellow flame results.

At B we see the effect of opening the apertures. Air now enters and mixes with the gas; thus primary air is supplied to the gas, while at the open end of the burner additional or secondary air is also consumed in the combustion process. A much hotter flame results from this arrangement, and semi-rotation of the device which opens the apertures allows a measure of control over the air–gas ratio.

2.3.2. Products of combustion

If the bunsen principle is used to mix gas and air with the flame entering the furnace, the products of combustion which accompany the combustion process have an important effect on the atmosphere produced within the furnace. Natural gas consists mainly of carbon and hydrogen; that is to say it is a hydrocarbon, producing considerable heat when combined or burnt with oxygen. A series of gases is produced during the combustion process, and as it is mainly these new gases that are radiated on to the furnace charge, clearly the surface layers of the red-hot steel are likely to be affected by their constant impingement. Depending on the gas–air ratio, two types of furnace atmosphere are likely to result from the bunsen-type burner previously illustrated.

2.3.3. Oxidising or decarburising atmosphere

Fig. 2.3 shows in diagrammatic form the conditions leading to an oxidising atmosphere within a gas-fired furnace. It may be noted that an excess amount of air enters the furnace; this is a very likely possibility when the air is supplied at low pressure, no more than about $3\,500N/m^2$ with a fan or blower. We see from the diagram that the products of combustion are:

(i) nitrogen (N_2);
(ii) carbon dioxide (CO_2);
(iii) water vapour (H_2O);
(iv) free oxygen (O_2).

Nitrogen may be considered as an inert gas; that is to say, it does not affect the surface of the heated steel. It is, however, present in the furnace in considerable volume, and this is due to the fact that air is composed approximately of one part oxygen and four parts nitrogen. This large volume of nitrogen sets a serious limitation on the maximum temperature available from a gas–air flame, and if a high-temperature flame is required it is necessary to supply pure oxygen and thus completely eliminate the nitrogen.

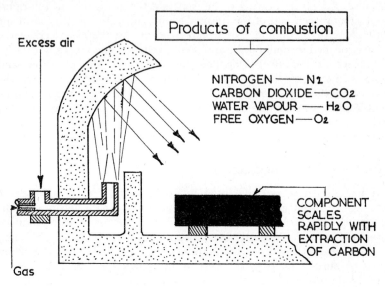

FIG. 2.3.—OXIDISING ATMOSPHERE WITHIN A GAS–AIR OPEN FURNACE

The three remaining gases all tend to cause oxidisation of the red-hot steel, especially the free oxygen which gives rise to severe surface scaling. The free oxygen passes into the furnace because the excess volume of air entering the burner meets with insufficient gas; thus not all the oxygen present in the air joins in the combustion process, and the oxygen which passes into the furnace causes rapid and severe scaling of the surface layers of the red-hot steel. At the same time there is a further tendency of the surface layers of the steel to become decarburised; that is to say, carbon tends to be extracted, and hence for the outside layers the percentage of carbon is below the stated value for the steel under heat treatment.

We see now that an oxidising or decarburising atmosphere, present in a gas-fired furnace through excessive supply of air, has a serious effect on the ultimate properties of a steel heated in it. The layer of oxide scale which forms on the surface of the steel acts as a heat insulator, preventing correct quenching of the steel, while the loss of carbon may reduce the hardening effect expected.

A great improvement in the furnace atmosphere is obtained by the simple expedient of ensuring that the air supply is slightly below that required for efficient combustion; the atmosphere thus produced is known as a reducing or carburising atmosphere.

2.3.4. Reducing or carburising atmosphere

The conditions of combustion which tend to produce a reducing atmosphere are simply shown in Fig. 2.4. Note that reduction of the air supply means that no free oxygen enters the furnace, but owing to lack

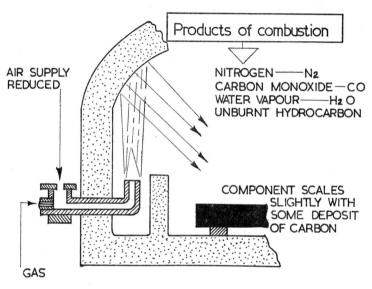

FIG. 2.4.—REDUCING ATMOSPHERE WITHIN A GAS–AIR OPEN FURNACE

of sufficient air some unburnt hydrocarbons do enter it. The tendency of a hydrocarbon is to extract oxygen from the surface layers of the red-hot steel, and at the same time deposit carbon, although the amounts involved are relatively small.

Some scaling, however, is still inevitable, and this is due to the presence of water vapour which is a product of combustion. If scaling is to be completely eliminated from the surface layers of steel undergoing heat treatment in a gas-fired furnace, the presence of water vapour (H_2O) must be prevented.

The simplest method is to keep the steel from coming into contact with the products of combustion, or in other words to ensure that it is heated in a separate container or muffle, with the furnace gases surrounding and heating, but not entering the muffle. A simple diagram illustrating the principle of a muffle furnace is shown in Fig. 65, Chapter 4, of *Workshop Processes, Volume* 2, by the writer of this book.

2.3.5. Controlled atmospheres

Several methods are in use whereby atmosphere control is achieved within a gas-fired furnace. A popular method is shown in diagrammatic form in Fig. 2.5. Gas and air are burnt in a combustion chamber, with

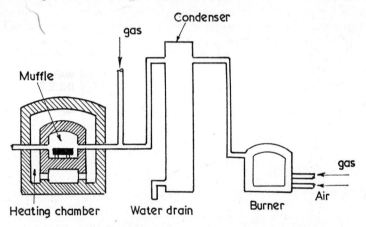

FIG. 2.5.—PRINCIPLE OF A CONTROLLED ATMOSPHERE FURNACE

the products of combustion passed, as shown in the diagram, to a separate condenser. The purpose of the condenser is to change the water vapour (H_2O) to liquid, and this is drained away. With the air supply to the combustion chamber restricted, no free oxygen enters the condenser, and to ensure that a truly reducing atmosphere is produced, some unburnt coal gas is added as the gas leaves the chamber and enters the muffle.

It may be seen that the heating of the muffle chamber is achieved by surrounding it with the products of combustion from the gas burners. This type of furnace is more expensive to operate, owing to the fact that heat must penetrate the muffle walls.

The use of cracked ammonia

Dissociated or cracked ammonia finds specialised use as a reducing atmosphere in furnaces heated by electrical methods. The apparatus or plant is available as a self-contained or compact unit, simply installed, and requiring only the connection of services such as:

(i) liquid-ammonia inlet;
(ii) water inlet;
(iii) drains and vents;
(iv) product outlet.

The principle underlying the operation of the ammonia dissociator consists in separating or cracking ammonia into its constituents hydrogen and nitrogen. This is achieved by passing the liquid ammonia into a vaporiser where the latent heat of evaporation is supplied, usually by electric immersion heaters.

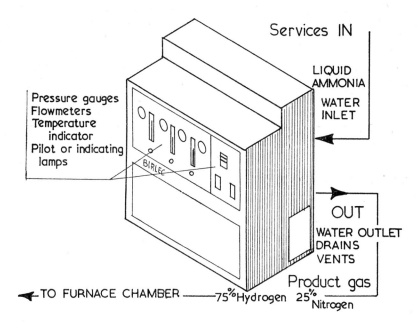

FIG. 2.6.—BIRLEC DISSOCIATED AMMONIA UNIT

The dissociation is carried out in a retort containing a suitable catalyst, after which the hot dissociated gas is cooled to approximately room temperature in a stainless-steel heat exchanger.

Very low costs are claimed for this method of producing a controlled atmosphere suitable for any of the following operations:

(i) bright annealing;
(ii) clean hardening;
(iii) sintering;
(iv) copper brazing.

The compactness of the unit is clearly seen by reference to Fig. 2.6; the panel includes pressure meters and flowmeters.

2.4. Typical gas-fired furnaces

Gas-fired furnaces, like other types of furnace, are of three main types as follows:

(i) for tool or die work (unit or standard production)
(ii) for dealing with batches (batch production)
(iii) for continuous heat treatment (flow production).

There are also many variations of the above main types; furnaces are needed for heating billets to the correct forging temperatures, while a wide range of furnaces is needed to melt the large number of different metals and alloys required in casting processes.

The hot-extrusion process also requires the heating of billets prior to extruding, and for fairly large-scale heating operations such as those described the gas-fired furnace finds universal application.

2.4.1. Standard-type furnaces

Fig. 2.7 shows a standard-type direct-fired gas heat-treatment furnace using a patented high-intensity combustion burner. This furnace may be operated within a temperature range of 380–1 200° C, and is thus

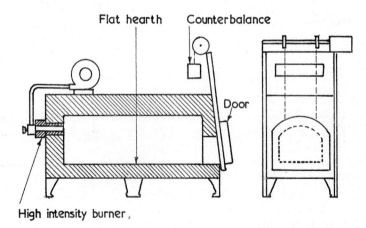

Fig. 2.7.—Standard Direct-fired Gas Furnace

suitable for operations such as hardening, annealing and tempering. The hearth is grooved to facilitate the charging of the furnace using a suitable mechanical loading device, and motorised door gear and automatic temperature control are also available.

Because combustion of the gas–air mixture is virtually completed in the gas tunnel, a precontrolled atmosphere enters the furnace, allowing an oxidising or reducing atmosphere as required.

At Fig. 2.8 we see a standard natural-draught gas-fired furnace suitable for temperatures within the range 600–1 100° C, with temperature uniformity held within ± 5° C. Direct flame impingement on the work

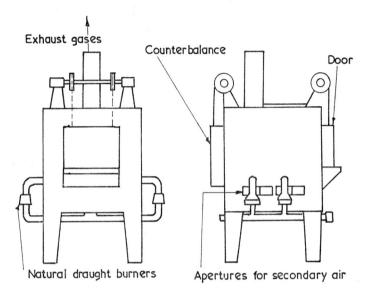

FIG. 2.8.—NATURAL-DRAUGHT GAS-FIRED OPEN FURNACE

is avoided; the hot gases or products of combustion circulate the working chamber and are then discharged through ports situated on either side of the door opening. In this way a curtain of exhaust gas prevents the entry of cold air into the furnace when the charging door is opened.

Adjustment of the burner controls allows an oxidising or reducing atmosphere as required, and the working temperature may be controlled manually or automatically. Note that two burners are arranged on each side of the furnace.

2.4.2. Batch-type furnaces

A wide range of special-type furnaces is available, specifically designed for the efficient and rapid heat treatment of components in batches. Heavy or bulky components are invariably heat treated in bogie-hearth furnaces. The bogie is essentially a movable hearth, thus allowing the component to be loaded outside the furnace, and a popular arrangement is to charge the furnace at one end as a heat-treated component is withdrawn at the opposite end. This principle is simply illustrated in Fig. 2.9. These furnaces may be electrically heated, and once again a controlled atmosphere may be introduced into the working chamber. A typical use for a bogie-hearth furnace would be the annealing of fairly large castings.

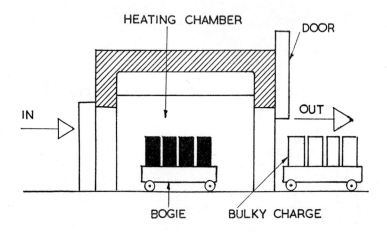

FIG. 2.9.—BOGIE-HEARTH FURNACE

2.4.3. Sealed-quench furnaces

Sealed-quench furnaces, as the name suggests, are designed to combine the techniques of heating and quenching in one operation, without the exposure of the components to the atmosphere. With the application of a controlled atmosphere, these furnaces are eminently suitable for such heat-treatment operations as hardening, carburising, carbon restoration and carbonitriding. The work may be conveniently loaded into suitable work baskets, jigs or trays, and automatic devices result in a considerable reduction of operating cost.

The principle underlying the application of a sealed-quench furnace is simply illustrated in Fig. 2.10. At A we see the charging position, while B shows the charge within the furnace. After the correct soaking period the charge is automatically quenched at C, after which it is removed from the furnace.

Automobile components are widely heat treated in furnaces of this type. By standardising the work carriers or baskets it is a simple matter to interconnect roller or conveyor tracks, thus ensuring speedy non-manual transportation of components through subsequent heat-treatment processes.

To meet the demands of continuous or flow production, continuous-conveyor furnaces represent perhaps the greatest technological advance in heat-treatment techniques. It is an axiom of efficient engineering manufacture that all stages involved in the production of a specified component be integrated with the machining and work-handling systems.

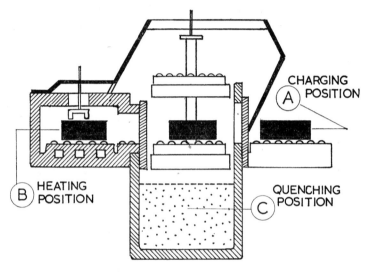

FIG. 2.10.—SEALED-QUENCH FURNACE

2.5. Continuous-conveyor furnaces

It is pointless to produce, say, crown wheels and pinions for the rear axles of motor cars at a high production rate using special-purpose machine tools, if the same components have to be carburised, hardened and tempered using primitive methods.

If full advantage is to be gained from flow production, it is necessary that on completion of machining the components are passed directly to degreasing and then to heat treatment, with no stop or break in the flow of components on their way to the assembly shops.

This means that heat treatment now becomes a production process directly linked by conveyor or other handling systems to the machine-tool elements of the production line. Fig. 2.11 illustrates the principle involved, and this application of heat treatment is likely to be greatly extended to meet the needs of increased production resulting from technological advances in the metal-cutting and metal-forming branches of engineering manufacture.

We may divide the continuous-conveyor-type furnaces as follows:

(i) belt;
(ii) roller-hearth;
(iii) shaker-hearth;
(iv) hump-back.

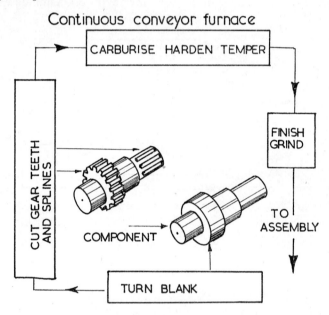

FIG. 2.11.—NEED FOR CONTINUOUS HEAT TREATMENT

2.5.1. Belt-conveyor furnaces

Essentially a belt-conveyor furnace operates on the principle of passing an endless belt through the heating chamber, thus allowing an uninterrupted flow of components through the chamber and if required through a quenching medium. The belt may be constructed from heat-resisting cast link, chain or slats for medium to heavy components, while less heavy components may be conveyed on a belt constructed from specially woven heat-resisting wire mesh.

Mesh-belt furnaces are widely used for copper brazing, sintering and annealing, with the work protected by a suitably controlled atmosphere. With a suitable reducing atmosphere the need for flux is obviated when the furnace is required to heat components to the brazing temperature, the brazing alloy entering the joint through capillary action. Similarly, a suitable atmosphere makes possible the bright annealing of mild-steel-, nickel- and copper-based alloy components. Fig. 2.12 illustrates in a simple manner the principle underlying the design and application of a mesh-belt-conveyor furnace.

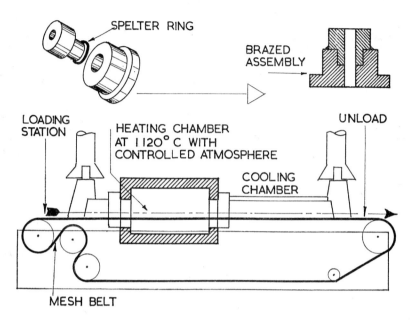

FIG. 2.12.—MESH-BELT CONVEYOR FURNACE

2.5.2. Roller-hearth furnaces

These are designed for the heat treatment of relatively heavy work, such as wire coils, pressings, forgings, tubes and sheets. The components are conveyed through the heating chamber on heat-resisting rollers. Once again a controlled atmosphere allows bright or clean annealing, while mechanical devices facilitate the loading and unloading of the components. A continuous heat-treatment line is easily arranged by using three roller-hearth furnaces in line, say for hardening, tempering and annealing. Fig. 2.13 shows the principle of a roller-hearth furnace.

2.5.3. Shaker-hearth furnaces

These are mainly designed for the continuous hardening of small components such as springs, nuts, bolts and other small steel components. The shaker hearth is given a slight oscillating movement, intended to

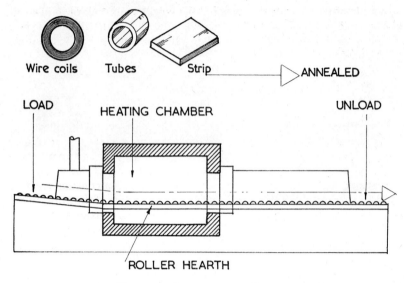

FIG. 2.13.—ROLLER-HEARTH FURNACE

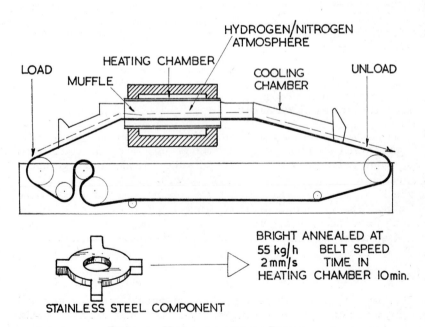

FIG. 2.14.—HUMP-BACK-CONVEYOR FURNACE

agitate or cause movement of the components. This ensures even or uniform heating to the correct temperature prior to quenching. Introduction of a controlled-temperature atmosphere provides for a clean or bright finish on the hardened components.

2.5.4. Hump-back-conveyor furnaces

This type of continuous furnace is designed for the heat treatment of alloy steels such as stainless steels which are rapidly affected by the furnace atmosphere. This means that a high-purity furnace atmosphere is an essential requirement, and the hump-back furnace, as the name suggests, has the heating chamber at the highest point of the furnace.

When this type of furnace is suitably charged with a controlled atmosphere at a positive pressure there is a minimum leakage of the atmosphere gas and minimum air infiltration. To reduce the risk of oxidisation of the heat-treated work as it leaves the heating chamber, a special water-cooled tunnel is included, the temperature of the workpieces dropping as they pass through it. Fig. 2.14 shows a diagrammatic arrangement of a hump-back-conveyor furnace.

The above examples include only a few of the continuous furnaces available. In many cases furnaces are designed and installed to meet particular requirements, the main object being to ensure that the heat treatment of components is a continuation of the production line; thus the efficiency of the furnace is measured in terms of the mass of charge that can be heat treated in unit time.

2.6. Electrically heated furnaces

Furnace heating by electrical methods offers several advantages. We have seen that the heat obtained when a mixture of gas and air is ignited results from a chemical action, and is accompanied by products of combustion which enter the heating chamber. The resultant furnace atmosphere is determined by the ratio of gas and air, and if components are to be heat treated free from scale or oxidisation a controlled atmosphere must be introduced into the heating chamber. At the same time the exhaust gases must be vented outside the working area, and a considerable amount of pipe or duct work is inevitable.

Electrical furnaces, on the other hand, need no pipe or duct work, and there are no products of combustion involved when electrical energy is converted into heat energy; that is to say, an electrical furnace does not burn or consume anything. The heat is obtained by the simple expedient of energy conversion, and in theory the transformation is 100% efficient. Electricity lends itself readily to instant and accurate control, and it is a simple matter to regulate the electrical input and thus the furnace temperature. Reference back to Fig. 2.1 shows that three main electrical heating principles are applied to the heat treatment of engineering components.

(i) resistance heating;
(ii) arc heating;
(iii) induction heating.

2.6.1. Resistance heating

The principle underlying resistance heating is that a high-resistance conductor, termed the heating element, opposes the passage of an electric current and rises in temperature as a result. In this way electrical energy is changed into heat energy, and this heat energy possessed by the heating element may be transferred to the work by radiation, convection or conduction. The heating elements may be in the form of wire, as in the domestic electric fire, or in the form of thicker-section strips. The metals used are usually nickel–chrome alloys, although silicon-carbide finds increasing use when temperatures in excess of 1 100° C are required.

Applications of resistance heating

Fig. 2.15 shows in diagrammatic form the main applications of resistance heating when applied to the heat treatment of engineering components.

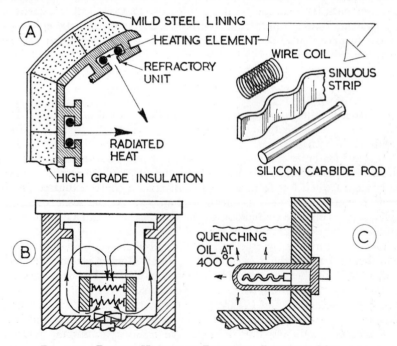

FIG. 2.15.—FURNACE HEATING BY ELECTRICAL RESISTANCE METHODS

At A we see the furnace chamber heated by radiation together with convection caused by hot-air movement. Elements are supported on electrical insulating material having a high refractory value, and may be arranged on the side walls or roof or under the chamber hearth. Note the different types of element form in use. When higher temperatures

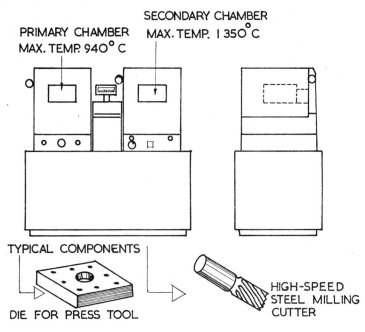

FIG. 2.16.—Two-chamber Electrical Resistance Toolroom Furnace

necessitate the use of silicon-carbide elements, means must be provided to increase the voltage to compensate for the increased resistance of the silicon-carbide elements as they age. A suitable ammeter indicates when a higher voltage is needed to maintain the heating efficiency of the elements. Safety precautions on standard-type electrical resistance furnaces include automatic cut-off of the electrical supply when the furnace door is opened, together with automatic heat-fuse protection against furnace overheating. Suitable atmospheres are readily introduced through an inlet pipe, and a standard thermocouple indicates the furnace temperature.

If it is necessary to protect the heating element from the furnace atmosphere, the element wire or strip must be surrounded by a suitable sheath or protective covering and heat transferred to the furnace by conduction. Such protection must be electrically insulating.

Fig. 2.15ʙ shows the use of electric heating when forced air circulation is required. A suitable fan circulates air through a duct crossed by a heated element, the air converging on the charge and then recirculating around the furnace chamber.

At Fig. 2.15c we see the popular electrical immersion-heater principle. Here the heating element is protected by a metal sheath; such a device can be used for maintaining an oil-quenching bath at a specified temperature. Fig. 2.16 illustrates a two-chamber electrical resistance furnace employed for the hardening of high-speed steel. This furnace is suitable

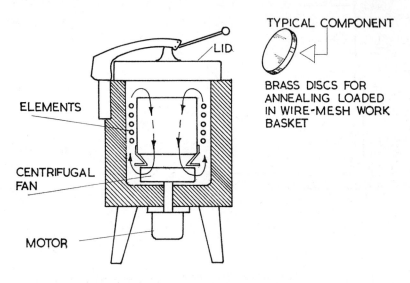

FIG. 2.17.—FORCED-AIR CIRCULATION ELECTRICAL RESISTANCE FURNACE

for toolroom use, allowing primary heating of the high-speed-steel tool in the first chamber, with rapid secondary heating to 1 300° C in the second chamber. Alloy steels used for the manufacture of dies and punches may also be hardened in this type of furnace, care being taken to ensure that the correct temperatures are used for the type of steel requiring heat treatment. Fig. 2.17 shows a simple section through a forced air circulation furnace. Temperatures up to 700° C are possible with this type of furnace; uniform heating is ensured by the forced circulation of air heated by resistance elements situated in the furnace walls as shown. A centrifugal fan supplies the necessary circulation of air in a closed circuit; no fresh air is admitted during the heating process. This type of furnace is eminently suited for tempering or secondary hardening operations on alloy tool steels, and for the heat treatment of non-ferrous alloys.

2.6.2. Electric-arc heating

The intense heat produced by an electric arc finds ready application in many fields of engineering heat treatment. If we consider the melting of metals as a primary heat-treatment process (that is to say the changing of the metal from solid to liquid, allowing it to be poured into suitable moulds), then the application of the electric-arc principle shows clearly the rapid advance of modern technology.

Two main arc heating principles are in use, both designed to melt metals or alloys:

(i) open-arc;
(ii) submerged-arc.

Open-arc principle

Fig. 2.18A shows the principle of the open arc. It may be seen that the arc passing between the ends of two graphite electrodes radiates heat, which is further radiated from the refractory lining enclosing the furnace. This principle is the basis of the electric-arc rocking melting furnace, in which a high-purity melt of metal is obtained. Metals in their liquid state possess the ability to absorb gases which lead to porosity and weakness

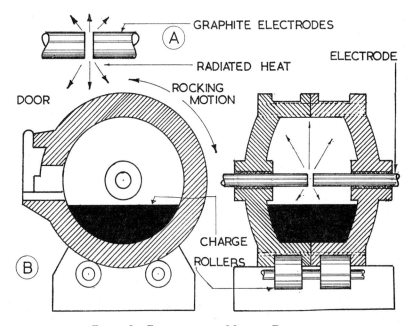

FIG. 2.18.—ELECTRICAL-ARC MELTING FURNACE

on solidification; also the non-ferrous metals are liable to severe oxidisation when the charge is exposed to the atmosphere.

The design of the electric-arc rocking furnace ensures complete freedom from contamination together with accurate control over the pouring temperature, both essential factors in the production of high-quality castings. Fig. 2.18B shows in simple form the design of a rocking furnace. Note that the furnace is able to rock or have partial rotation on the rollers; this action of rocking reduces the possibility of inclusions or segregation in the castings produced from the furnace charge. The angle of rock increases as the charge heats up.

A charging door on the mid-circumference of the furnace chamber incorporates a pouring spout in the lower edge, enabling simple and rapid filling of moulds.

Power input to the furnace is obtained by adjustment of the electrodes, thus shortening or lengthening the arc length. A fully automatic system consisting of a motorised leadscrew ensures full power during the melt without the need for constant attention. This type of furnace is ideal as a batch-melting unit for the more difficult metals and alloys such as gunmetal, aluminium bronze, stellite and stainless steel.

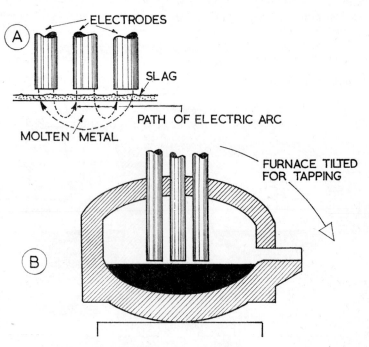

FIG. 2.19.—PRINCIPLE OF THE SUBMERGED-ARC FURNACE

Submerged-arc principle

Fig. 2.19A shows the principle of submerged-arc furnace heating. Three electrodes are seen, with their tips in close proximity to the slag lying on top of the molten metal. The current, supplied to the electrodes from transformers, jumps the gap between electrode and slag, and passes through the molten metal. The arcs provide intense heat, and conduction currents give efficient mixing of the metal. On completion of the melt the furnace is tilted, as seen in the simple diagrammatic illustration at Fig. 2.19B. Clearly there are no products of combustion within the furnace chamber, and the slag present on the surface of the metal prevents oxidisation and carbon pick-up from the graphite electrodes. Once again the application of the electric-arc principle makes possible high-purity melts of the more difficult casting metals.

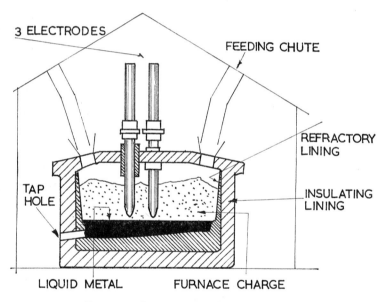

FIG. 2.20.—SUBMERGED-ARC MELTING FURNACE

At Fig. 2.20 we see a further application of the arc principle in reducing metal oxides or ores to liquid metal. The ores reduced in this way are those not suitable for blast-furnace operations. The technique illustrated in Fig. 2.20 does not require high-grade metallurgical coke, and thus removes the need for high-cost coking plant and equipment. As in the blast-furnace technique, a measured charge is periodically introduced into the furnace, with provision for the collection of usable product gas.

2.6.3. Induction heating

We have seen, in our short discussion on furnace principles and design, that the primary purpose of a furnace is to bring the charge to the temperature required in the minimum time and with minimum heat loss. The induction-heating technique has made great strides within the last few decades, because the process is ideally suited for a wide range of heating requirements. In order to clarify the techniques in use, Fig. 2.21 shows in diagrammatic form the three main applications of the induction-heating process.

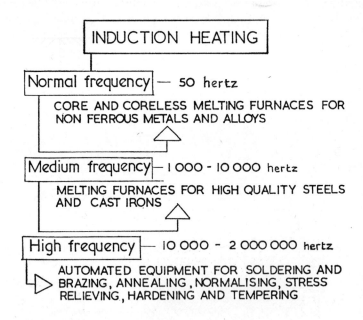

FIG. 2.21.—APPLICATIONS OF INDUCTION HEATING

In each case the heating effect is obtained by electric currents induced in the metal (which must be a conductor of electricity) by the magnetic field of a coil supplied with alternating current. As well as having the advantage of a complete absence of products of combustion, the electrical or eddy currents induce movement or stirring of the metal when the process is used for melting, and thus high-purity alloys, particularly the non-ferrous types, are well suited to this process. Let us now consider the main types of induction heating as outlined in Fig. 2.21.

Normal-frequency induction heating

As the name suggests, the main advantage of this process consists in the use of normal or mains current at a frequency of 50 hertz. Normal-frequency induction furnaces are of two types:

(i) core or channel furnace;
(ii) coreless furnace.

The core furnace is widely used for the melting of brass, and aluminium is also finding increasing melting applications within recent years. For example, a core or channel furnace is ideally suited to the melting of aluminium alloys required for the pressure-die-casting process described in Chapter 1. The uniform stirring action promoted by the electric currents ensures rapid melting and uniform metal temperature, and the complete absence of any contaminating gas makes possible an ideal casting metal.

The compactness of the induction-heating furnace allows the unit to be part of the flow- or mass-production line, an important factor in the need for quality components at competitive prices.

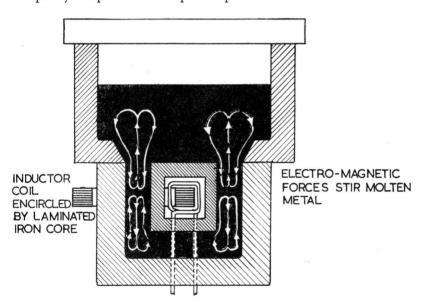

INDUCTOR COIL ENCIRCLED BY LAMINATED IRON CORE

ELECTRO-MAGNETIC FORCES STIR MOLTEN METAL

FIG. 2.22.—NORMAL-FREQUENCY CORE MELTING FURNACE

Fig. 2.22 shows the principle of the core or channel furnace. The operating principle is similar to that of an ordinary transformer, the inductor coil acting as a primary winding. The molten metal forms a loop around the inductor coil, acting as a secondary winding, and a laminated iron

c

core embraces both inductor coil and molten-metal loop, thus concentrating a magnetic field linking the two. Note the electromagnetic forces, which not only generate the heat but also provide a powerful stirring or mixing action, distributing the heat evenly throughout the furnace charge. We see now that the heating effect is directly applied to the charge, and as a consequence no part of the furnace is hotter than the metal within the furnace. This makes for ideal working conditions—no fumes, dust or over-heated atmosphere—and in this way the unit can be incorporated in line with the type of pressure-die-casting machines previously described.

Medium-frequency induction furnaces

These furnaces are widely used for the melting of all types of metals, in particular alloy steels, special cast irons and other non-ferrous metals and their alloys. Fig. 2.23 illustrates the principle involved.

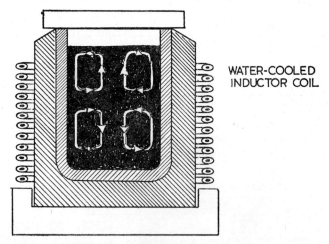

WATER-COOLED
INDUCTOR COIL

Fig. 2.23.—Medium-frequency Induction Melting Furnace

The furnace is encircled by an inductor coil, which is of extruded section and water cooled. A medium frequency current at between 1 000 and 10 000 hertz is applied to this coil, resulting in intense eddy currents in the furnace charge. Once again heat is transferred to the metal, and the charge is agitated, ensuring a high-purity melt.

Tapping the furnace is achieved by tilting, using hydraulic rams, which gives a steady pouring stream.

High-frequency induction heating

The introduction of high-frequency heating has revolutionised the whole aspect of heat treatment with regard to engineering components. There is practically no heat-treatment process that cannot be adapted to high-frequency heating. The processes listed below are all possible with high-frequency induction heating:

    (i) soldering and brazing;
    (ii) normalising, annealing and stress relieving;
    (iii) hardening and tempering;
    (iv) forging;
    (v) sintering;
    (vi) melting.

The principle underlying high-frequency heating is simply illustrated in Fig. 2.24, which also shows some typical applications.

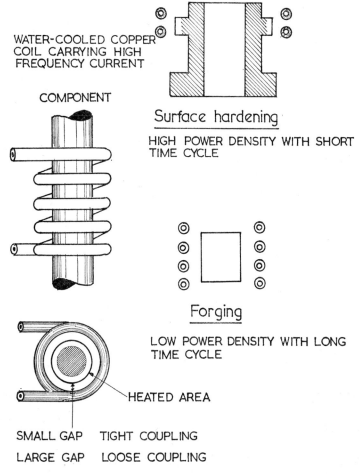

WATER-COOLED COPPER
COIL CARRYING HIGH
FREQUENCY CURRENT

COMPONENT

Surface hardening

HIGH POWER DENSITY WITH SHORT TIME CYCLE

Forging

LOW POWER DENSITY WITH LONG TIME CYCLE

HEATED AREA

SMALL GAP   TIGHT COUPLING

LARGE GAP   LOOSE COUPLING

FIG. 2.24.—INDUCTION-HEATING TECHNIQUES

A high-frequency current is applied to the water-cooled coil, resulting in eddy currents near the surface of the component placed within the coil. A rapid rise in temperature takes place at the outer layers of the metal, and the following set of rules shows the factors that affect the depth of heating:

(i) The higher the frequency, the shallower the depth of current penetration.
(ii) The greater the power concentration, the higher the surface temperature.
(iii) The longer the current is applied, the deeper the heat penetration.

Thus we may summarise the main applications of high-frequency heating as follows:

(i) high-power density and short-time cycle for shallow heating, for example as required for soldering, brazing and surface hardening;
(ii) low-power density and longer-time cycle for deep heating, as in forging, sintering and annealing.

The proximity of the workpiece to the heating coil also has an effect on the efficiency of the heating process, although this is more pronounced at the lower frequencies. When the gap is small the set-up is known as 'tight-coupling', and when large as 'loose-coupling'. Greater efficiency is obtained with tight-coupling, although more care is needed in the design and construction when high-frequency induction heating is to be used as an automatic or self-feeding device.

It must be noted that the current application is controlled electronically, with heating cycles taking only a matter of seconds. With the use of special loading and unloading fixtures many heat treatments now form part of the production line, for it is a simple matter to incorporate air or oil quenching as a natural follow-on to the heating processes.

Examples of high-frequency induction heating

[Perhaps a few examples will serve to demonstrate the high efficiency of the high-frequency induction-heating process.]

EXAMPLE 1

At Fig. 2.25A we see part of the front suspension of a modern motor car. The forging shown as A is to be silver-soldered to the steel tube indicated as B.

This operation is carried out as follows:

(i) Forging, spelter ring and flux loaded onto fixture.
(ii) Tube positioned.

(iii) Charge lifted by pneumatic ram, bringing spelter ring within the heating coil.

(iv) Current applied.

(v) Current switched off and time lapse allowed for solder to set.

(vi) Ram lowered, part removed and cycle repeated.

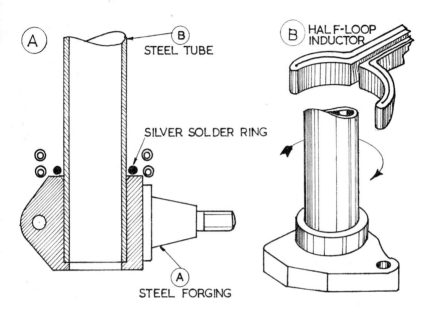

Fig. 2.25.—Use of Half-loop Inductor for Silver-soldering

Should the forging be of irregular shape a half-loop coil is used, necessitating revolving the component to provide even application of heat to the soldered joint. In the above example the silver-soldering cycle is completed in less than 60 seconds, with a sound, reliable joint produced. At Fig. 2.25B we see the application of a half-loop inductor.

EXAMPLE 2

Fig. 2.26 shows a motor-car hypoid pinion machined from case-hardening low-alloy steel. In order to enable the pinion to withstand shock loading it is necessary to temper the portions indicated.

This operation is carried out in a special fixture using high-frequency heating, at a rate of production of 90 components per hour. Scaling is negligible, owing to the very rapid heating time, and as the heat is applied only to the surface layers distortion of the pinion gear is not possible.

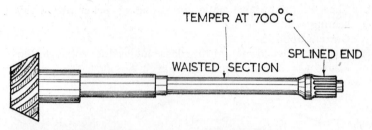

MOTOR CAR HYPOID PINION IN CASE-HARDENING LOW-
ALLOY STEEL. WAISTED SECTION TEMPERED TO HRC 35-45
SPLINED END TEMPERED TO HRC 50.
PRODUCTION TIME-90 COMPONENTS PER HOUR USING
INDUCTION HEATING EQUIPMENT.

FIG. 2.26.—INDUCTION TEMPERING OF MASS-PRODUCED HYPOID PINION

EXAMPLE 3

We have seen in the previous examples that the great merit of high-
frequency heating lies in the fact that the heat may be applied at any
particular depth required. Fig. 2.27A shows a special-purpose shaft, made
from medium-carbon steel: it is required to harden only the gear teeth
to a depth of 1·25 mm. This effect is shown at B, and clearly the localised

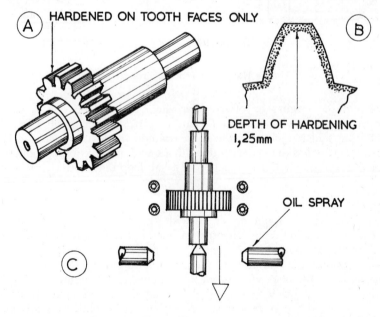

FIG. 2.27.—LOCALISED TOOTH HARDENING WITH INDUCTION HEATING

hardening required involves a difficult and lengthy operation if attempted by normal methods.

The use of a suitable high-frequency induction coil makes this hardening operation a relatively easy matter, and a simple set-up is shown at Fig. 2.27c. Note the application of an oil spray to quench the heated teeth on completion of the heating cycle. Once again the induction-heating unit may become part of a flow-production line, with complete absence of fumes, dust or excessive heat.

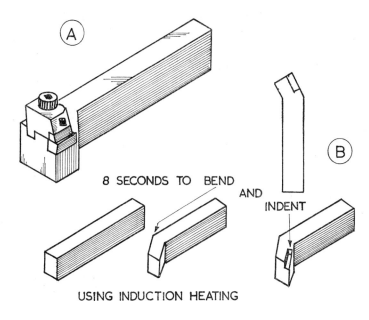

FIG. 2.28.—INDUCTION HEATING FORGING

EXAMPLE 4

Fig. 2.28A shows a tool shank required for holding a tungsten–carbide tip. The finished shape or profile is shown at B, and it can be seen that the shank requires two simple forging operations, namely:

  (i) bending;
  (ii) indenting.

These operations are achieved in minimum time using high-frequency induction heating, and as deep penetration of heat is required a low-power-density current is used in conjunction with an extended time period. Even so the heating time is only about 8 seconds; thus the shanks may be forged at a rate of approximately 300 per hour.

2.7. Oil-fired furnaces

The application of oil-fired furnaces in Great Britain is mainly confined to steam generation for the heating of factories and other industrial or domestic establishments. Fuel oils emanate mainly from Middle-East sources and are thus relatively expensive. The type of fuel oil used for industrial purposes is known as a 'heavy' type. The following notes may prove of value in giving some indication of the principles and techniques underlying the use and application of oil-fired installations.

Viscosity

This is a measure of the fluidity of the oil, or in other words it indicates the time taken in seconds for a given quantity of oil at a temperature of 38° C to flow through a standard orifice. The viscosity of a fuel oil is measured in this country by an apparatus known as a Redwood Viscometer; other countries use different viscometers such as the Saybolt or the Engler. Conversion tables may be used to compare or convert one value to another.

Flash point

Increase in the temperature of a fuel oil results in the vaporisation of the lighter or more volatile fractions of the fuel oil, and the flash point of a particular oil indicates the temperature at which the vapour ignites when exposed to a naked flame.

Principles of combustion

Heavy fuel oil consists of about 84·6% carbon, 11·3% hydrogen and 4·1% sulphur. In order to achieve complete combustion it is essential to expose the maximum surface area of the oil, and this is done by breaking up the oil into a spray a minute droplets or globules. Before the oil is reduced to a fine spray some preheating is necessary in order to increase the viscosity or flowing properties.

2.7.1. Oil Burners

Several principles are adopted in order to ensure that the fuel oil is reduced to a spray of fine droplets; the four main techniques are given below:

   (i) pressure-jet or mechanical atomisers;
  (ii) air-blast atmomisers;
 (iii) rotary-cup atomisers;
 (iv) steam atomisers.

In all cases the oil burner must satisfy the following requirements if efficient and economical heating of the furnace is to be obtained:

(i) Reduction of the necessary amount of fuel to a fine spray of minute droplets over the entire range of working temperatures.
(ii) A suitable standard of oil–air mixing over the entire range of temperatures, and particularly at full load conditions.
(iii) Ability to operate over long periods without the need for cleaning or replacement.

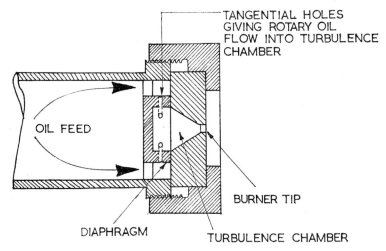

FIG. 2.29.—PRESSURE-JET OIL BURNER

Pressure-jet atomiser

Fig. 2.29 illustrates in simple form the principle underlying a typical pressure-jet oil burner. The sectional view shows the linear flow of pressurised oil transformed into rotary flow through the change in direction induced by the oil flowing through holes tangentially drilled in the diaphragm. The oil leaves the burner tip as a thin, hollow cone where the minute droplets combine with air supplied by natural or mechanical draught to produce a hot, fierce flame.

Air-blast atomiser

Fig. 2.30 illustrates a typical low-pressure air-blast atomiser. The preheated fuel oil is fed through the central tube, the rate of flow being controlled with a regulator. The air is given a measure of rotational velocity by adjustment of the swirler plate. It may be noted that a small quantity of primary air is mixed with the oil, and final atomisation takes place at the nozzle, where the oil–air mixture combines with secondary air.

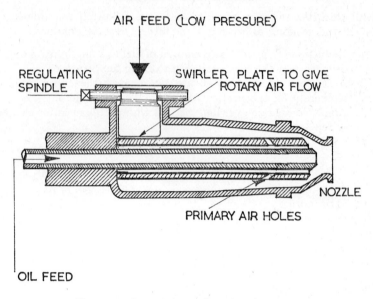

FIG. 2.30.—LOW-PRESSURE AIR-BLAST ATOMISER

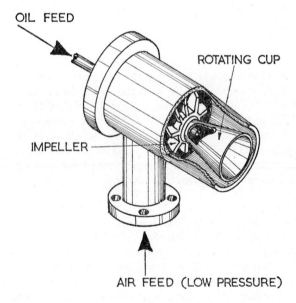

FIG. 2.31.—ROTARY-CUP ATOMISER

Rotary-cup atomiser

The principle of an air-driven rotary-cup oil burner is simply illustrated in Fig. 2.31. The low-pressure air supply enters at the bottom of the device, striking the impeller, which rotates at about 80 rev/s. The cone-shaped cup is integral with the impeller. The oil enters the cup via the small nozzle shown at the cup centre, and spreading around the inner surface of the revolving cup leaves a high velocity in the form of a wide-angle spray, thus ensuring a fine mist of minute oil droplets.

2.7.2. Oil storage

Unlike a gas furnace, which requires no prior storage of fuel, oil-fired furnaces necessitate adequate and safe storage of the fuel oil. All oil-storage devices must meet the requirements of safety and fire precautions as laid down by local authorities. It is also necessary to heat the oil either by steam heating or with electrical immersion heaters. Fig. 2.32 shows a typical residual storage tank, horizontally mounted; note the slope of the tank, approximately 20 mm per metre.

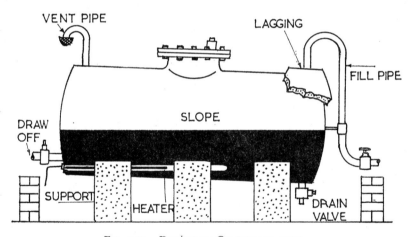

FIG. 2.32.—DETÁILS OF OIL-STORAGE TANK

Summary

Engineering is the business of producing the components and commodities necessary in the modern world in which we live. Not only must the components be produced as cheaply as possible but they must also possess the qualities that ensure reliable and trouble-free service in use.

Heat-treatment furnaces play a vital part in this important matter of component reliability. We have seen that the primary purpose of any heat-treatment furnace consists of rapid and uniform heating of the charge within the furnace; the source of heat may be chemical or electrical.

Gas-fired furnaces are certain to come to the forefront, following the exploitation of natural gas in the North Sea, while the use of oil-fired furnaces may decline owing to the ever-increasing transportation costs of fuel oil.

If the furnace charge is exposed to the products of combustion that result when gas and air are burnt, deterioration of the surface layers of the charge is certain. Excess air gives rise to an oxidising atmosphere, while insufficient air leads to a carburising atmosphere. If the furnace charge is protected or isolated from the products of combustion the furnace is known as a muffle furnace; the alternative method of protection consists in feeding an inert gas into the furnace chamber, providing a controlled atmosphere.

The use of electrical furnaces eliminates the problems associated with products of combustion, and we have seen that the principle of heat generation by converting electrical energy to heat energy has many applications in the heat treatment of engineering components.

Perhaps the most important factor of furnace design, irrespective of the method adopted for heating, is the incorporation of the heat-treatment process into the production line. This means that processes ranging from soldering to annealing can be carried out on a flow-production basis, with maximum utilisation of mechanical loading devices or the use of conveyor or roller tracks.

Not only is the human element reduced to a minimum but automatic methods of temperature control ensure a steady flow of heat-treated components having the required mechanical properties, certain to stand up to the sort of service conditions for which the component is intended. Clearly the supervision and operation of the furnaces briefly described in this chapter demands technicians of the highest calibre, and while the foregoing notes give only a brief indication of the types and principles of the furnaces in use, it is hoped that the technician who is concerned with the maintenance or supervision of these furnaces is made aware of the vital contribution that efficient furnaces make to the art of engineering manufacture.

EXERCISE 2

1 Outline, in some detail, the principles of gas–air combustion, making special reference to the following:

(i) primary air;
(ii) secondary air;
(iii) products of combustion.

2 Describe **two** methods of providing a muffle gas-fired furnace with a controlled atmosphere.

3 Describe, choosing suitable engineering components, **three** heat-treatment processes requiring a controlled atmosphere.

4 Explain the effects of the following atmospheres on the surface layers of low-carbon-steel components:

(i) oxidising atmosphere;
(ii) reducing atmosphere.

5 Sketch, naming the metal from which the component is made, suitable components that may be heat-treated in any **three** of the furnaces listed below:

(i) a natural-draught gas-fired standard furnace;
(ii) a bogie-hearth furnace;
(iii) a sealed-quench furnace;
(iv) a continuous-conveyor furnace;
(v) a belt-conveyor furnace.

6 Outline the advantages offered by the use of electrically operated heat-treatment furnaces.

7 Name the three main types of electrically heated furnaces applicable to the heat-treatment of engineering components, giving in each case a suitable component.

8 Explain the principle of any **two** of the following electrical heat-treatment furnaces:

(i) an electric-arc furnace;
(ii) an electrical resistance furnace;
(iii) a high-frequency or induction-heating furnace.

9 Make a neat sketch of a typical fuel-oil burner, explaining the essential conditions for maximum combustion efficiency.

10 Explain the meaning of the following terms with respect to fuel oil intended for heat-treatment furnaces:

(i) viscosity;
(ii) flash point.

3

FURTHER HEAT-TREATMENT PROCESSES

3.1. Introduction

We have seen in the previous chapter the basic principles underlying the
heating and design of heat-treatment furnaces intended to meet the needs
of modern engineering manufacture. At this stage we should be familiar
with the more common heat-treatment processes; reference to Fig. 3.1

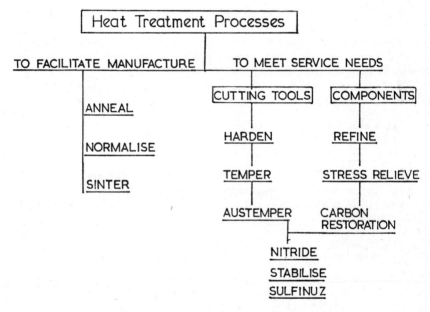

Fig. 3.1.—Outline of Heat-treatment Processes

will assist revision. Note that the processes are divided into two separate
categories, namely those intended to facilitate the manufacture or production of engineering components, and those that enable the component
to stand up better to the conditions likely to be encountered in service.
The need for components well able to stand up to severe service conditions
is clearly exemplified if one considers the steering, shock-absorbing and

driving arrangements for the modern high-speed motor car, while the need for cutting tools possessing the necessary physical properties of hardness and toughness also needs no emphasising.

Suitable heat-treatment processes change or modify the structure of a metal, and in this way its physical properties are enhanced to suit the service application.

Reference back to Fig. 3.1 shows that we have further divided heat-treated components into two categories:

(i) service components;
(ii) cutting tools;

and the following notes give a simple approach to the main heat-treatment processes as applied to the production of efficient and reliable cutting tools.

3.2. Hardening of high-speed steel

Despite the ever-increasing application of more modern cutting-tool materials such as cemented carbides or ceramics, high-speed steel still finds wide application in the form of drills, milling cutters, lathe tools, reamers and form tools. High-speed steel is not the easiest of materials to heat treat. It is denser than high-carbon steel, and it is also a relatively poor conductor of heat. If we add to this the fact that the hardening temperature is in the region of 1 300° C and the tool is likely to have many sharp edges or narrow sections, then clearly scaling must be avoided at all costs.

At Fig. 3.2A we see an end view of a high-speed-steel milling cutter. The effect of scaling is illustrated at B, where it can be seen that loss of metal results, necessitating considerable grinding of the faces in order to restore the cutting edges.

At the same time it is certain that the furnace atmosphere responsible for the scaling has also affected the surface layers of the steel, resulting in a deterioration of the cutting properties of the cutter. The presence of the scale may also have an adverse effect on the quenching process; hence a scale-free surface is essential for the efficient and economical hardening of high-speed steel.

Fig. 3.3 shows in simple form the essential stages in the hardening of a typical high-speed-steel cutting tool. Note that the hardening process is separated into distinct operations:

(i) warming;
(ii) preheating;
(iii) final heating;
(iv) tempering.

HELICAL MILLING CUTTER IN HIGH-SPEED STEEL
HEATED TO I 300°C IN OPEN GAS-FIRED
FURNACE

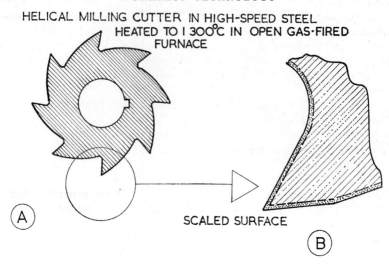

SCALED SURFACE

Fig. 3.2.—Scaling of High-speed Steel

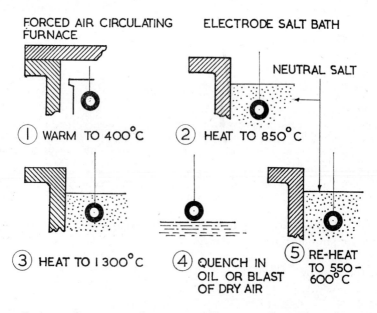

Fig. 3.3.—Operational Sequence for High-speed Steel Hardening

The hardening technique illustrated in Fig. 3.3 is suitable for a standard high-speed steel having the following composition:

	%
Tungsten	18–22
Chromium	4·5
Carbon	0·8
Molybdenum	0·3
Vanadium	1

Although a controlled-atmosphere furnace may be used for the hardening of high-speed steels (such a furnace is illustrated in Fig. 2.16) modern techniques tend to favour the use of a furnace containing a molten inert salt. Such salts must be free from cyanides, and are generally alkali chlorides or alkaline-earth metal chlorides, while for temperatures in excess of 1 000° C barium chlorides are used.

No scaling takes place in these salt baths, and a popular method of heating consists in the use of immersed electrodes operating on the principle that the molten salt is an electrical conductor allowing a heavy current at low voltage to pass, thus transforming electrical energy to heat energy. Such furnaces allow high output rates, distortion of even small and intricate tools being at a minimum. The following notes give a good idea of the essential stages involved, as indicated in Fig. 3.3:

(i) Preheat to approx. 400° C. This may be carried out in a forced-air electrically heated furnace (see Fig. 2.17).

(ii) Transfer to salt bath already at a working temperature at 850–900° C.

(iii) Transfer to salt bath at a temperature of 1 300° C and allow to soak.

(iv) Remove and quench in oil or air blast.

(v) While still warm from final quenching, immerse in neutral salt bath at 550–600° C for $1\frac{1}{2}$–2 hours. This is the secondary hardening process, and may be likened to a form of tempering, although the process is accompanied by a slight increase in the hardness value of the steel.

3.3. Nitriding

Nitriding is an irreversible surface-hardening process applicable only to certain types of steel. A typical example of a nitriding steel is as follows:

	%
Chromium	1·6
Aluminium	1·1
Carbon	0·4
Molybdenum	0·2

The great advantage offered by the nitriding process is that a complicated precision die can be given a very hard case of up to 0·80 mm without the necessity of a quench from an elevated temperature. If we refer to Fig. 3.4, which gives a diagrammatic representation of the stages necessary

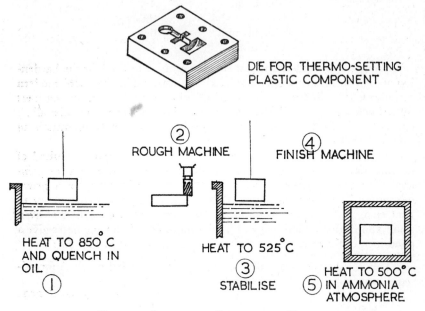

DIE FOR THERMO-SETTING PLASTIC COMPONENT

② ROUGH MACHINE   ④ FINISH MACHINE

HEAT TO 850° C AND QUENCH IN OIL
①

HEAT TO 525° C
③ STABILISE

HEAT TO 500° C
⑤ IN AMMONIA ATMOSPHERE

FIG. 3.4.—OPERATIONAL SEQUENCE FOR NITRIDING

to produce a nitrided die intended for producing thermosetting plastic components, we see that the following sequence is required:

(i) The steel is heated to 850–900° C and quenched in oil, then tempered at 600–650° C.

(ii) The die is now machined close to finished size, and to prevent the possibility of distortion owing to a redistribution of stresses following the machining it is given a stabilising process. This consists in heating the die to 525° C, allowing to cool in air.

(iii) Final machining now takes place, and the die is ready for the nitriding process.

(iv) The nitriding process consists in heating the steel in a furnace provided with an ammonia atmosphere. The temperature of the furnace is held at 500° C, and the die may be in the furnace for a period extending to 90 hours.

We have seen in the previous chapter that dissociated ammonia is used as a protective atmosphere, the ammonia breaking up into the constituents of hydrogen and nitrogen. Much the same thing happens in the nitriding furnace, except that the dissociated nitrogen combines chemically with the alloying elements in the steel, forming very hard substances, called nitrides.

The depth of the chemical change is related to the time the steel is left in the furnace, and a standard depth of nitrided case would be from 0·4 to 0·8 mm.

Remember that **no** quenching or cooling is necessary; thus the risk of cracking or distortion following finish machining is eliminated. Also, no scaling takes place, and the die is readily repolished—an important process, as we have seen in Chapter 1, for the presence of even minute scratches on a die used for pressure die casting leads to early failure, owing to the severe thermal stressing suffered by the die.

The hardness of the nitrided case is permanent, and it cannot be softened to any appreciable extent; thus even if the working temperature of the die approaches 500° C there is no loss of hardness of the case. Perhaps the only disadvantage of the nitriding process is the very slight expansion of the die which takes place, but due allowance can be made for this at the machining stage.

Although we have chosen a die intended for the pressure die-casting process as an example of a nitrided component, components such as heavy-duty ball, thrust and roller bearings, together with camshafts and crankshafts, are all better able to withstand abrasion and fatigue when given a hard nitrided case.

3.4. Carbonitriding

This process is carried out for the types of component just described; that is to say for severely stressed parts subject to abrasion and fatigue. We have seen that the nitriding process described in the previous paragraph is a somewhat lengthy and hence costly process; carbonitriding has been developed to produce a heat-treatment technique well suited to the mass- or flow-production of components needed in large quantities.

Essentially the process consists of heating the components in a suitably controlled atmosphere within a furnace chamber held between 800° and 900° C.

Both carbon and nitrogen must be present in the furnace atmosphere, and these are absorbed by the surface layers of the steel. Normal practice consists in supplying to the furnace a neutral or mildly carburising gas, a typical method being to pass town gas with a controlled mixture of air over a heated catalyst. This is now known as a carrier gas; in order to carbonitride the outer layers of the steel the following technique is adopted.

The carbon is introduced into the furnace atmosphere by a precisely regulated flow of hydrocarbon gas, propane or butane being suitable for this purpose. This gas carburises the steel, while the nitrogen essential for the carbonitriding process is obtained by introducing a small amount of anhydrous ammonia into the furnace atmosphere.

Alternatively, the above gases may be introduced by drip-feeding an organic liquid into the furnace. A suitable fan adequately distributes the dissociated gas throughout the furnace chamber. This principle is simply illustrated in Fig. 3.5, where a mixture of iso-propyl alcohol and benzole is seen to dissociate into the gases shown.

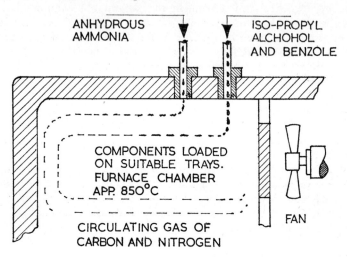

FIG. 3.5.—PRINCIPLE OF CARBONITRIDING

The advantages of carbonitriding may be summarised as follows:

(i) faster penetration rate, allowing lower temperatures to be employed, with reduced possibility of work distortion;

(ii) increased hardenability of the case; an oil quench produces full hardening of a carbon steel;

(iii) increased wear-resistance of the carbonitrided surface;

(iv) application of the process to the many types of continuous furnaces available, as outlined in the previous chapter.

3.5. Gas carburising

Fig. 3.6A illustrates a bevel pinion used in the transmission system of a modern motor car. Made from a low-carbon alloy steel, the component requires case-hardening to increase the resistance of the teeth to abrasion and wear. Clearly large quantities need to be heat-treated, and a batch-type furnace, say of the sealed-quench type, would be ideal for the heat treatment of these components.

We have seen in previous volumes that both pack and cyanide hardening may be employed to add the required carbon to the outer layers of
the steel, but in both these techniques it is difficult to control the amount
and depth of carbon case. The pack-hardening method is also a lengthy
and complicated affair, not suitable for the efficient handling of small- or
medium-sized components. These defects have led to the introduction of
gas carburising, which is at the present moment accepted as the most
efficient method of adding carbon to the outside layers of suitable low-
carbon alloy steels.

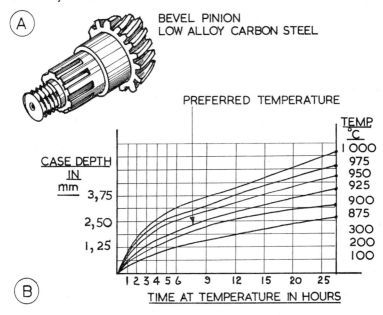

FIG. 3.6.—RELATIONSHIP BETWEEN DEPTH OF CASE, TIME AND TEMPERATURE
WHEN GAS CARBURISING

Essentially the process is similar to that of carbonitriding, except that
ammonia is not introduced into the furnace atmosphere. Modern practice
favours the furnace chamber at a temperature of about 925° C. The
graph illustrated at Fig. 3.6B gives an indication of the effect of case depth
in terms of time and temperature in the furnace chamber. Note that, as
mentioned, 925° C is the temperature most widely used.

For example, if a case depth of 0·6 mm is required the time in the furnace
is approximately 1½ hours, the furnace being held at a temperature of
925° C.

The process of gas carburising allows greater control of the depth and
distribution of carbon in the case; once again the process may be carried
out in a range of continuous furnaces, ensuring high production rates by

mechanised methods of charging and unloading the components using standard-type trays, baskets or conveyor systems.

Unlike those which have undergone the true nitriding process, gas-carburised components require quenching; this process is readily incorporated, using mechanical devices.

We see now that gas carburising represents an advanced technique for the efficient heat treatment of components required in large numbers, such as those to be found in the auto-engineering industry. The ever-increasing efficiency of the modern motor cycle or car with respect to maximum speed and braking power must of necessity result in very severe stressing of the component parts of engine, transmission and braking assemblies.

It is a matter of vital concern that the heat treatment of such components be carried out to the utmost degree of exactitude, and the introduction of the carbonitriding process makes this possible with a high rate of product output.

3.6. Homogeneous carburising

So far we have dealt with the case-hardening of low-carbon, or low-carbon alloy steels—that is to say the increasing of the carbon percentage in the outer layers of a low-carbon steel component, producing on quenching a hard, wear-resistant case.

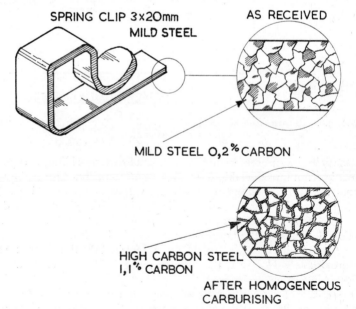

SPRING CLIP 3×20mm
MILD STEEL

AS RECEIVED

MILD STEEL 0,2% CARBON

HIGH CARBON STEEL
1,1% CARBON

AFTER HOMOGENEOUS
CARBURISING

Fig. 3.7.—Homogeneous Carburising

Homogeneous carburising is the thorough or surface-to-surface carburising of low-carbon steel components, generally restricted to components not exceeding 3 mm thickness. Let us take as an example the spring clip illustrated in Fig. 3.7. Clearly, considerable material expense is saved if the strip is made from (say) 0·2% carbon steel, and in addition the part is easily bent to shape using press tools.

Homogeneous carburising converts the low-carbon steel into a high-carbon steel; up to 1·1% carbon is possible, and the part may be quenched and tempered to give the required resilience. Very accurate control of the carbon percentage can be achieved, and the gas-carburising process ensures a completely unscaled component which can be chromium plated at the minimum expense.

3.7. Carbon restoration

As the name suggests, this process consists in restoring to steel components any carbon that may have been lost from the outer layers during previous hot-working processes. The production of steel strip, bar and rod proceeds from heating a steel ingot to passing it through a series of rolls, reducing the section and increasing the length. This process is the familiar hot-rolling of steel, and is inevitably accompanied by considerable scaling of the surface layers of the rolled section. This means that these outer layers have been decarburised, and the carbon percentage of the section is thereby reduced.

In order to simplify a description of the carbon restoration process, let us consider the manufacture of the high-tensile-steel cold-headed bolt illustrated in Fig. 3.8A. If we trace the manufacturing processes we shall see both the necessity for and the application of the carbon restoration process.

At B we see the stages necessary to reduce the white-hot steel ingot to the stock size from which the bolt is to be manufactured. Although the cold-heading process illustrated at C gives additional strength owing to the grain flow associated with the forging process, the sectional view through the bolt indicates that the specified carbon percentage is not present in the outside layers. This deficiency of carbon is certain to lower the mechanical properties of the heat-treated high-tensile-steel bolt, and it is therefore necessary to restore to these outer layers the carbon lost through decarburisation during the primary forming stages.

Fig. 3.8D shows in simple diagrammatic form the principle underlying the technique of carbon restoration. Essentially it consists in heating the components in an atmosphere having a carbon potential equivalent to that desired. This is shown in Fig. 3.8D, where we see the component in a circulating atmosphere having the correct carbon potential. Both carbon potential and temperature may be preset with suitable control systems, as simply illustrated in the diagram.

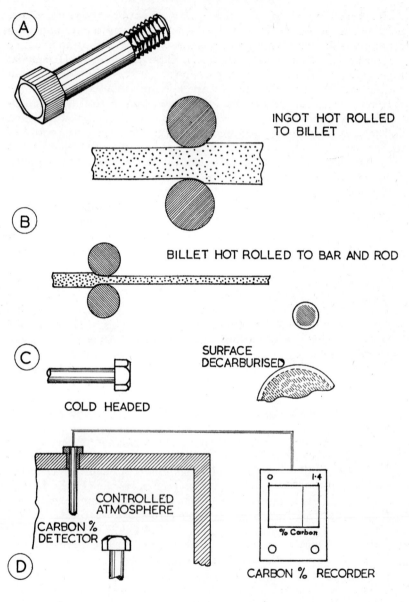

A

INGOT HOT ROLLED
TO BILLET

B

BILLET HOT ROLLED TO BAR AND ROD

C

SURFACE
DECARBURISED

COLD HEADED

D

CONTROLLED
ATMOSPHERE

CARBON %
DETECTOR

% Carbon

CARBON % RECORDER

% CARBON RESTORED TO
CORRECT VALUE

FIG. 3.8.—EXAMPLE OF CARBON RESTORATION

The carbon restoration process is usually combined with the final stages of heat treatment; thus the component is heated to the hardening temperature, and with the carbon potential dial set to the required value the percentage carbon of the outer layers can be restored to coincide with the carbon percentage of the core. In this way the heat-treated high-tensile-steel bolts are certain to have the mechanical properties expected from the carbon steel from which they are manufactured.

3.8. The Sulfinuz process

This is a salt-bath heat-treatment process carried out to improve the wear-resistance properties of ferrous components subject in service to rolling or sliding friction.

Protected by ICI patents, this process has found increasing application for a large number of engineering components, typical examples being crankshafts, camshafts, machine-tool spindles, valve guides, cylinder liners and a great many other components. Consider the assembly illustrated

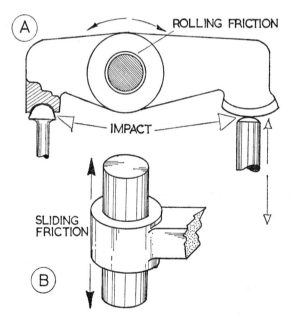

FIG. 3.9.—COMPONENTS SUBJECT TO SLIDING AND ROLLING FRICTION

at Fig. 3.9A. Here we see the rocker arm as used on automobile internal-combustion engines. Note that the rocker arm has a semi-rotating action on the spindle actuated by the push rod shown, thus giving a downwards movement to the tappet. Clearly at the high speeds at which the engine is run there is severe abrading or wear on both the mating spindle and the rocker-arm pad.

A phosphor-bronze bush could be used as a bearing medium between the spindle and rocker-arm bore, but the continual abrading action at the rocker-arm pad would still lead to frictional wear or scoring of the pad.

The Sulfinuz heat-treatment process removes the need for a phosphor-bronze bush, while abrading of the rocker-arm pads is also eliminated.

At Fig. 3.9B we see a familiar type of engineering assembly, namely the sliding of one part on another. Unless the lubrication of the assembly is maintained under all working conditions scuffing is likely to take place, leading to failure or seizure of the mating parts. For the applications just described the Sulfinuz heat-treatment process is ideal.

Fig. 3.10 illustrates in simple form the Sulfinuz process. At A we see the component immersed in a salt bath containing cyanide and sulphur compounds. The bath is maintained at a temperature of between 540° and 600° C, the component being kept in the molten salt for about $1\frac{1}{2}$ hours.

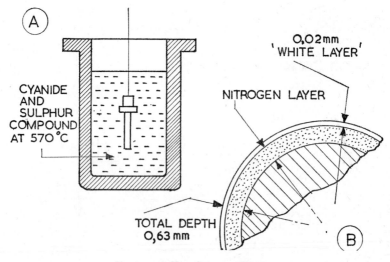

FIG. 3.10.—THE SULFINUZ PROCESS

The effect of this treatment on the surface layers of the component is illustrated at Fig. 3.10B. A 'white layer', rich in nitrogen and sulphur, exists at the immediate surface, extending to a depth of about 0·01–0·02 mm. This white layer is followed by a layer of nitrogen of depth 0·5 mm; thus the total diffusion depth amounts to approximately 0·5–0·6 mm.

The existence of these diffused layers gives excellent resistance to sliding wear and scuffing. Typical applications of the Sulfinuz process include the following:

    (i) cutting edges of high-speed cutting tools;
    (ii) valve spindles and valve guides;
    (iii) machine-tool spindles and slides.

3.9. Austempering and martempering

Before leaving the subject of heat treatments, it is of interest to consider some newer applications of the tempering of straight carbon steels.

The time-honoured method of hardening and tempering consists in heating the carbon steel to the upper critical temperature, then quenching in water or oil. Tempering consists of reheating the hardened steel to an appropriate temperature according to the degree of toughness required from the hardened and tempered component.

3.9.1. Purpose and method of austempering

The purpose of austempering is to heat treat a component and obtain a high hardness value together with a high toughness value. Fig. 3.11A shows a blade intended for the rotary cutter of a power lawn mower. Made from 0·8% carbon steel, the blade needs a good degree of hardness

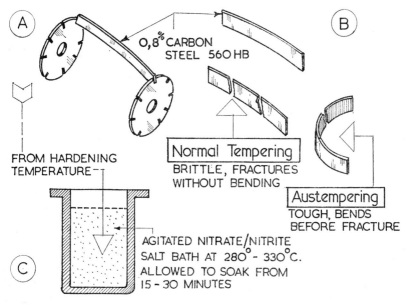

FIG. 3.11.—EXAMPLE OF AUSTEMPERING

and a good degree of toughness. At B we see the effect of bending two blades, one hardened and tempered in the conventional manner, the other hardened and austempered.

Clearly the austempered blade is capable of considerable bending before fracture, while the conventionally hardened blade is brittle, breaking in two places with no prior bending. Note that both blades possess the same degree of hardness, namely 560 BHN, yet it is evident that the austempered blade is far superior for use in the cylindrical cutter of the lawn mower.

The method of austempering is also illustrated in simple detail at Fig. 3.11c. The blades are taken straight from the hardening furnace and immersed in a bath containing molten nitrate–nitrite salts at between 280° and 330° C; the blades remain in the bath for about 20 minutes, and are then allowed to cool in still air.

3.9.2. Martempering

This heat-treatment process is preferred to conventional tempering when distortion and risk of cracking need to be kept to a minimum. The principle is identical with that adopted for austempering, the component being taken from the hardening furnace and immersed in a molten bath of nitrate–nitrite salts. The salt bath, however, is at a lower temperature than that used for austempering, about 200–250° C, and the part is allowed to remain in the bath until it reaches the bath temperature, whereupon it is removed and allowed to cool off in still air. The process is suitable for the heat treatment of high-carbon steel taps and dies, the distortion and cracking risk being considerably reduced.

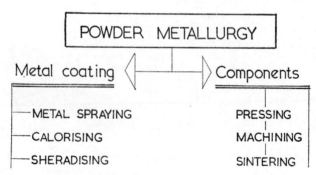

FIG. 3.12.—POWDER-METALLURGY TECHNIQUES

3.10. Powder metallurgy

Although powder metallurgy cannot be considered in the strict sense as a heat-treatment process, it is still worth while including this interesting topic at this stage. We may separate the applications of powder metallurgy to engineering manufacture as follows:

(i) use of metal powders as protective coatings;
(ii) compacting or pressing of metal powders into components.

Fig. 3.12 shows a simple line diagram outlining the techniques employed for both the above applications.

3.10.1. Protective coatings

Components may be given a protective coat to increase resistance to corrosion by either **calorising** or **sheradising**. In both processes the steel components are heated in a suitable powdered metal, zinc and aluminium finding greatest use. In this way the surface layers of the steel component acquire a high-resistance coating and are relatively unaffected by the corrosive effects of the atmosphere.

Alternatively, metal powders may be sprayed on to the surface of steel components, giving a semi-permanent protective coating against corrosion; zinc is the metal mostly used for this technique.

3.10.2. Pressing metal powders

Perhaps the widest application of powder metallurgy is in the production of components by pressing or compacting metal powders in suitable moulds or dies.

The principle of pressing is simply illustrated in Fig. 3.13. A carefully

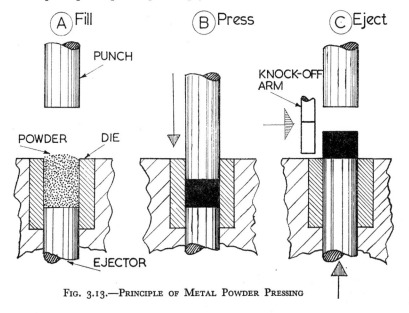

FIG. 3.13.—PRINCIPLE OF METAL POWDER PRESSING

prepared amount of powder enters the die as shown, whereupon the punch descends, compacting the powder to the shape of the die cavity. The ejector now lifts the pressing out of the die, and a knock-off arm sweeps it to one side. Another constant amount of powder fills the die and the

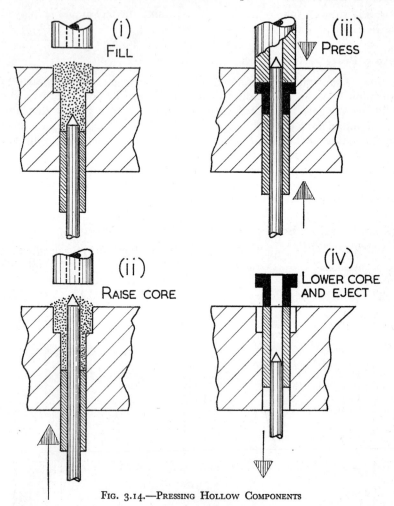

FIG. 3.14.—PRESSING HOLLOW COMPONENTS

sequence is repeated. It is clear that production rates can be high when the process is fully automated.

At Fig. 3.14 we see the technique adopted for pressing a hollow or cored component. The sequence of operations is as follows:

(i) powder enters the die;
(ii) core raised;

(iii) punch descends;
(iv) punch and ejector are raised and component removed.

The pressings produced in this way are fairly robust and may be handled without damage. For maximum strength, however, it is necessary to carry out a **sintering** process.

3.10.3. Sintering

The purpose of sintering a metal-powder pressing is to confer greater strength to the pressing. The pressing may be heated in a controlled-atmosphere furnace or vacuum furnace; for example, trays of pressed components are readily sintered in the furnace illustrated at Fig. 2.14. The sintering temperatures vary according to the powdered metal used, but in general they are a little below the melting point of the powdered metal. Volumetric changes take place during the sintering process; for example, a porous bronze pressing increases slightly in volume, while a tungsten-carbide tip contracts.

3.11. Example of sintered components

The great advantage offered by the production of components by the pressing and sintering technique is that the powder or constituents used can be chosen so that the component possesses the properties required. Also, for some components powder metallurgy is the only possible manufacturing technique, while in other applications powder metallurgy offers a more rapid and cheaper method of manufacture. Thus we may outline the application of powder metallurgy in the field of engineering manufacture as follows:

(i) manufacture of anti-friction bearings;
(ii) manufacture of hard metal components;
(iii) manufacture of intricate shapes in iron.

3.11.1. Porous bronze bearings

Fig. 3.15A illustrates a typical application for a porous bronze bearing, while at B we see the pressing and sintering conditions. A typical composition for this bearing would be:

	%
Copper	89
Tin	10
Graphite	1

We see that the addition of the graphite gives the bearing a built-in lubricating property, while further impregnating with oil increases the anti-friction properties.

Bearings of this kind are very widely used for applications where the bearing needs to be sealed, such as rotating shafts in refrigerators and washing machines. In use the bearing gives many years of trouble-free service.

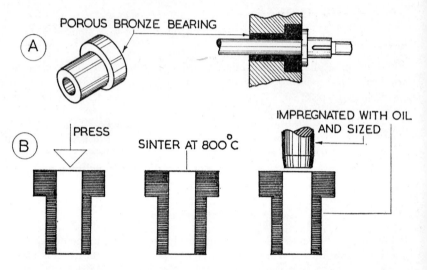

FIG. 3.15.—PRODUCTION OF A POROUS BRONZE BEARING

3.11.2. Tungsten filaments

We are all familiar with the tungsten wire filaments which produce the light source in an electric bulb. The production of tungsten filament wire can be achieved only by the application of powder metallurgy; the basic sequence of operations is simply illustrated at Fig. 3.16.

The tungsten powder is first obtained by a chemical process, namely the hydrogen reduction of tungstic acid.

This powder is now pressed into rectangular blocks and then pre-sintered at 1 100° C. Full sintering then takes place by passing a heavy current through the blocks, the pre-sintering process giving sufficient rigidity for this operation. A temperature just short of 3 000° C is attained during the full sintering process.

The bars are then hot swaged and finally drawn into wire of the required diameter.

3.11.3. Tungsten-carbide tips

Once again powder metallurgy is the only process by which the familiar tungsten-carbide tips may be produced. As well as tips intended for lathe

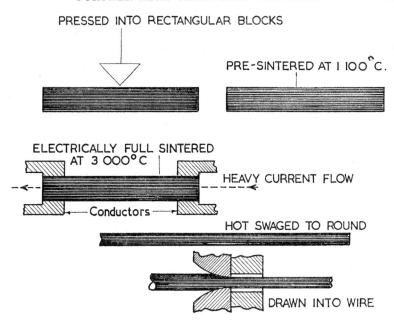

FIG. 3.16.—PRODUCTION OF TUNGSTEN FILAMENT WIRE

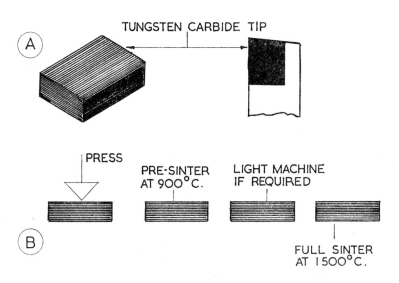

FIG. 3.17.—PRODUCTION OF TUNGSTEN-CARBIDE TIPS

D

tools or milling cutters, tungsten-carbide–cobalt alloys are widely used for such applications as drawing dies, stone- and rock-cutting tools, and indeed any application where a very hard working surface is required.

Fig. 3.17A shows a typical tungsten-carbide tip, and the sequence of manufacture is further illustrated at Fig. 3.17B.

Tungsten-carbide and cobalt powder are thoroughly mixed and then pressed, using a technique similar to that illustrated at Fig. 3.14. Presintering in a vacuum or hydrogen atmosphere at approximately 900° C gives the pressing sufficient rigidity to permit any machining required.

Full sintering takes place at a temperature of about 1 500° C; once again a controlled atmosphere is vital.

3.11.4. Dense iron and steel components

In many instances powder metallurgy provides more economical manufacture of small intricate shapes in iron and steel, as compared with more conventional methods of forging or casting followed by machining.

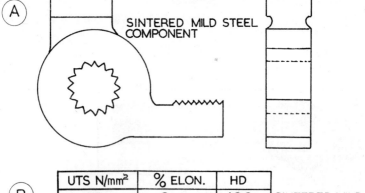

FIG. 3.18.—EXAMPLE OF SINTERED MILD STEEL COMPONENT

Fig. 3.18A shows a typical steel component produced by pressing, followed by sintering. The accompanying table gives an indication of the physical or mechanical properties of the component, and it may be appreciated that the values will meet a wide range of applications.

3.11.5. Further applications of powder metallurgy

The above examples represent only a small fraction of the scope and types of components available by the pressing and sintering of metal powders. For example, powder metallurgy is ideally suited for the manufacture of components requiring porosity, typical examples including filters used in the engineering and chemical industries. Also the manufacture of highly magnetic materials is well suited to the pressing and sintering technique, while a highly refractory metal such as tungsten can be mixed in powder form with powdered metals such as silver and platinum, thus producing a component with excellent, yet extremely hard-wearing electrical contact faces.

Summary

Heat treatment, once considered the province of highly skilled individual application, has now emerged as a production technique, able to take its place alongside the more conventional techniques of machining, pressing and other high-speed methods of metal fabrication.

We have seen that the purpose of all heat treatments is to change or modify the structure of metal, giving to the component the properties required. In general, two main advantages stem from the application of a correct heat-treatment process:

(i) simplification of manufacture;
(ii) ability of the component to stand up to service conditions.

In addition to the well-established techniques of annealing, normalising and stabilising, all calculated to render the metal more amenable to the manufacturing process, suitable heat-treatment processes now make possible the following operations on a flow-production basis:

(i) carbonitriding;
(ii) gas carburising;
(iii) homogeneous carburising;
(iv) carbon restoration;
(v) the Sulfinuz process;
(vi) austempering and martempering.

In all the above processes it is vital to apply the heat within strictly controlled limits and to ensure that the correct atmospheric conditions are present within the furnace. The preceding chapter has made clear the wide range of furnaces now available, with heating carried out by gas–air combustion or using electrical energy.

Increasing use is now being made of suitable salts, which effectively isolate the component from the atmosphere, and may at the same time give superior properties to the surface layers of the metal.

Finally, powder metallurgy, although not strictly a heat-treatment process, uses heat and controlled atmospheres during the production cycle, the heat-treatment of sintering process bringing about considerable changes in the structure of the component, thus making it suitable for service conditions.

EXERCISE 3

1 Describe with the aid of neat diagrams a sequence of heat-treatment operations for hardening a high-speed-steel side and face milling cutter, 175 mm diameter, 25 mm bore and 20 mm width. Explain how scaling is kept to a minimum.

2 Make a neat sketch of an engineering component suitable for hardening by nitriding. Explain the advantages offered by the process.

3 Describe the difference between nitriding and carbonitriding. For what type of component is carbonitriding best suited?

4 With a neat diagram illustrate the principle of **one** of the following case-hardening heat-treatment processes:

   (i) nitriding;
  (ii) carbonitriding.

5 Explain what is meant by the term 'gas carburising', giving three advantages offered by this process.

6 Sketching a typical component, outline the principle of homogeneous carburising.

7 Describe the circumstances that would warrant the heat-treatment process of carbon restoration, using a typical engineering component to illustrate your answer.

8 Outline the Sulfinuz process of heat treatment, giving **two** components suitable for this heat-treatment process.

9 Describe, with the aid of typical components, any **two** of the following heat-treatment processes:

   (i) martempering;
  (ii) austempering;
 (iii) calorising.

10 Give **two** typical applications of the adoption of powder metallurgy for the manufacture of engineering components.

4

MEASURING TECHNIQUES

4.1. Screw-thread form

The measurement of screw threads is much complicated by the complex geometric nature of the screw-thread form. To illustrate this point we may consider the basic form of the ISO metric thread, which is intended to replace both Whitworth and BSF forms. The diagram at Fig. 4.1 shows the basic thread form of a bolt in its maximum-metal condition, mated to a nut in its maximum-metal condition; in other words, we have a perfect fit, something very difficult to achieve in actual practice.

Note that in its maximum-metal condition the bolt has an optional rounded crest and root, while a nut in maximum-metal condition is

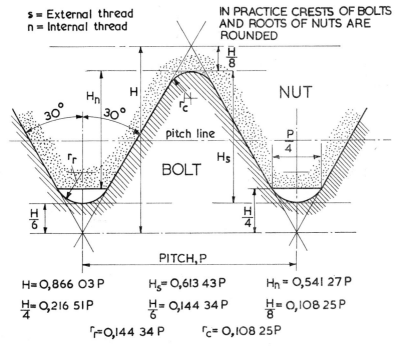

$$H = 0{,}866\ 03\ P \qquad H_s = 0{,}613\ 43\ P \qquad H_n = 0{,}541\ 27\ P$$

$$\frac{H}{4} = 0{,}216\ 51\ P \qquad \frac{H}{6} = 0{,}144\ 34\ P \qquad \frac{H}{8} = 0{,}108\ 25\ P$$

$$r_r = 0{,}144\ 34\ P \qquad r_c = 0{,}108\ 25\ P$$

Fig. 4.1.—Basic Form of ISO Metric Screw Thread

usually rounded at the root only; the crest is flat. Note also that all the screw-thread proportions may be expressed in terms of the pitch of the thread, as indicated by the relevant formulae given with the diagram. Clearly the measurement of screw threads must involve the accurate determination of all the linear, angular and non-linear dimensions that make up the screw-thread form, and we see at once that a screw thread of only a few turns must involve a great deal of work and precise calculation if all the relevant dimensions are to be measured.

4.2. Elements

Fortunately only three elements are involved in the measurement of screw threads, and these are:

    (i) effective diameter;
    (ii) major diameter;
    (iii) minor diameter.

Fig. 4.2 shows these elements, together with the other main features of the screw-thread form. The quality of the thread produced is determined by the amount of tolerance given to the effective, major and minor diameters.

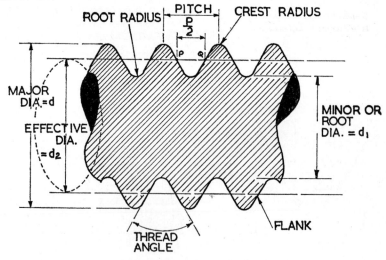

Fig. 4.2.—Screw-thread Elements

Effective diameter

This is the diameter of an imaginary cylinder co-axial with the thread, which has equal metal and space widths; in other words it is the diameter of the cylinder shown in broken line in Fig. 4.2, intersecting the thread flanks so that the distance PQ is equal to one-half the pitch. Fig. 4.1

shows this diameter passing through the thread form, and indicated as the pitch line on the diagram. The theoretical value of the diameter of this imaginary cylinder is more commonly referred to as the **simple** effective diameter, but errors in pitch and flank angles lead to a value known as the **virtual** effective diameter. In other words, a bolt having errors of pitch or flank angle may not allow a nut of perfect thread form to assemble. Clearly, if the effective diameter of the nut is increased so that it is just able to screw on, assembly is possible, and the increased effective diameter of the nut is now equivalent to the virtual effective diameter of the bolt.

Major diameter

This is the diameter of an imaginary cylinder parallel with the crests of the thread; in other words, it is the distance from crest to crest for an external thread, or root to root for an internal thread.

Minor diameter

This is the diameter of an imaginary cylinder which just touches the roots of an external thread, or the crests of an internal thread.

4.3. Classes of fit for ISO threads

The quality of accuracy of a screw thread depends on the purpose or application of the thread. We have seen that the important elements of a screw thread are as follows:

(i) effective diameter;
(ii) major diameter;
(iii) minor diameter.

Provided a thread is machined with the above elements within the tolerances laid down, complete interchangeability is possible according to the class of fit of the screw thread.

The basic screw thread form shown at Fig. 4.1 is that of the International Organisation for Standardisation (ISO) and is to replace the BSW, BSF and Unified threads, although the ISO metric thread is closely related to the Unified thread. The class of fit between a bolt and nut can be taken to indicate the degree of fit between an external and internal thread; that is to say, close tolerance threads produce a tighter fit than threads with greater tolerances. Three main classes of fits are provided for in the ISO range of screw threads, and these are as follows:

(i) fine;
(ii) medium;
(iii) coarse.

Fine threads will require grinding, medium threads are those for general use, while coarse threads are those produced by threading hot-rolled bars and long blind holes, and threads to meet the requirements of dirty or corrosive conditions.

It is important to remember that a fine class of thread refers to the quality of the fit, and not to a fine pitch thread.

The class of fit depends on two factors:

   (i) tolerance grade;
  (ii) tolerance position;

the tolerance grade specifying the width of the tolerance band, while the tolerance position determines the allowance or deviation from the basic size. This system is identical in principle to that adopted in BS 4500, and is simply illustrated at Fig. 4.3. We see from the diagram that the deviation from the zero line or basic size is given a symbol.

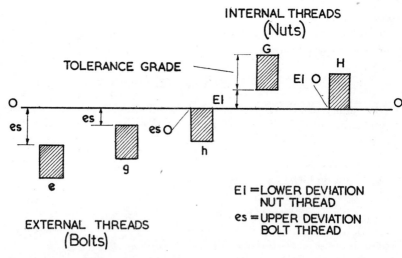

Fig. 4.3.—Tolerance Positions and Grades for ISO Screw Threads

EI is the lower deviation from basic size of the nut thread. At position H it may be seen that zero deviation is provided for, while position G provides an allowance equivalent to the distance shown as EI. Thus a thread with an EI deviation or allowance must provide a free fit with a mating bolt and would be suitable when free assembly is essential. Position H is the normal tolerance position for nuts, and such a nut mated to a bolt having a tolerance position of g will provide a free fit. Note that the tolerance position for a nut is given as a capital letter, while that for a bolt is given in lower case or a small letter.

The shaded areas in the diagram represent the tolerance grade, and are designated by numbers, thus each number refers to the width of the tolerance band or the amount of tolerance. Such tolerances are arrived at by means of a mathematical formula, and the table below shows the tolerance grade applicable to the class of fit required. Clearly the better the fit the smaller the tolerance, and it is important to note that the tolerances apply to each of the four diameters of the mating threads.

| Class of fit | Tolerance grade | | | | | |
| | External threads | | | Internal threads | | |
	Major Dia.	Effective Dia.	Minor Dia.	Major Dia.	Effective Dia.	Minor Dia.
Fine	4	3 4	—	—	4	4
Medium	6	5 6 7	—	—	5 6 7	5 6 7
Coarse	8	8 9	—	—	8	8

TABLE 4.1.

It may be appreciated at this stage that a very wide range of screw thread fits are possible under the system just described, for any tolerance grade can be applied with any tolerance position, and the combination of both tolerance grade and tolerance position produces a particular class of fit.

The following table gives the recommended tolerance class for general purpose threads used in engineering manufacture. This table applies to uncoated threads, that is to say as machined, and of normal length of engagement.

| Class of fit | Tolerance class | |
	Bolt	Nut
Fine	4h	5H
Medium	6g	6H
Coarse	8g	7H

TABLE 4.2. Uncoated threads.

If the thread is to have a thin coating, for example cadmium plating to give increased resistance to corrosion, then the recommended tolerance classes are as shown in Table 4.3, and apply to the thread profile before the application of the coating.

Class of fit	Tolerance class	
	Bolt	Nut
Fine	4g	4H 5H
Medium	6g	6H
Coarse	8g	7H

TABLE 4.3. Thin-coated threads.

It must be appreciated that the medium and coarse classes of fit will prove tighter fits than the equivalent uncoated threads as the thickness of the coating encroaches upon the allowance or the amount of the deviation from basic size.

In the case of threads requiring a heavy coating, Table 4.4 is used.

Class of fit	Tolerance class	
	Bolt	Nut
Medium	6e	6G
Coarse	8g	7H

TABLE 4.4. Thick-coated threads.

4.4. Designation of ISO threads

In order to completely specify a screw thread it is necessary to state the following details:

    (i) thread system;
    (ii) size of thread;
    (iii) thread tolerance.

The ISO system uses the same basic thread form as shown in Fig. 4.1 for all the following thread series. This series comprises three main types of threads as shown:

    (i) a coarse-thread series;
    (ii) a fine-thread series;
    (iii) a constant-pitch series.

4.4.1. ISO coarse-thread series

It is generally intended that this series will replace both Whitworth and British Standard Fine as used at the present time. The thread pitches of the ISO coarse series are finer than Whitworth for threads of equivalent diameter and can, therefore, be used to replace either BSW or BSF.

The pitch increases or varies with the diameter of the coarse-thread series, and ranges from a diameter of 1·6–68 mm; the pitch of the 1·6 mm thread is 0·35 mm, while the pitch of the 68 mm diameter thread is 6 mm.

All threads in this series are designated by the symbol M and the diameter of the thread; thus a coarse thread of 20 mm diameter with a pitch of 2·5 mm is designated as M20, and a 30 mm diameter coarse thread as M30. In other words, **only** the thread diameter is given, the thread pitch must be looked up in the relevant tables. As we have seen, the limits of size or the tolerance class of both the effective diameter and major or minor diameter are given by a number indicating the tolerance grade, and a letter for the tolerance position (lower case for bolts—upper case for nuts) as shown in Table 4.3 and Fig. 4.3. Perhaps the example at Fig. 4.4A will help to show the method used.

4.4.2. Fine-thread series

The ISO fine-thread series is intended for use where maximum strength is required from a threaded component, or when relatively thin tubes require to be threaded. Because the depth of thread depends on the pitch value it follows that the finer the pitch the shallower the depth of thread, and hence the greater the core diameter, resulting in a stronger-threaded component.

The fine-thread series starts at 8 mm diameter with a pitch of 1 mm, and finishes at 68 mm diameter with a pitch of 4 mm, the pitches being graded according to the thread diameters.

This series is designated by the symbol M followed by a multiplication sign and the thread pitch.

Thus, a thread of 10 mm diameter and a pitch of 1·25 mm is indicated as follows—M10 × 1·25. Once again the effective diameter and minor diameter are given as in the previous example, and Fig. 4.4B shows the designation of a threaded nut.

4.4.3. ISO constant pitch series

A very wide range of constant pitch series is available as Table 4.5 shows. By constant pitch we mean that the pitch of the thread remains constant for all the diameter ranges listed in the table, for example, in the diameter range—18–150 mm—the pitch remains constant at 2 mm. Constant pitch threads are very suitable for adjusting collars or retaining

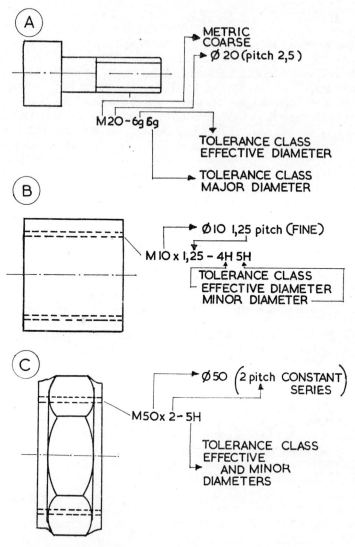

FIG. 4.4.—DESIGNATION OF ISO SCREW THREADS

nuts for shafts and sleeves, or for general use in well-planned compact design work.

The designation of constant pitch threads follows that for fine threads. For example, a 2 mm constant pitch thread of 50 mm diameter is designated thus—M50 × 2 — 4g.

Note that in the above example, the tolerance class of both the effective diameter and minor diameter are the same, and it is not necessary to repeat the tolerance class. Fig. 4.4c shows a typical example of a constant pitch thread properly designated.

Constant pitch in mm	Diameter range in mm	
	From	To
0·35	2·5	3·5
0·5	4	5·5
0·75	6	11
1	8	30
1·25	10	14
1·5	12	80
2	18	150
3	30	250
4	42	300
6	70	300

TABLE 4.5. ISO constant pitches.

4.4.4. Screw-thread measuring elements

In order to determine the accuracy of a screw thread, it will be necessary to measure all of the following:

(i) effective diameter;
(ii) major diameter;
(iii) minor diameter;
(iv) pitch;
(v) thread form.

The first four are all linear dimensions and must be subject to tolerances according to the class of fit required; the object of all thread measurement is to ensure that these tolerances are within the limits laid down.

4.5. Use of limit and tolerance tables

Let us consider the methods adopted to determine the tolerances or limits of size of the ISO metric coarse thread used in Fig. 4.4A. Reference needs to be made to the appropriate British Standard, in this case BS 3643; ISO Metric Screw Threads. Table 4.6 shows an extract from the relevant table in BS 3643, and covers the limits and tolerances for the thread we wish to measure, namely an M20 — 6g6g external thread as shown at Fig. 4.4A. The top extract refers to an external thread or bolt, while the bottom extract refers to an internal thread or nut; the following notes will give some idea of the correct use of the tables.

Nominal diameters

Three choices are provided and wherever possible a designer must make use of the first choice available in the tables. If this is not possible, a diameter from the second-choice column is chosen. We see that 20 mm diameter is a preferred size, for it is in the first-choice column.

Pitch

The pitch of the thread is given in the pitch column, and may, as we have seen, be a coarse, fine or constant pitch.

Length of engagement

This column gives the recommended normal length of engagement, and threads outside this recommended range are designated as either short or long.

Tolerance class

Remembering that we are using the bolt shown in Fig. 4.4A to demonstrate the use of the tables, we may now write down the tolerance class of the bolt thus: 6g6g, or 6g. In other words, effective diameter tolerance class = 6g, major diameter tolerance class = 6g.

Referring to the table, the following information is immediately available:

Allowance or minus deviation . . .	0·080 mm
Maximum major diameter	19·958 mm
Minimum major diameter	19·623 mm
Tolerance on major diameter . . .	0·335 mm
Maximum effective diameter . . .	18·334 mm
Minimum effective diameter . . .	18·164 mm
Tolerance on effective diameter . . .	0·170 mm
Maximum minor diameter . . .	16·891 mm
Minimum minor diameter	16·541 mm
Tolerance on minor diameter . . .	0·350 mm

ISO metric screw threads coarse series—limits and tolerances for normal length of engagement (dimensions in millimetres).

BOLTS

Nominal diameters			Pitch	Normal length of engagement		Tolerance class	Allowance	Major diameter			Effective diameter			Minor diameter		
1st choice	2nd choice	3rd choice		Over	Up to			Max.	Tol.	Min.	Max.	Tol.	Min.	Max.	Tol.	Min.
20			2·5	10	30	6e	0·080	19·920	0·335	19·585	18·296	0·170	18·126	16·853	0·350	16·503
						6g	0·080	19·958	0·335	19·623	18·334	0·170	18·164	16·891	0·350	16·541
						8g	0·042	19·958	0·530	19·428	18·334	0·265	18·069	16·891	0·445	16·446
						4h	0·	20·000	0·212	19·788	18·376	0·106	18·270	16·933	0·286	16·647
						6h	0·	20·000	0·335	19·665	18·376	0·170	18·206	16·933	0·350	16·583

NUTS

Nominal diameters			Pitch	Normal of engagement		Tolerance class	Allowance	Major diameter min.	Effective diameter			Minor diameter		
1st choice	2nd choice	3rd choice		over	up to				Max.	Tol.	Min.	Max.	Tol.	Min.
20			2·5	10	30	6G	0·042	20·042	18·642	0·224	18·418	17·786	0·540	17·336
						7G	0·042	20·042	18·698	0·280	18·418	17·896	0·560	17·336
						5H	0·	20·000	18·556	0·180	18·376	17·649	0·355	17·294
						6W	0·	20·000	18·600	0·224	18·376	17·744	0·450	17·294
						7H	0·	20·000	18·656	0·280	18·376	17·854	0·560	17·294

TABLE 4.6.

The above information represents the limits of size to which the bolt must be machined, and we see now that by using the tables in the manner shown, it is a relatively simple matter to ascertain the relevant limits of size applicable to any specific ISO thread, for the Tables of Limits of Size in BS 3643 cover the whole range of coarse, fine and constant pitches. In other words, provided the thread is of normal length of engagement and is chosen from the ISO range of screw threads, **all** the high and low limits of size of the measuring elements of the screw thread are immediately available.

Note that it is the effective diameter which carries the smallest tolerance, and thus provides the most difficult dimension to machine within its limits during manufacture.

Note also that no limits are given for the major diameter of a nut thread. This diameter is controlled by the outside diameter of the tap used to produce the thread; thus as far as possible all taps have maximum outside diameter giving ample metal to take up wear and prolong their useful life.

4.6. Measuring the effective diameter

We see from Table 4.6 that the tolerance on the effective diameter of a 20 mm diameter coarse-thread bolt is relatively small, namely 0·170 mm for a tolerance class of 6g. It is not often that the effective diameter of a tapped thread is measured in order to ensure that it has been produced within the limits laid down, but it is certain that the taps used to produce the thread have been submitted to a close dimensional check.

In order to show the technique of effective diameter measuring, we may consider measuring the effective diameter of a tap to cut a 20 mm diameter coarse thread of 2·5 mm pitch with a tolerence class of 6g. Perhaps the simplest method is to make use of the 3-wire system, as illustrated at Fig. 4.5A.

Note the use of an external micrometer, together with three small-diameter wires. Clearly, only two essentials or elements are involved in the set-up shown:

(i) diameter of wires (d_w);
(ii) micrometer reading (P).

4.6.1. Wire diameters and their calculation

For best results the wires chosen should make contact with the thread flanks as shown in the diagram at Fig. 4.5B, that is to say, the contact points of the wires should be on the pitch line or effective diameter. In these circumstances it is not difficult to calculate the wire diameter in terms of the thread angle, and the thread pitch. The method is outlined below.

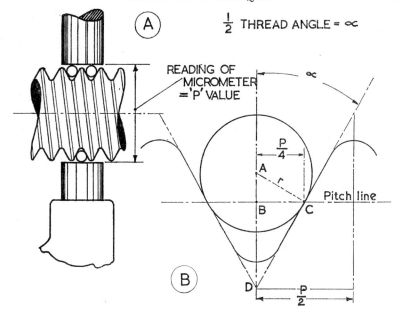

FIG. 4.5.—MEASURING EFFECTIVE DIAMETER USING THREE-WIRE SYSTEM

With flank of thread tangential to radius of wire angle ACD = 90° and DAC = (90 − α).

In triangle ABC:

$$\sin (90 - \alpha) = \frac{BC}{AC}$$

and

$$AC = \frac{BC}{\sin (90 - \alpha)}$$

$$\therefore AC = \frac{BC}{\cos \alpha} \left(\text{since } \sin \left(90 - \frac{\alpha}{2} \right) = \cos \frac{\alpha}{2} \right).$$

Since AC = r and wire diameter = 2r:

$$d_w = \frac{2\,BC}{\cos \alpha}$$

As BC lies on the pitch line:

$$BC = \frac{P}{4}$$

Hence:

$$d_w = \frac{2\,P}{4 \cos \alpha} = \frac{P}{2 \cos \alpha}$$

$$\text{or } d_w = \frac{P \sec \alpha}{2} \left(\text{since } \frac{1}{\cos \alpha} = \sec \alpha \right).$$

This formula gives the ideal wire diameter, where P is the pitch of the thread to be measured and α is half the thread angle.

For ISO, American and Unified threads the thread angle is 60°, hence the correct wire diameter simplifies to:

$$d_w = \frac{P \sec 30°}{2} = 0.577 \, P$$

Using this formula to determine the ideal wire diameter for the 20 mm ISO coarse thread of 2·5 mm pitch, we have

$$d_w = 0.577 \, P$$
$$d_w = 0.577 \times 2.5$$
$$d_w = 1.443 \text{ mm}$$

In actual practice measuring wires are available in sets of two or three. These wires are lapped to within 0·002 5 mm, and it is vital that they are kept in sets as received, as a mean value is taken of the wires that make up a set.

In most cases the manufacturers give not only a certificate of accuracy with these wire sets but also tables giving the expected readings when the wires are used to measure the effective diameter of specified pitches. It should be appreciated that only in very rare cases does the wire diameter coincide with the ideal size, for in practice the diameter slightly exceeds that of the ideal value, but this has little effect on the resulting accuracy of the effective diameter under test.

4.6.2. Practical application of the three-wire system

Returning now to the 20 mm diameter tap, we will assume that we have available three wires, the mean diameter being 1·443 mm. These wires are set into the V grooves of the thread, a little smear of Vaseline helping to keep them in place while a 0–25 mm external micrometer is carefully placed in position. This is the set-up previously illustrated at Fig. 4.5A. While the technique is easily illustrated, it is not so easily carried out in practice, the difficulties increasing with the tap diameter.

We need now to calculate the effective diameter with the following elements known:

(i) the reading of the micrometer (this is the distance across the top of the wires, usually referred to as the P diameter);
(ii) the wire diameters (using the mean value given by the manufacturers);
(iii) the thread angle (this pre-supposes that the thread angle is correct).

As a simple exercise in the use of trigonometry as applied to workshop problems, we will first, using basic principles, establish a formula applicable to ISO form screw threads.

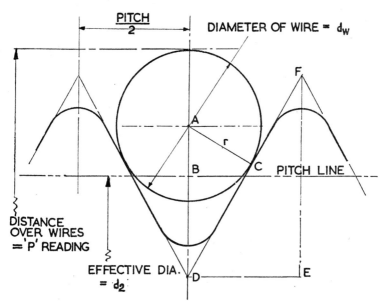

FIG. 4.6.—GEOMETRY OF EFFECTIVE DIAMETER

Referring to Fig. 4.6:

$$\sin 30° = \frac{r}{AD}$$

$$AD = \frac{r}{\sin 30°} = \frac{r}{0 \cdot 5} = 2r = d_w \qquad (1)$$

$$\tan 30° = \frac{p/2}{EF}$$

$$EF = \frac{p}{2 \tan 30°} = \frac{p}{2 \times 0 \cdot 5774} = \frac{p}{1 \cdot 1548} = 0 \cdot 866p \qquad (2)$$

$$DB = \frac{EF}{2} = \frac{0 \cdot 866p}{2} = 0 \cdot 433p \qquad (3)$$

$$AB = AD - DB$$

Substituting (1) and (3):

$$AB = d_w - 0 \cdot 433p$$

The distance over the wires, or the P value may now be stated:

$$P = \text{effective diameter} + 2(d_w - 0\cdot433p) + 2r$$
$$= d_2 + 2d_w - 0\cdot866p + d_w$$
$$= d_2 + 3d_w - 0\cdot866p$$

Hence $\quad d_2 = P - 3d_w + 0\cdot866p$

Or effective diameter = micrometer reading over wires $- 3d_w + 0\cdot866p$.

Because the tap is used to thread nuts we must now ensure that the effective diameter of the tap is within the limits laid down. On reference back to Table 4.6 we see that an internal thread of 20 mm diameter and 2·5 mm coarse pitch must have its effective diameter within the following limits of size for a tolerance class of 6g:

$$\text{Maximum effective diameter} = 18\cdot642 \text{ mm}$$
$$\text{Minimum effective diameter} = 18\cdot418 \text{ mm}$$
$$\text{tolerance} = 0\cdot224 \text{ mm}$$

The simplest technique is to insert the wires and take a reading using a 0–25 mm external micrometer. Let us assume that the reading is 20·75 mm; this is the distance across the top of the wires or the P reading.

From the formula:

$$\text{effective diameter} = P - 3d_w + 0\cdot866p$$
$$= 20\cdot75 - 3 \times 1\cdot443 + 0\cdot866 \times 2\cdot5$$
$$= 20\cdot75 - 4\cdot329 + 2\cdot165$$
$$= 16\cdot421 + 2\cdot165$$
$$= 18\cdot586 \text{ mm}$$

Thus the effective diameter of the 20 mm diameter ISO coarse thread 2·5 mm pitch tap under test is 18·586 mm. This value is 0·056 mm below the top limit of 18·642 mm, and 0·168 mm above the bottom limit of 18·418 mm.

This is quite acceptable, with the advantage that the effective diameter of the tap is just below the top limit, giving a good measure of wear before the value falls to the minimum value of 18·418 mm.

4.6.3. The two-wire system

The use of only two wires precludes the application of an external micrometer held by hand; a specially designed machine is required which maintains the axis of the micrometer spindle square to the thread axis.

Fig. 4.7A shows the principle underlying the two-wire system, while at B we see a simplified diagram of the measuring machine used. Essentially the instrument ensures that the axis of the micrometer is maintained at 90° to the axis of the screw thread under test. The lower slide is capable of movement parallel with the thread axis while the top slide has movement at 90° to the thread axis.

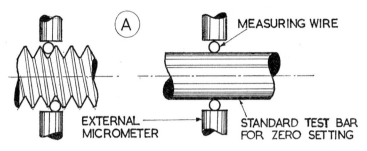

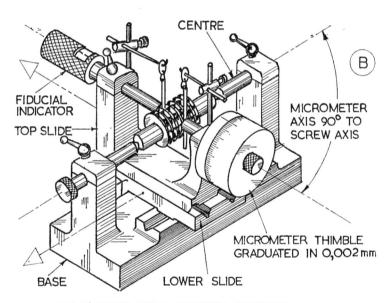

COMPONENT HELD BETWEEN CENTRES,
MEASURING WIRES SUSPENDED ON
IDENTIFICATION TAGS

FIG. 4.7.—TWO-WIRE SYSTEM WITH MEASURING MACHINE

A standard test bar of known diameter is inserted between centres and a reading is taken with two measuring wires interposed between the outside diameter of the test bar and the two micrometer faces. Errors likely to arise due to variation in the tightening pressure are removed by the use of a fiducial indicator on the micrometer thimble; all readings being taken with the indicator at the zero position.

The test bar is now removed and replaced with the screw thread to be measured. Any variation from the first setting gives the error present in the effective diameter; thus if the micrometer reading is minus 0·05 mm, and the test bar is set up so that zero on the micrometer dial indicates the minimum effective diameter, then the thread under test is not acceptable because the effective diameter is 0·05 mm undersize.

Alternatively the test bar may be dispensed with, and the effective diameter of the screw thread calculated from the following formula applicable to ISO threads:

$$\text{diameter over wires} = \text{effective diameter} + 3d_w - 0\text{·}866p$$
$$\text{(where } d_w = \text{diameter of measuring wires,}$$
$$p = \text{pitch of thread)}$$

4.7. Measuring the major diameter

The major diameter of a screw thread is the distance from crest to crest at 90° to the centre line or axis of the screw thread. An external micrometer is quite acceptable provided the ratchet device is used, but for high precision the machine illustrated at Fig. 4.7B may be employed. The procedure is to hold the screw thread by hand and use the machine as a bench micrometer.

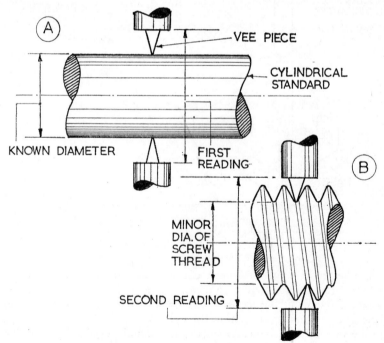

FIG. 4.8.—MEASURING MINOR DIAMETER

4.8. Measuring the minor diameter

External micrometers are seldom used to measure the minor diameter of screw threads because of the difficulty of ensuring that the measurement takes place at 90° to the thread axis.

The usual procedure is to use the measuring machine illustrated at Fig. 4.7B, together with a cylindrical standard of known diameter and two V pieces.

A reading is first taken with the two V pieces in position as shown at Fig. 4.8A. The cylindrical standard and V pieces are now removed and replaced with the screw thread, as shown at Fig. 4.8B.

Any variation between the reading obtained from this set-up and the first reading gives the minor diameter of the screw thread under test.

4.9. Measuring the pitch

Errors in the pitch of a nut or bolt have a serious effect on the accuracy of fit produced. The effect of pitch error on the effective diameter is approximately double; that is to say, if a bolt has a pitch error of 0·01 mm, then the actual or virtual effective diameter shows an error of twice this value, namely 0·02 mm. Provided, however, that the tools forming the threads are accurately produced, pitch errors are seldom found in nuts or bolts, as the taps and dies used are carefully ground and checked. It is very necessary to measure the pitch of, say, a tap used to produce a 20 mm ISO coarse thread, and in general two methods are employed:

   (i) optical projection;
   (ii) pitch measuring machine.

4.9.1. Optical projection

A toolmaker's microscope may be used, the principle of optical projection underlying the technique involved. The tap is set between centres on the microscope table, care being taken to ensure that the table is rotated by an angular amount equivalent to the helix angle of the thread. With a master thread profile mounted in the projection head, a sharp image of the thread is projected on to the screen to match the master profile, and a reading is taken on the micrometer dials controlling movement of the table along the screw axis.

The table is now traversed until the magnified image of the next thread matches the master profile, and the reading taken at the micrometer indexing dial.

The pitch is now the distance traversed by the table, and if the pitch is correct the amount of traverse will equal the stated value for the pitch. This principle is simply illustrated at Fig. 4.9, and it may be appreciated that both depth of thread and flank angles may also be checked or measured, using this principle of optical projection.

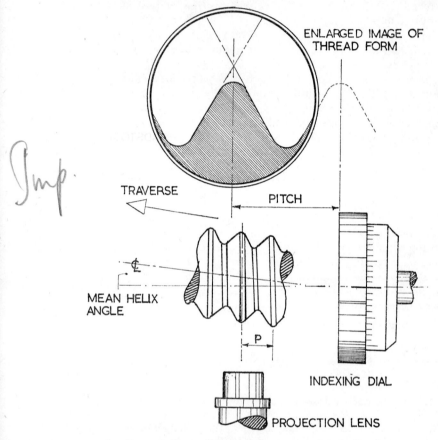

FIG. 4.9.—PITCH MEASUREMENT BY OPTICAL PROJECTION

4.9.2. Pitch-measuring machine

The pitch of a thread is defined as the distance between corresponding points on adjacent thread forms, measured parallel to the thread axis, in the same axial plane and on the same side of the axis. A pitch-measuring machine is specifically designed to achieve the above measurement to a high degree of accuracy, and Fig. 4.10 shows the essential geometrical movements. The headstock, which is fixed to the base, carries a micrometer head, rotation of which produces movement of the carriage along the bed of the base. A second carriage, guided at 90° to the first, carries a sensitive indicating unit, comprising a radiused stylus and visual scale allowing a zero reading to be taken.

In operation, the screw thread to be checked is placed between centres, and the correct stylus mounted in the indicating head. A range of styli is supplied with the machine, together with tables giving the correct stylus to be used according to the type and pitch of thread under test.

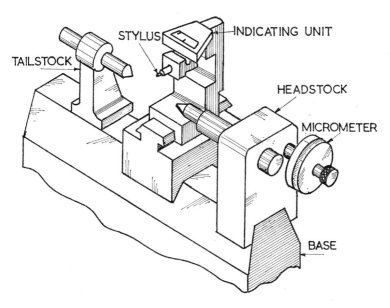

FIG. 4.10.—PITCH-MEASURING MACHINE

For best results it is necessary that the stylus point makes contact on or near the effective diameter. With the correct stylus in position, the second carriage is moved forward so that the stylus fits into the thread groove as shown at Fig. 4.11A, with the indicator pointer at zero as shown at Fig. 4.11B.

The stylus, by reason of an ingenious mounting device, is capable of free movement, riding up and down the thread flanks on linear movement of the screw thread by rotation of the micrometer head. In other words, the exact distance required at Fig. 4.11A, that is to say the pitch of the thread, obtained by a second zero reading from one thread groove to another, is achieved by noting the indexing on the micrometer head.

For example, if the micrometer lead screw has a pitch of 0·5 mm, two complete turns of the micrometer head indicate a thread pitch of 1 mm. A set of interchangeable dials is available graduated to suit particular pitches, while the fixed dial is graduated in 0·002 mm intervals.

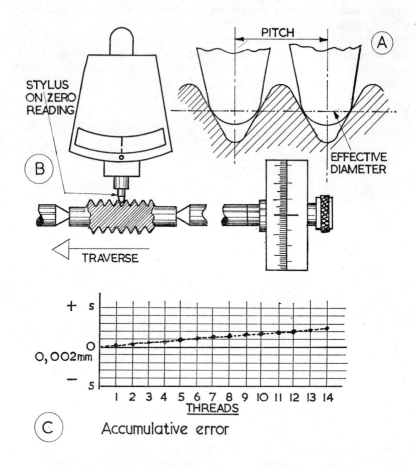

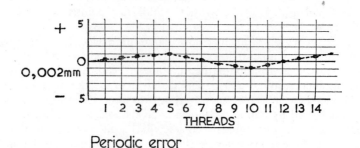

Periodic error

FIG. 4.11.—PITCH-MEASURING TECHNIQUE

It must be noted that each individual pitch is measured, and this allows plotting a graph of pitch error for each turn. Fig. 4.11c shows two typical pitch errors. The first graph indicates an accumulative error, that is to say the error is progressive, increasing with each turn. The second graph indicates a periodic error, the error fluctuating at certain periods or distances along the thread.

4.10. Measuring internal threads

The determination of the accuracy of the elements of an internal thread is a difficult matter. With regard to the effective diameter, a diameter-measuring machine may be utilised provided the thread diameter is of reasonable size, say in excess of 20 mm. Special attachments are needed, including setting blocks and styli. The principle of operation is not unlike that adopted for the determination of effective diameter of an external screw thread as shown in Fig. 4.6. Alternatively, and particularly in the case of small-diameter internal threads, a semi-cast of the thread form may be made, using either dental plaster or sulphur.

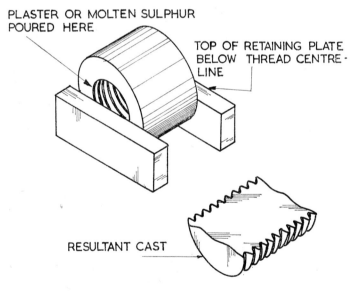

PLASTER OR MOLTEN SULPHUR POURED HERE

TOP OF RETAINING PLATE BELOW THREAD CENTRE-LINE

RESULTANT CAST

Fig. 4.12.—Casting Technique for Internal Threads

The technique is simply illustrated at Fig. 4.12, where it may be seen that the cast does not rise above the centre line of the thread. The purpose of this is to ensure that the cast may be lifted clear of the thread, and not screwed out. The cast may readily be mounted in a suitable optical projector to allow comparison of thread profile and flank angles against a master thread form. The major diameter of an internal thread is best measured using taper parallels in conjunction with an external micrometer; large diameters may be checked using precision rollers and slip gauges. Both techniques are illustrated at Fig. 4.13.

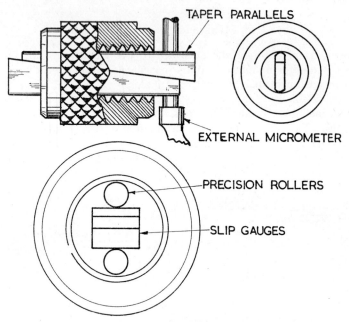

FIG. 4.13.—MEASURING INTERNAL MINOR DIAMETERS

4.11. Angle gauges

In the same way that slip gauges are built up to give a linear dimension, so also may angle gauges be built up to give a required angle. Fig. 4.14 shows a typical set, comprising thirteen angle gauges, one square plate and one parallel straight-edge, making fifteen pieces in all. The gauges are carefully hardened and seasoned to ensure permanence of angular accuracy, and the measuring faces are lapped and polished to a high degree of accuracy and flatness. This allows the 'wringing' of one angle gauge to another; with the set shown, any angle can be built up in steps of 3 seconds from 0° to 360°.

We see from Fig. 4.14 that the following angle gauges are available:

Degrees: 1, 3, 9, 27, 41
Minutes: 1, 3, 9, 27
Seconds: 3, 6, 18, 30

Note that

$$0\cdot05 \text{ minutes} = 3 \text{ seconds}$$
$$0\cdot10 \quad ,, \quad = 6 \quad ,,$$
$$0\cdot30 \quad ,, \quad = 18 \quad ,,$$
$$0\cdot50 \quad ,, \quad = 30 \quad ,,$$

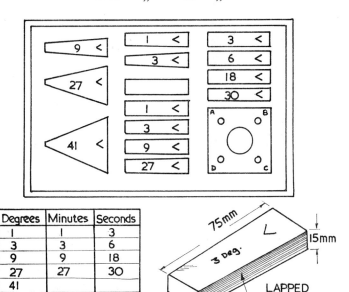

Degrees	Minutes	Seconds
1	1	3
3	3	6
9	9	18
27	27	30
41		

FIG. 4.14.—SET OF ANGLE GAUGES

4.11.1. Application of angle gauges

Angle gauges may be used to advantage in inspection and toolroom departments when a precise angular measurement is required. In many cases a visual check is possible, obtained by comparison of the angle gauge build-up against the component, with a suitable source of white light in the background.

Fig. 4.15A shows a die insert of air-hardening alloy tool steel, having the angle finish ground as shown in the diagram.

The angle gauges required to build up 37° 10′ 18″ are listed below:

$$\text{Degrees} \quad 27 + 9 + 1 = 37°$$
$$\text{Minutes} \quad 9 + 1 = 10′$$
$$\text{Seconds} \quad 18 = 18″$$

Note that six angle gauges are used, the total angle being obtained by **addition** of the individual values. The build-up is shown at Fig. 4.15B, where it may be seen that the engraved Vs which indicate the direction of angle are all in line, showing that each angular value is added. When the combination has been wrung together it should be laid on a Grade A surface plate or toolmaker's flat and each gauge pressed into contact with the plate. This technique ensures that the gauges lie in one plane.

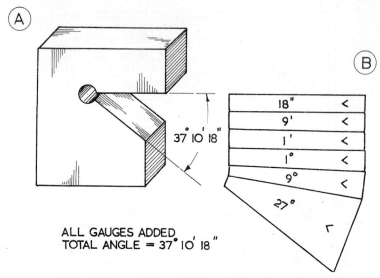

FIG. 4.15.—DIRECT USE OF ANGLE GAUGES

To test the accuracy of the angle in the die insert, we must place the insert on an illuminated glass surface plate, or in front of an inspection light box, with the built-up combination carefully inserted in position. If no white light can be seen between the gauge faces and die faces, then the die faces are within 0·002 mm of the angle-gauge faces.

4.11.2. Use of the square plate

Fig. 4.16A shows a plan view of a 120° V gauge, used to determine or measure large radii. It is important that the 120° angle be ground and lapped to a high degree of accuracy, and the use of angle gauges in conjunction with the square plate illustrates the versatility of the angle-gauge principle. At B we see the combination required to check the 120° angle, while at C the set-up is shown as placed on an illuminated glass surface plate. Note the use of the parallel straight-edge together with standard slip gauges to extend the measuring range of the angle-gauge combination. The lettering on the four corners of the square plate is used when a very high degree of accuracy is required; the square plate has its 90° angles guaranteed to within 2 seconds of arc, and a test certificate is issued with each set of angle gauges. This certificate gives the measured angle of each gauge, and as the square plate has four 90° angles the letters A, B, C and D are used to identify them.

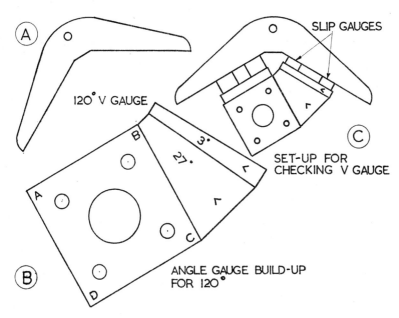

FIG. 4.16.—USE OF SQUARE PLATE

So far we have used angle gauges to obtain a visual comparison of an angular dimension under test, and while very good results are possible it is difficult to give an estimate of the actual angular error. For very precise angular measurement, angle gauges need to be used in conjunction with an Angle Dekkor.

4.12. The Angle Dekkor

An Angle Dekkor is a special type of autocollimator; that is to say it is a type of optical telescope which makes use of parallel rays of light emitted from the instrument. Consider Fig. 4.17A. A source of light originates at A and passes through the lens, striking the highly polished and perfectly flat reflecting surface indicated as B. This lens has the ability to transmit parallel beams of light, and also to catch parallel beams of reflected light. In Fig. 4.17A, if the reflecting surface is truly at 90° to the axis of the lens, the reflected beams clearly follow the same path back through the lens on reflection from the flat polished surface.

At Fig. 4.17B we see the effect of a slight tilt of the reflector in one plane only. The reflected rays now follow a different path back to the lens, reaching the plane of origin at a different point, as indicated by C in the diagram. The difference between point A and its reflected image, point C, is obtained from the formula:

$$AC = 2 \propto \text{rad} \times F$$

where F is the focal length of the lens.

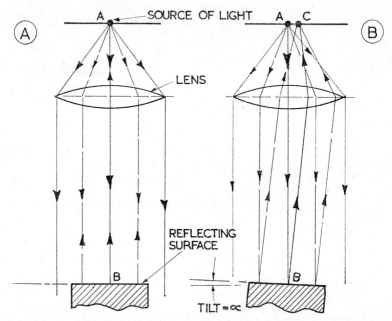

FIG. 4.17.—OPTICAL PRINCIPLE OF ANGLE DEKKOR

Note that the distance between the lens and reflector has no bearing on the accuracy or magnification, although the greater the distance between the lens and the reflector, the smaller must the displacement angle be if the reflected beams of light are to re-enter the lens and thus be shown as the image of a line engraved on a graticule situated at the focal point of the lens.

4.12.1. Reading the Angle Dekkor

The purpose of an Angle Dekkor is to measure small variations in angular setting; in other words, to determine angular tilt. In operation the measuring principle is that of measurement by comparison; the Angle Dekkor is set to give a fixed reading from a known angle, as shown

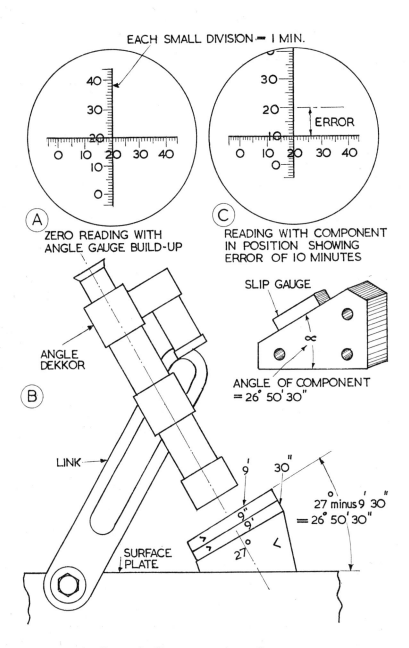

EACH SMALL DIVISION = 1 MIN.

(A) ZERO READING WITH ANGLE GAUGE BUILD-UP

(C) READING WITH COMPONENT IN POSITION SHOWING ERROR OF 10 MINUTES

ANGLE DEKKOR

(B)

LINK

SURFACE PLATE

SLIP GAUGE

∝

ANGLE OF COMPONENT = 26° 50' 30"

27 minus 9' 30" = 26° 50' 30"

9' 30"
9"
9'
27°

Fig. 4.18.—Reading the Angle Dekkor

E

at Fig. 4.18B. Here we see an angle build-up of 26° 50′ 30″ obtained by wringing the following angle gauges

Degrees   + 27
Minutes   —   9
Seconds   —   30

Note that both the 9 minute and 30 second angle gauges are in the reverse direction to the 27 degree gauge; thus the arc of 9′ 30″ must be substracted from 27°, giving an angular inclination of 26° 50′ 30″.

The Angle Dekkor is now set, using the special attachment and link, so that a zero reading is obtained on the illuminated scale. This scale is engraved on the graticule, and may be seen at Fig. 4.18A as the horizontal or fixed scale. Each small division represents 1 minute of arc, and a zero reading is obtained when the 20 division on the reflected scale coincides with the 20 division on the fixed scale.

The angle-gauge build-up is now removed and replaced by the component under test, a straight-edge being used to ensure that there is no change in lateral positions. Any variation in the angle α of the component from 26° 50′ 30″ means that the zero reading of the Angle Dekkor will not be repeated, and the new position of the reflected scale with respect to the fixed scale gives the angular tilt of the component from 26° 50′ 30″.

We have in effect made a comparison of the readings, using known angular standards to obtain a zero reading, and then found the variation from the known angle by a suitable magnification device incorporating a visual and easily read scale. This is identical in all respects with the use of a comparator and slip gauges, and demonstrates how basic principles always find ready application in all types of precision measurement. With practice, accuracy to about 15 seconds of arc is attained using Angle Dekkor and angle gauges, although great care needs to be taken to ensure that absolute cleanliness is observed during the measuring set-up.

At Fig. 4.18c we see the new reading obtained by looking in the eyepiece with the component replacing the angle-gauge build-up. Remember that the Angle Dekkor works on an optical principle, namely the reflection of light rays, and this means that a dead-flat reflecting or polished surface is needed. In most cases a slip gauge in good condition can be used as a reflector, a little Vaseline or Plasticine ensuring close contact to the face of the component. The reading at c shows that the reflected scale falls 10 minutes below the original or zero setting; in other words the 10 division now coincides with the 20 division of the fixed scale. The error from the first setting, therefore, is 10 minutes; hence the angle of the component is 26° 40′ 30″.

4.12.3. Applications of Angle Dekkor and angle gauges

Although the Angle Dekkor is supplied with an adjustable mounting allowing fairly rapid setting at any angle of inclination to a high-class surface plate, as illustrated at Fig. 4.19, it may be utilised to obtain precise angular settings for machining operations. For example, if a slot is to be milled at a precise angle to a previously machined datum face, a horizontal milling machine being used for the operation, a parallel bar or straight-edge may be positioned with the aid of an Angle Dekkor.

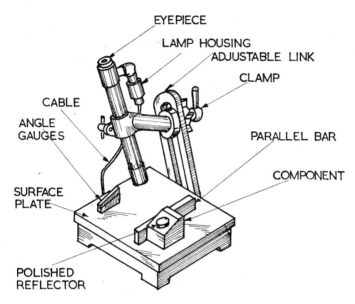

FIG. 4.19.—ANGLE DEKKOR SET-UP

This parallel bar is then used as a datum face, the component being securely clamped when in close contact with it. The setting-up technique is illustrated at Fig. 4.20A. Note the reflecting mirror attached to the column of the horizontal milling machine; a little Plasticine or clay may be used to ensure firm holding of the reflector.

An Angle Dekkor is now set up and a zero reading obtained; this means that the axis of the optical beam is truly at 90° to the table feed. If in Fig. 4.20B the slot to be milled is at an angle of 28° 15′ to the datum face, the following angle gauges are needed:

$$\text{Degrees} \quad + 27 + 1 \quad = \quad 28°$$
$$\text{Minutes} \quad + 27 - 9 - 3 \quad = \quad 15′$$

Note that both the 9 and 3 minute gauges are wrung with their angles in opposition to the remainder of the angle gauges; this has the effect of subtracting their values. The build-up can be seen in Fig. 4.20A, the small engraved V on each gauge indicating the angular inclination. With the correctly assembled angle-gauge build-up in good contact with the datum face of a parallel bar, the bar is adjusted so that a zero reading is obtained on the Angle Dekkor. In other words, the angular inclination between the datum face of the parallel bar and the feed direction of the table is now 28° 15'. The parallel bar must be firmly clamped in this position, a check being made to ensure that no movement takes place during clamping; a few gentle taps will soon allow a zero reading on the Angle Dekkor to be regained.

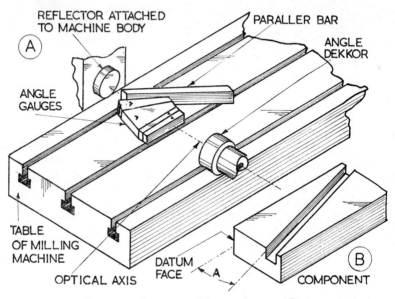

REFLECTOR ATTACHED TO MACHINE BODY

PARALLER BAR

ANGLE DEKKOR

A

ANGLE GAUGES

TABLE OF MILLING MACHINE

OPTICAL AXIS

DATUM FACE

A

COMPONENT

B

FIG. 4.20.—SET-UP FOR MILLING ANGULAR SLOTS

All that now remains is for the workpiece to be clamped to the milling-machine table, in close contact with the pre-set parallel bar. With a suitable cutter mounted in the arbor, the angular accuracy of the milled slot shown at Fig. 4.20B is assured to a very high degree of accuracy.

It should be clear at this stage that the applications and usefulness of angle gauges are very wide indeed; Fig. 4.21 gives some idea of the sort of angular measurements easily checked by careful and intelligent use of the Angle Dekkor.

Reference to Fig. 4.21A shows that the setting of an adjustable angle plate to a precise angle is easily carried out with angle gauges and the Angle Dekkor. Note the use of a parallel bar to bring the angle-gauge build-up to a reasonable working height. With careful positioning of the angle plate it is possible to obtain multiple images in the eyepiece in one setting of the Angle Dekkor.

Checking the sloping angle of a V block is also a simple matter using the Angle Dekkor and angle gauges. The set-up is illustrated at Fig. 4.21B. Once again the principle consists in the comparison of the reading obtained from the polished slip gauge in close contact with the work surface, and a zero reading obtained from the slip-gauge build-up.

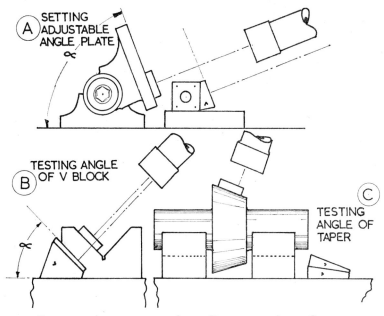

FIG. 4.21.—APPLICATIONS OF ANGLE DEKKOR AND ANGLE GAUGES

There are many other angular checks that can be carried out with a combination of angle gauges and Angle Dekkor, and in general an accuracy of within 10 seconds of arc is achieved. At Fig. 4.21c a simple method is shown for checking the included angle of a component turned or ground between centres.

4.13. The Autocollimator

Similar in principle to an Angle Dekkor, the autocollimator is capable of measuring very small angles of tilt. The accuracy is maintained over a distance of 30 metres, that is to say with the collimator set up 30 metres away from the component under test. The optical principle, as can be seen from Fig. 4.22A, is very similar to that of the Angle Dekkor, remembering that in Fig. 4.22 we show how the illumination is obtained from the small low-voltage lamp. At Fig. 4.22B we see a simple view of a typical autocollimator; it may be noted that unlike an Angle Dekkor, which is clamped to a bracket attached to a surface plate, the autocollimator is equipped with three adjustable feet.

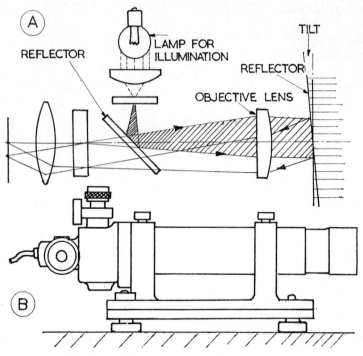

FIG. 4.22.—PRINCIPLE OF THE AUTOCOLLIMATOR

4.13.1. Reading the Autocollimator

An autocollimator, like an Angle Dekkor, is capable of measuring very small angular displacements to a high degree of accuracy. The body or tube of the instrument can be rotated through 90°, allowing displacements in both the horizontal and vertical planes to be measured. This principle is simply illustrated at Fig. 4.23A; the accuracy of the 90° rotation is controlled by fixed stops, and the set-up shows the autocollimator used to measure angular tilt or displacement in the horizontal plane. A zero reading is first obtained in the following manner. The position of the autocollimator is adjusted until the two target wires set in the focal plane of the instrument are each covered by their reflected image. This means that a polished reflecting surface is required to reflect back the light beam from the autocollimator.

As we see from the diagram at Fig. 4.23A, the autocollimator is to measure small angular tilt in the horizontal plane, that is to say tilt of the reflector in the direction indicated by arrow T. Any such horizontal tilt means that the original setting will not be regained; in other words the image of the vertical target wire moves to the right, as shown in the eyepiece view at Fig. 4.23B (the left-hand view showing the zero setting).

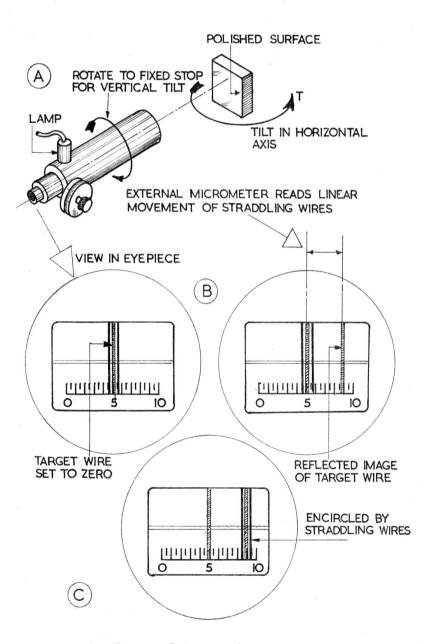

FIG. 4.23.—READING THE AUTOCOLLIMATOR

We see from the diagram that the angular tilt is equivalent to about 4 minutes of arc; this amount may be read off directly from the scale, each small division representing $\frac{1}{2}$ minute or 30 seconds of arc. If greater accuracy is required, use can be made of the straddling wires in conjunction with the external micrometer. Rotation of the micrometer drum controls linear movement of the straddling wires; thus in the initial or zero setting it is necessary to rotate the drum until the wires straddle or encompass the reflected image from the vertical target wire, as shown at B.

Clearly if we now rotate the micrometer drum, moving the wires until they straddle the new position of the reflected image of the vertical target wire following displacement or tilt of the reflector, a very precise determination of angular tilt can be made, with accuracy to within plus or minus one half-second of arc. The micrometer drum is graduated into 60 divisions, and as one complete revolution of the drum is equivalent to a straddling-wire movement of one division on the scale, or 30 seconds of arc, each division on the micrometer drum is equivalent to an angular tilt of $\frac{1}{2}$ second of arc.

4.13.2. Applications of the Autocollimator

With the aid of additional equipment such as a reflector carriage, optical square or precision polygon, a wide range of measuring techniques are possible with an autocollimator; the following examples are intended to give a brief survey of the adaptability of this instrument.

1. *Testing the flatness of a horizontal surface*

The testing of a flat surface such as the guideway of a machine tool or the working area of a surface table requires a reflector carriage similar to that illustrated at Fig. 4.24A. Note that the reflector needs an exceedingly high degree of surface flatness; it is recommended that for a 50 mm diameter reflector the reflecting surface should be optically flat to within 0·000 075 mm. Assuming we are to test the flatness of a machine-tool guideway, it is first necessary to mark off the length under test into intervals equivalent to the base length of the reflector carriage. With the reflector carriage in the first position, as shown at Fig. 4.24B, an arbitrary reading is taken. It is not strictly necessary to zero the autocollimator, the arbitrary reading acting as a zero reading.

The reflector carriage is now moved along the length under test, and a reading is taken at the intervals marked off, as shown in the diagram, which considerably exaggerates the profile of the surface under test. For best results the following precautions should be taken:

(i) Keep all surfaces absolutely clean.
(ii) By tilting the reflector carriage, check whether forward or back-

ward tilts give a positive or minus reading on the autocollimator scale. This will enable a correct interpretation to be made of the surface under test.

(iii) Keep the central point of the reflector in line with the optical axis of the autocollimator as shown in the diagram.

(iv) After the last reading, return the reflector carriage to the first position and recheck the reading to find out whether any inadvertent movement of the autocollimator has taken place.

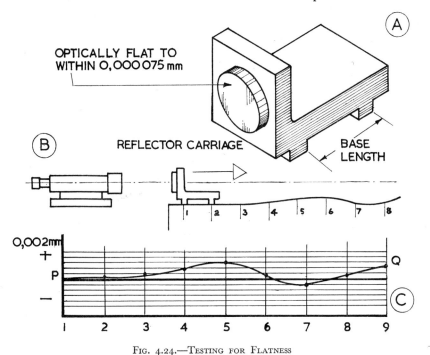

FIG. 4.24.—TESTING FOR FLATNESS

In order to obtain a visual picture of the surface under test it is necessary to plot the readings obtained at each interval along the length under test, plotting the intervals along the horizontal axis, and linear displacement along the vertical axis, as shown at Fig. 4.24c. The linear displacement of the reflector carriage is a known value, dependent on the base length; for example, on a reflector carriage of 125 mm base length, the stamp '30 sec = 0·018 mm' indicates that a 30 second tilt of the reflector is equivalent to a linear displacement of 0·018 mm.

A typical graph is illustrated at Fig. 4.24c. The angular displacements or autocollimator readings have been converted to linear displacements, giving the profile shown. Note that the true profile, or variation from true flatness, is obtained by joining P to Q, that is to say the first reading to the last reading, and the actual profile of the surface is the deviation from the straight line PQ.

2. *Testing the flatness and squareness of machine-tool elements*

As we have stressed in earlier volumes, the inherent geometry of a machine tool determines the geometric accuracy of the surface generated, and for this reason it is very necessary to ensure that machine-tool

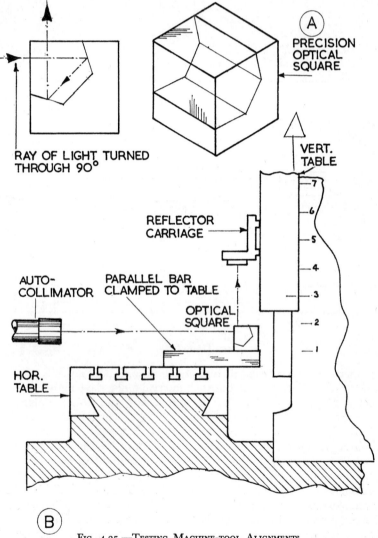

FIG. 4.25.—TESTING MACHINE-TOOL ALIGNMENTS

elements possess the required flatness and squareness. To test squareness, that is to say the accuracy of one surface at 90° to another, we need the optical square illustrated at Fig. 4.25A. This is a precision piece of equipment consisting of a glass prism in a steel or alloy block. The optical principle is illustrated also, and it may be seen that a ray of light entering the optical square is turned through 90° by virtue of the reflecting faces.

The application of the optical square is shown at Fig. 4.25B, where we see a vertical guideway being checked for 90° accuracy to the table of the machine tool. The reflector carriage has a magnetic base and is attached to the vertical table. The optical square may be placed directly on to the horizontal table, or on to a precision parallel bar, according to the requirements of the set-up, while the autocollimator is suitably mounted at a convenient distance.

The procedure differs little from that adopted for the checking of a flat surface; the vertical table is moved at intervals equal to the base length of the reflector carriage, with readings taken at each interval. Once again a graph is plotted showing either angular or linear variation from 90° to the horizontal table. In this way the path of the vertical table is readily checked, as may be the flatness of both tables.

3. *Checking the accuracy of rotary tables and dividing heads*

For this technique a precision polygon is required. A typical polygon is illustrated at Fig. 4.26A; it is made from tool steel, with the reflecting

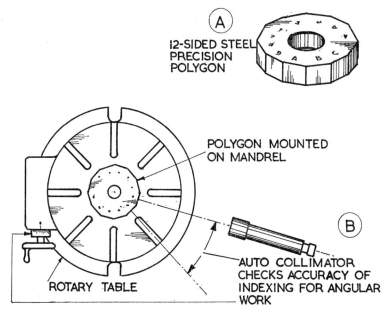

FIG. 4.26.—USE OF PRECISION POLYGON FOR ROTARY CHECKING

faces optically flat and suitably identified. A test certificate is issued with each polygon, giving the respective errors; thus adjustments can be made for each of the twelve faces according to their error from the perfect angle.

A plan view of the set-up for checking the angular indexing accuracy of a rotary table is simply illustrated at Fig. 4.26B; once again a graph may be plotted showing the errors present in the rotary table.

Summary

In this chapter we have seen some of the more specialised forms of measurement, requiring not only the use of expensive equipment, but also the services of a highly skilled and experienced mechanical engineering technician. Screw threads, in particular, present severe problems owing to their complex form, and success can only be achieved if the appropriate measuring instruments are employed.

The measurement of angular inclination, as we have seen, is readily achieved using autocollimators or Angle Dekkors in conjunction with angle gauges. There are few machine-tool movements that cannot be checked with an autocollimator and reflector carriage; the autocollimator is capable of working at a distance of 30 metres from the reflector carriage.

EXERCISE 4

1 With a simple sketch, show a perfect nut engaging with a perfect bolt, and indicate the following screw-thread elements:

(i) effective diameter;
(ii) major diameter;
(iii) minor diameter;
(iv) pitch.

2 Name and define the three main elements that control the accuracy of a screw thread.

3 Describe in some detail the types of screw threads available with the ISO system, and explain the principles underlying the designation of these screw threads.

4 With neat sketches, illustrate how the effective diameter of an M30 tap may be checked using the three-wire system. Show also the method of measuring the major diameter.

5 With a neat diagram show clearly the essential principles or movements of a machine designed to measure the effective diameter of external screw threads using the two-wire system.

6 Describe one method of measuring the pitch accuracy of an external screw thread. What is meant by:

(i) cumulative pitch error;
(ii) periodic pitch error?

7 A 50 mm diameter, 2 mm constant pitch screwed ring gauge is to be checked for the following elements:

(i) minor diameter;
(ii) thread profile.

Describe the measuring technique required for each of the above.

8 List and give the values for a set of angle gauges capable of building up any angle in 3 second steps. Sketch the build-up required for an angle of 37° 10′ 18″.

9 Describe a practical application of an Angle Dekkor as used for the determination of a precise angle.

10 A 40/1 standard Cincinnati dividing head is suspected of inaccurate indexing through continual usage. Describe a method of determining the accuracy of the dividing head with respect to angular indexing.

5

INSPECTION TECHNIQUES

5.1. Introduction

While all forms of measurement are carried out in order to determine an actual size or angle, the degree of accuracy being determined by the type of measuring equipment used, the purpose of inspection is to ascertain whether the dimensions are within the specified limits. In other words, all inspection techniques are designed and operated to ensure **dimensional control**. We have seen in earlier volumes that the greatest manufacturing problem facing engineers is the machining on a mass-production basis of large numbers of components so as to provide the requisite types of reliable and trouble-free fit.

While all measuring techniques are very necessary during the manufacture of machine tools, jigs, fixtures and gauges, it is clear that individual measurement of machined dimensions is wholly impracticable in terms of both time and cost. We have seen, too, that British Standard 4500:1969 provides the engineer with a wide range of fits, together with limits or tolerances according to the quality of fit or size of work. Thus the main problem is to ensure that all dimensions are machined within the limits laid down. Most inspection techniques stem from the application of simple limit gauges.

5.2. Principles of inspection techniques

Let us consider the inspection of the component illustrated at Fig. 5.1A to check the external diameters. There are four diameters involved, and as the machine tool which produced this component is capable of turning out a component every 20 seconds it is clear that a cheap yet efficient inspection technique is required.

5.2.1. Limit gauges

Adjustable limit gauges may be used, set to the high and low limits of the machined dimensions. This means that four gauges are needed, each requiring hand application; but while they give a clear indication of the acceptability of the diameters, they do not show whether the dimension is approaching a high limit owing to wear of the cutting tool. Neither

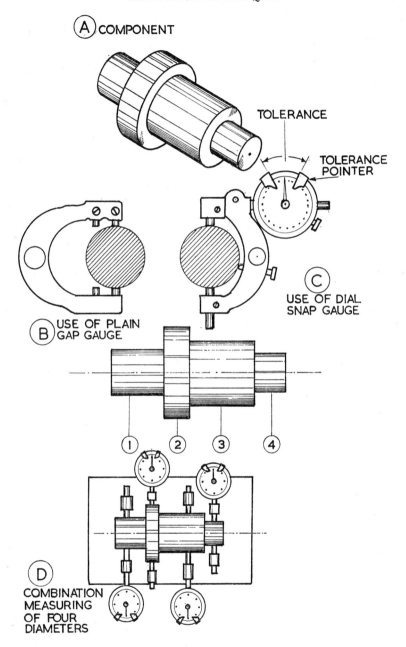

Ⓐ COMPONENT

TOLERANCE

TOLERANCE POINTER

Ⓒ USE OF DIAL SNAP GAUGE

Ⓑ USE OF PLAIN GAP GAUGE

① ② ③ ④

Ⓓ COMBINATION MEASURING OF FOUR DIAMETERS

FIG. 5.1.—PRINCIPLES OF MEASURING AND INSPECTION TECHNIQUES

does a limit gauge show ovality of the diameter or eccentricity with respect to the other machined diameters.

A typical adjustable limit gauge is shown at Fig. 5.1B, while at Fig. 5.1c is shown a simple expedient which allows a visual indication of any changes in size. This is a dial snap gauge, consisting of a sensitive dial together with adjustable tolerance pointers set at the high and low limits of the diameter. Once again, four such gauges are required; but while they are capable of indicating ovality by rotation of the component, they do not show concentricity of the diameters about the centre line of the component.

5.2.2. Combination measuring technique

We may regard the combination measuring technique as a logical development of the caliper limit-gauge principle. The technique now is to combine all the measuring or inspection procedures into one operation; this is achieved by using a simple jig or receiving fixture. The component is now mounted on suitable V blocks, with the dial gauges arranged to suit. A master component is needed to set the dial gauges to zero, and the four diameters of the component are simultaneously checked on insertion into the jig. Rotation of the component immediately shows acceptability or non-acceptability. Any tendency for the diameters to approach high limit can be noted, and in this way action can be taken to remedy the fault before oversize components are produced. A plan view of the set-up is shown at Fig. 5.1D; the dial indications are arranged horizontally.

Which principle of inspection is employed depends on several factors; these may be summarised as follows.

5.2.3. Application of inspection principles

Limit gap gauges

Suitable for small batches where tolerances are fairly large—for example, components machined on capstan lathes with no tolerance less than plus and minus 0·025 mm. All limit gap gauges are fairly robust in construction, well able to stand up to workshop conditions; for we must remember that a capstan operator is concerned mainly with production together with piecework or bonus, and a delicate or sensitive measuring device is likely to have a short life if exposed to workshop usage.

Dial snap gauges

This type of gauge, as we have seen, not only shows the limits of size by suitable adjustment of the tolerance pointers but also indicates variation in size, as the dial possesses a suitable scale according to the degree of accuracy required. The gauge, therefore, is ideal for small batches of machined components that are to be produced to close limits of accuracy, say less than plus and minus 0·025 mm.

The advent of the jet engine for aircraft has necessitated the precision machining of fairly large cylindrical components to very close limits of accuracy in relatively small numbers.

Such components are invariably produced on combination turret lathes by highly skilled craftsmen, and the use of dial snap gauges greatly simplifies the checking of the machined diameters. We shall see later on in this chapter that the dial gauges may be of the pneumatic type, that is to say air-operated.

Combination measuring devices

A large number of engineering components are produced on special-purpose machine tools specifically designed for high production speeds. This manufacturing technique requires manual loading of the component only; all machining and transfer from one stage to another is fully auto-mated, and testing stations incorporating combination measuring or inspection devices are included in the transfer line. In this way, rationali-sation of the manufacturing procedure is achieved—a necessary condition for the efficient and economical manufacture of a mass-produced com-ponent involving a large number of machining operations.

5.2.4. Importance of the inspection technique

In order to consider and appreciate the importance of the inspection technique, we may with advantage take as a simple example the develop-ment of machining and inspection of the light-alloy cylinder head illustra-ted at Fig. 5.2A. Reference to the graph shows that in 1950 the cylinder head was produced using 26 universal milling machines, requiring 26 operators, the component being unloaded and checked at each operation, with a monthly output per worker of 250 components. Inspection of the component was achieved with limit gap gauges at each machining operation.

In 1953 a semi-automated transfer line is used with thirteen stations. Only one loading of the cylinder head is required, automatic transfer of the component taking place from each machining stage to the next, with combination measuring devices used to check the component on un-loading from its fixture. Clearly any faults developing during the machining operation are not detected until the component is checked on removal. With this method production increases to 800 components per month per worker.

Finally, in 1960, we see the effect of a fully rationalised manufacturing and inspection technique; the whole machining sequence is now fully automated. There are 27 machining stages, with three inspection stations strategically positioned. Provided the machining is within the limits laid down, electrical devices indicate the acceptability of the component for the next machining stage, and in this way the component is completely machined and inspected at the rate of 6 500 per month per worker.

All this is carried out quite independently of the human element, and we see now that the use of limit gauges is completely outdated with respect to the inspection of mass- or flow-production engineering components. We need, however, to take a closer look at the principle underlying the application of limit gauges.

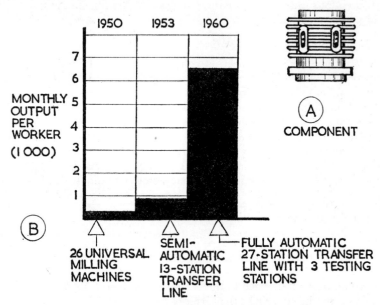

FIG. 5.2.—NEED FOR IMPROVED INSPECTION TECHNIQUES

5.3. Limit-gauge design

The use of limit gauges to maintain dimensional control extends back over 100 years. In 1905 William Taylor, of Messrs Taylor, Taylor and Hobson, introduced his now famous 'Taylor principle', and this principle must still be applied should a small batch of components require a set of limit gauges for their inspection.

The two basic features of the Taylor principle may be stated as follows:

(i) The GO gauge must incorporate as many dimensions as possible.
(ii) Each NO GO dimension must be checked separately.

In order to appreciate the application of the Taylor principle let us consider the gauges required for checking the machined component illustrated at Fig. 5.3A. If separate GO gauges are used to check the out-

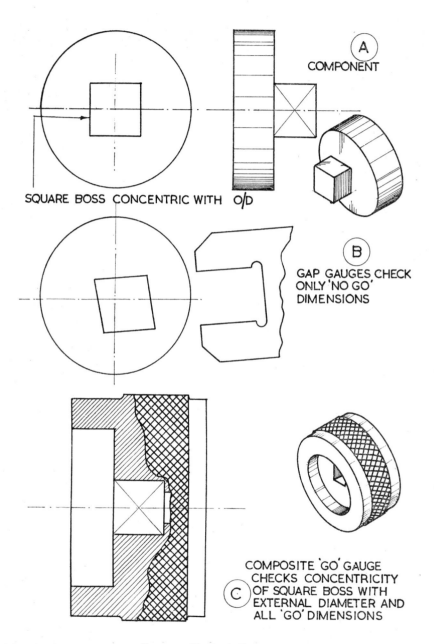

SQUARE BOSS CONCENTRIC WITH O/D

(A) COMPONENT

(B) GAP GAUGES CHECK ONLY 'NO GO' DIMENSIONS

(C) COMPOSITE 'GO' GAUGE CHECKS CONCENTRICITY OF SQUARE BOSS WITH EXTERNAL DIAMETER AND ALL 'GO' DIMENSIONS

FIG. 5.3.—TAYLOR'S PRINCIPLE

side diameter and the length of side of the square boss, then such gauges would accept a component as shown at Fig. 5.3B. The high-limit gap gauge illustrated would accept the square boss, thus indicating that the length of side was not less than the low limit, but such a gauge would give no indication of the squareness of the boss, or its concentricity with the centre of the diameter. A gap gauge on high limit would be used to check the outside diameter, but while indicating that the diameter at the points of contact were not outside the high limit, such a gauge would not indicate the roundness of the diameter.

The correct GO gauge is illustrated at Fig. 5.3C, and it may be seen that this composite gauge ensures the following conditions:

   (i) No part of the diameter is in excess of the high limit.
  (ii) The lengths of the square sides are not greater than the high limit.
 (iii) The square sides have 90° accuracy.
 (iv) The square is concentric with the component centre line.

Provided the component fits into this composite GO gauge all the above conditions are checked. It is possible, however, that the diameter may be undersize, that is to say under the low limit, while the length of side of the square boss also may be less than the low limit.

To ensure that neither the outside diameter nor the length of side of the square boss is below the low limit, separate gap gauges are used to check these dimensions, as shown at Fig. 5.3B.

5.3.1. Limit gauging of external screw threads

In accordance with the Taylor principle, the GO dimensions of an external screw thread must be checked with a full-form GO gauge, and two NO GO gauges—one to check the effective diameter and the other the major diameter of the thread.

The GO gauge

A full-form GO ring gauge suitable for checking an external screw thread is illustrated at Fig. 5.4A. All dimensions are on high limit; thus if the thread enters the full length of the gauge, no dimension is in excess of the high limit. Note that the thread profile has full form, as shown in the diagram.

The NO GO gauge

The NO GO ring gauge is intended to check that the effective diameter is not less than the low limit specified for the particular thread under test, and as can be seen from Fig. 5.4B, the length of the gauge extends over a distance of about three threads, with the thread form reduced or truncated

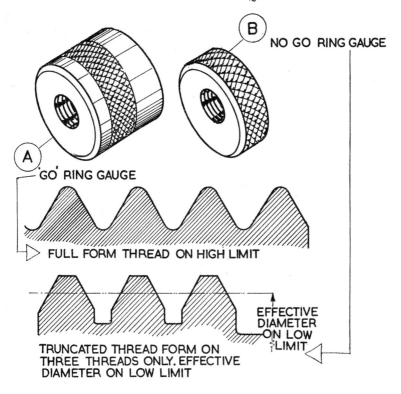

B NO GO RING GAUGE

A GO RING GAUGE

FULL FORM THREAD ON HIGH LIMIT

EFFECTIVE
DIAMETER
ON LOW
LIMIT

TRUNCATED THREAD FORM ON
THREE THREADS ONLY. EFFECTIVE
DIAMETER ON LOW LIMIT

FIG. 5.4.—LIMIT GAUGING OF SCREW THREADS

to ensure that the gauging is on the flanks of the threads. The remaining gauge is a simple NO GO plug-gap gauge used to ensure that the major diameter is not below the low limit.

Caliper thread gauges

The thread ring gauges shown are both difficult and costly to produce, and increasing use is now being made of adjustable caliper thread gauges. A typical caliper gauge is illustrated at Fig. 5.5, where it can be seen that both GO and NO GO sizes are incorporated on the one gauge. The hardened and tempered ground rollers are free to rotate, thus reducing wear and prolonging the useful life of the gauge; the outer rollers have a full-form thread on high limit, while the inner rollers are truncated and are set to the low limit of the effective diameter, and gauge over a distance of about three threads only.

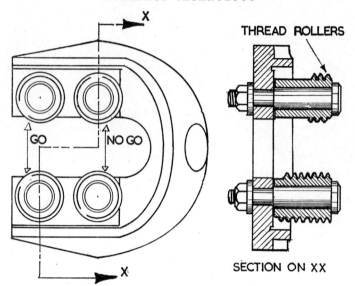

FIG. 5.5.—CALIPER GO AND NO GO THREAD GAUGE

5.3.2. Limit gauging of internal threads

The same gauging principle is applied to the checking of internal threads, that is to say a full-form GO thread plug gauge, together with a reduced form NO GO thread plug gauge. To ensure that the minor diameter is not oversize, a plain plug NO GO is used.

Both gauges are illustrated at Fig. 5.6; note that the thread plug gauge

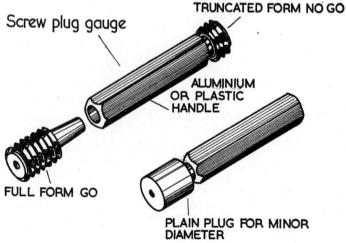

FIG. 5.6.—THREAD PLUG GAUGES

is double-ended, with a full form GO gauge at one end and a NO GO truncated thread form at the other end.

5.4. Applications of the combination inspection technique

It is an axiom of efficient and economical manufacture that the inspection of the machined dimensions keeps pace with the increased rates of production made possible by new developments in metal forming and removal. In the same way that modern machine tools such as automatic lathes operate on the principle of maximum metal removal in one setting or chucking of the component, so also do combination inspection techniques check several dimensions in one setting. Essentially the technique is one of inspection by comparison; a master component is used to set the inspection devices to zero, the machined component replaces the master and any variation from the zero readings is indicated by the recording instruments used.

5.4.1. Combination inspection with dial indicators

Standard units of the caliper type may be assembled on a suitable fixture to suit the particular requirements of machined components. The indicator dials are available in various degrees of accuracy according to the amount of tolerance given on the machined dimensions, and tolerance pointers may be set to indicate the high and low limits of the dimensions under test.

Fig. 5.7A illustrates a high-accuracy dial indicator, manufactured by C. E. Johansson of Sweden, and called a small-type Mikrokator. This instrument operates on the twisted-strip principle which was simply described in *T.3 Workshop Technology*, Chapter 2, Fig. 2.15. At Fig. 5.7B we see some of the standard equipment by which inspection fixtures may be built up using the mikrokators just described. The baseplate is machined to accommodate several standard elements, permitting inspection in the vertical or horizontal plane. Suitable V blocks are used to locate the component, preferably on the bearing surfaces, and simultaneous checking of the diameters, lengths, roundness, squareness, axial truth and taper is readily achieved.

Fig. 5.7c illustrates a typical example of the application of the combination inspection device involving horizontal mounting of the component. The assembled fixture is light in weight and easily transportable, can be used in close proximity to the machining station or production line, and is eminently suitable for the inspection to close limits of turned or ground cylindrical components similar to the example shown at Fig. 5.7c.

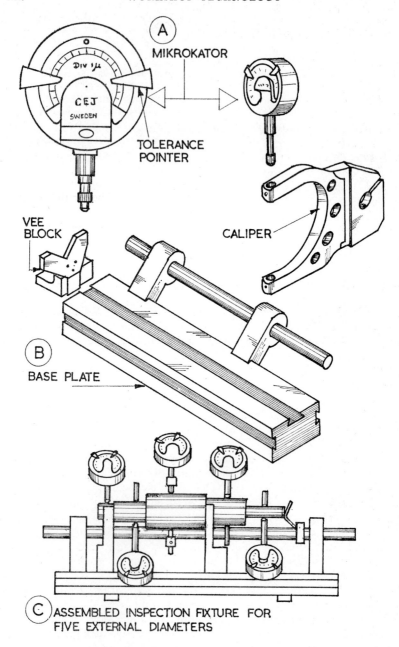

Ⓐ MIKROKATOR

Div 1µ

CEJ

SWEDEN

TOLERANCE POINTER

VEE BLOCK

CALIPER

Ⓑ BASE PLATE

Ⓒ ASSEMBLED INSPECTION FIXTURE FOR FIVE EXTERNAL DIAMETERS

FIG. 5.7.—PRINCIPLE OF STANDARD EQUIPMENT FOR COMBINATION INSPECTION

5.4.2. Combination inspection with indicating signals

The use of dial indicators or mikrokators makes possible not only the inspection of a number of dimensions but also their measurement. The tolerance pointers, set to the high and low limit of the dimension under test, give the limitations of the pointer reading; any reading outside the tolerance pointers indicates rejection of the dimension.

At the same time, the position of the pointer within the tolerance pointers gives the size of the component and also indicates whether the dimension is approaching high or low limit. For example, steady approach of the pointer to the high-limit tolerance pointer over a period of time indicates wear of the cutting tool, and action can be taken to reset the cutting tool, thus bringing the dimension (say) to just below the middle limit.

Mikrokators are now available with built-in electrical contacts; thus an oversize dimension is immediately indicated by an amber signal lamp. Similarly, a dimension within the limits is indicated by a green lamp, while an undersized dimension is indicated by a red lamp. The use of signal lamps of this kind enables semi-skilled inspectors to carry out rapid inspection of machined components without the need for close study of the indicating dials. Provided the dimension under test results in illumination of the green signal lamp the dimension is within the limits laid down. This technique results in considerable speeding-up of the inspection procedure.

Signal lamps and selective assembly

An important advantage of the use of the signal-lamp technique is that instruments are now available which will indicate the actual position of the dimension within the tolerance allocated. This means that components may be readily sorted for purposes of selective assembly; that is to say high-limit holes are mated to high-limit shafts, middle-limit holes to middle-limit shafts and low-limit holes to low-limit shafts.

Perhaps a simple example will help to make clear the principle involved.

Fig. 5.8A shows a simple design sketch of a shaft and mating pulley. The designer, using BS 4500:1969, has specified an H7 hole and a g6 shaft, giving a close running fit. As we have seen in the previous volume, an H7 hole will be produced by boring or broaching while a g6 shaft will be ground to size.

Referring to the tolerance tables given in BS 4500, we find that the tolerance and limits for a 19·05 mm diameter hole are as follows:

$$\begin{array}{rcl}
\text{High limit of hole} & = & 19\text{·}075 \text{ mm} \\
\text{Low limit of hole} & = & 19\text{·}05 \text{ mm} \\
\text{Tolerance} & = & 0\text{·}025 \text{ mm}
\end{array}$$

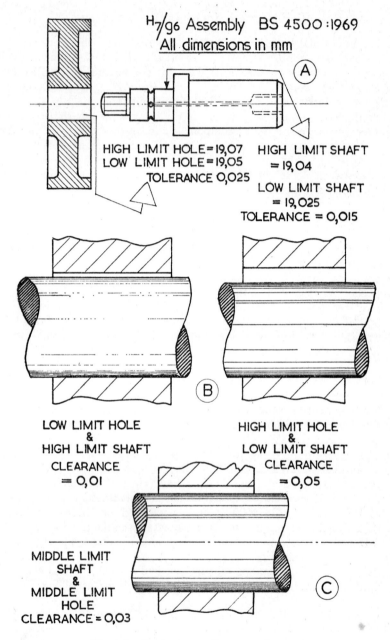

$H_7/g6$ Assembly   BS 4500 : 1969
All dimensions in mm

HIGH LIMIT HOLE = 19,07
LOW LIMIT HOLE = 19,05
TOLERANCE 0,025

HIGH LIMIT SHAFT
= 19,04

LOW LIMIT SHAFT
= 19,025
TOLERANCE = 0,015

LOW LIMIT HOLE
&
HIGH LIMIT SHAFT
CLEARANCE
= 0,01

HIGH LIMIT HOLE
&
LOW LIMIT SHAFT
CLEARANCE
= 0,05

MIDDLE LIMIT
SHAFT
&
MIDDLE LIMIT
HOLE
CLEARANCE = 0,03

Fig. 5.8.—Principles of Selective Assembly

For the shaft the limits and tolerance are as follows:

$$\text{High limit of shaft} \quad = \quad 19{\cdot}04 \text{ mm}$$
$$\text{Low limit of shaft} \quad = \quad 19{\cdot}025 \text{ mm}$$
$$\text{Tolerance} \quad = \quad 0{\cdot}015 \text{ mm}$$

Provided the holes and shafts are machined to within the limits given they are acceptable. It is possible, however, that two undesirable matings may occur, namely:

(i) assembling a high-limit shaft to a low-limit hole;
(ii) assembling a low-limit shaft to a high-limit hole.

A simple diagrammatic representation of both occurrences is shown at Fig. 5.8B, and it may be seen that the actual running fit obtained in each case leaves a great deal to be desired. Clearly in the first case, with a high-limit shaft and a low-limit hole, we have a minimum clearance, and there is a risk of seizure. On the other hand, a low-limit shaft mated to a high-limit hole gives excessive clearance, as can be seen from the diagram. The ideal conditions are shown at Fig. 5.8c, where we see a middle-limit hole assembled to a middle-limit shaft.

With the aid of suitable equipment it is possible to set the measuring device so that signal lamps will indicate the following results when the dimension is checked:

(i) oversize;
(ii) undersize;
(iii) middle limit;
(iv) approaching low limit;
(v) approaching high limit.

This means that the signal box is equipped with five lamps, each giving immediate indication of one of the above results. In this way it is possible to grade the shafts and holes so that the best possible fit results, namely:

(i) middle-limit holes to middle-limit shafts;
(ii) low-limit holes to low-limit shafts;
(iii) high-limit holes to high-limit shafts.

Fig. 5.9 illustrates a typical signal box. The setting of the instrument is achieved with the aid of master specimens carefully machined to within the desired tolerance zones.

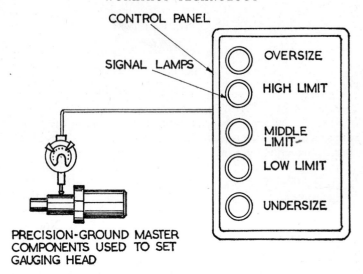

FIG. 5.9.—USE OF SIGNAL LAMPS

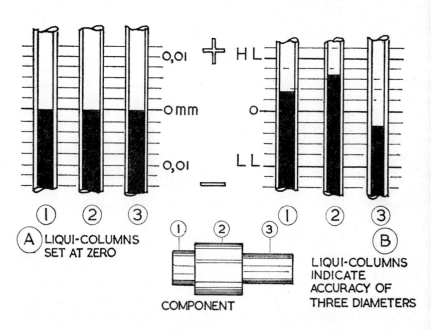

FIG. 5.10.—USE OF LIQUICOLUMNS FOR PNEUMATIC GAUGING

5.5. Pneumatic gauging

In its simplest form 'pneumatic gauging', or 'air gauging' as it is more commonly called, makes use of water-filled tubes in conjunction with suitable scales. This device is simply illustrated at Fig. 5.10A, which shows three liquicolumns, as we may call them, all reading zero. These zero readings are obtained with a master component in position; thus we see at once that once again a combination inspection technique is employed, with three diameters checked simultaneously.

At Fig. 5.10B we see the result of replacing the master with a machined component. Any variation of the diameters under test from the master diameters is immediately indicated by a rise or fall of the liquicolumn, and with the gauging scale calibrated in 0·002 mm it is clear that pneumatic or air gauging offers a rapid, easily read method of determining the accuracy or acceptability of machined dimensions. Note that the principle employed is common to all combination inspection techniques; namely setting up the measuring or checking device with a precision master component, with immediate and rapid indication of variation from this master. It is clear that with the type of scale illustrated at Fig. 5.10 very little skill is needed from the user of the equipment; provided the liquicolumns fall within the high and low limits the machined diameters are acceptable.

For example, it is clear that the three diameters under test in Fig. 5.10B are within the limits of acceptability, while concentricity of the diameters is readily checked by rotation of the component. Note that, while a scale is shown in Fig. 5.10A, this is not strictly necessary. For example, a line can be adjusted with a master component machined to low limits, and similarly a master component on high limit can be used to set a line indicating high limit.

In this way the high and low limits of several machined dimensions are simply and clearly indicated to the operator of the gauging device, who may have little idea of the actual limits of size. Provided that all the liquicolumns fall between the two lines indicating high and low limit the machined component is acceptable and may be passed to assembly.

5.5.1. The use of air pressure

Linear movement of the liquicolumns is brought about by changes of air pressure. Consider Fig. 5.11. Air at constant pressure is introduced into the chamber as shown in the diagram, through an orifice indicated as Oa. The orifice indicated at Ob permits air to escape from the chamber, while an opening at G leads to a simple manometer. If the surface shown as S is brought into close contact with the orifice Ob the escape of air is prevented, and the pressure within the chamber will equal that of the air supply, giving a linear rise in the column of liquid on the right-hand side of the manometer. If the surface S is moved slightly away from the orifice Ob, in other words through a small linear movement *H*, a small quantity of air is allowed to escape, with the result that the pressure within the chamber is now less than that of the air supply resulting in a lower reading of the manometer.

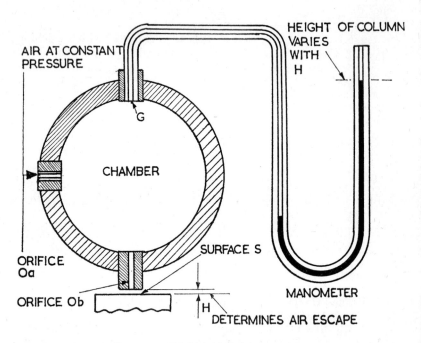

FIG. 5.11.—THE AIR-PRESSURE PRINCIPLE

It is clear that increase in distance *H* is equivalent to increase in the escape of air, or increase in the diameter of the escape orifice Ob, and it has been found that provided the ratio of inlet and escape orifices, together with the ratio of the air supply and pressure within the chamber, are kept within certain values, the pressure within the chamber is a linear function of the distance *H*. In other words, small variations in distance *H* caused by differences resulting from the comparison of a machined diameter or dimension against a master component give rise to differences in pressure within the air chamber, these pressure differences resulting in rise or fall of a liquicolumn.

The diagram shown in Fig. 5.11 is a much simplified representation of the pneumatic gauging principle, for it is an essential condition of accuracy that the air pressure supplied to the chamber is maintained at a constant value. In general, two main air gauging systems are in common use, namely a low-pressure system and a high-pressure system.

5.5.2. Low-pressure air gauging

Low-pressure air or pneumatic gauging makes use of liquicolumns or manometers, a typical example being the Solex system. Fig. 5.12 shows in simple detail the basic principle underlying the Solex pneumatic gauge. As we have already pointed out, constancy of air pressure is an essential element in air gauging, and this is achieved in the first air control chamber, where air under pressure passes through restriction jets before entering a dip tube at comparatively low pressure, as shown in the diagram.

The pressure in the air control chamber is equal to the head of water forced down the dip tube, excess air bubbling from the bottom of the dip tube. Provided the level of water remains constant so also does the pressure in the dip tube, and this pressure is slightly in excess of that required at the gauging head.

The reduced pressure to the gauging head is achieved by means of a suitable control jet with a flexible lead taking the air pressure to the gauging head, as shown in the diagram. Note the introduction of a manometer between the control jet and the gauging head; any variation in the air pressure owing to increase or decrease in escape air is immediately recorded by linear movement of the liquid column within the glass tube of the manometer. With the insertion of a suitably calibrated scale behind the glass tube of the manometer, and using the measuring heads illustrated at Fig. 5.12B, a wide range of gauging operations are possible, very suitable for the simultaneous gauging of a number of machined dimensions. The plug gauge shown on the left is widely used for the checking of machined bores to close limits of tolerance. With three jets arranged at 120° to each other, insertion and rotation of the plug gauge reveals not only diametral errors but also any tendency to ovality or out-of-roundness. Note that a measuring jet does not touch the surface under test; thus there is no wear or deterioration of the measuring elements. As may be seen from the right-hand illustration at Fig. 5.12B, the measuring jet may be arranged vertically, giving in effect a vertical comparator with the height of the liquicolumn at zero with the master component under the measuring jet. It may be appreciated at this stage that there is practically no limit to the type of checking possible by pneumatic gauging. Provided a component can be suitably located and placed in position with respect to the gauging jets, then diameters, widths, lengths, alignment, roundness and concentricity can all be checked, with each item or element indicated by movement of its respective liquicolumn.

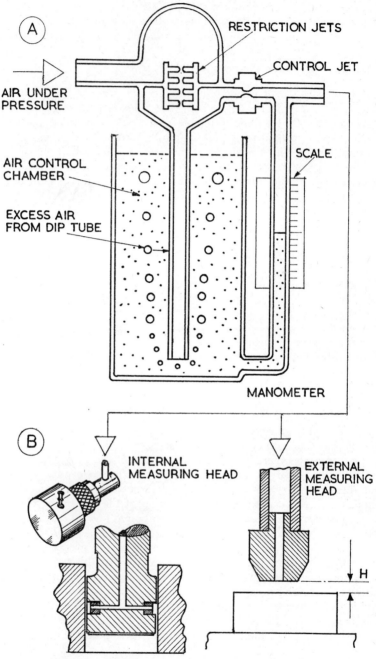

FIG. 5.12.—PRINCIPLE OF LOW-PRESSURE AIR GAUGING

5.5.3. High-pressure air gauging

This is a popular type of air gauging which uses higher pressures than are required for the manometer system. The glass tubes are replaced by dial-type indicators, or deltameters as they are more commonly called. Clearly the replacement of a glass tube with a dial provides a more versatile method of inspection and measurement, for the dials are robust and sturdy and easily adaptable to measuring devices such as internal and external calipers. At the same time the small size of the dial allows it to be placed close to the measuring position, while complete mobility is also possible with a flexible lead.

Fig. 5.13 shows the basic principle involved, and it must be appreciated at this point that the measuring system differs a great deal from the Solex pneumatic system just described. As may be seen on reference to the diagram, two basic units are required:

   (i) measuring head;
   (ii) recording dial.

The measuring head houses a movable spindle or plunger, its movement leading to changes in air pressure to the recording dial, giving pointer movement. In other words very small linear movements of the measuring plunger are converted to relatively large movements of the pointer; magnification ratios of 30 000 are easily achieved. It is evident that with the aid of the flexible air connection the measuring head can be placed at any convenient machining or measuring point, while the recording dial can be placed for maximum ease of reading.

A simple diagram illustrating the principle of the measuring head is shown at Fig. 5.14. The air intake is shown at A; the air will have been passed through an air cleaner for thorough removal of moisture and any foreign bodies. In addition the air has been reduced in pressure to about 250 kN/m^2, a special reducing valve being used for this purpose. With the measuring plunger or spindle in the neutral or zero position, the same quantity of air passes both sides of the restrictions shown as aa and bb; thus an equal quantity of air flows through the output tubes and hence to both sides of a bellows system in the recording dial, giving a zero reading.

If, now, the measuring plunger is pushed upwards, say by variation of a dimension under test from the master setting, the passage of air at aa is greatly restricted, while the aperture at bb is increased, allowing an increase in the flow of air at this point. In other words, the *pressure in the upper chamber increases* while that in the lower decreases. The increased pressure is conveyed to one side of the bellows system in the recording dial, while the opposite side gets a reduction in pressure, resulting in movement of the dial pointer to indicate a positive error. Similarly, an undersize component will result in downward movement of the plunger,

F

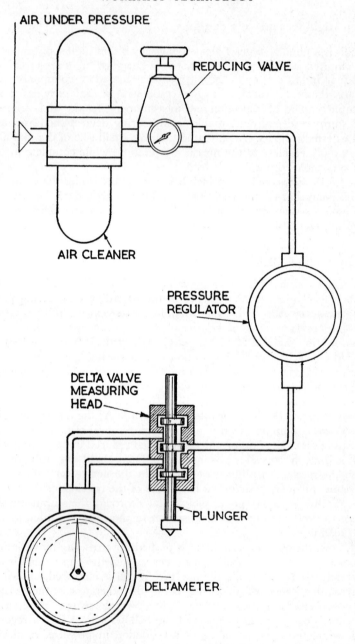

AIR UNDER PRESSURE

REDUCING VALVE

AIR CLEANER

PRESSURE
REGULATOR

DELTA VALVE
MEASURING
HEAD

PLUNGER

DELTAMETER

FIG. 5.13.—PRINCIPLE OF HIGH-PRESSURE AIR GAUGING

in which case the air pressure in the upper chamber increases, with a corresponding pressure decrease in the lower chamber, and a minus reading is obtained on the dial.

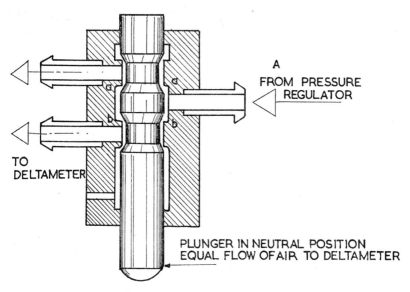

FIG. 5.14.—MEASURING HEAD

Should the measuring head be required to check an internal diameter, it is a simple matter to change the positions of the flexible connections so that inward movement of the plunger results in a minus reading on the dial. The actual shape of the measuring head may vary according to the particular operation for which it is required, but in most cases the actual contact point is spherical and tungsten-carbide tipped to promote a long and accurate life.

Fig. 5.15 shows the dial face of a typical deltameter. The relatively large diameter of 130 mm allows a magnification ratio of about 30 000; that is to say a plunger movement of 0·025 mm results in a pointer movement of 750 mm. For example, the distance between the divisions on the dial shown in Fig. 5.15 is about 30 mm, while the dial is graduated in 0·001 mm. Thus the pointer will move through one division on the dial for a movement of 1 micrometre of the plunger. This represents a very high degree of precision measurement, but alternative scales are available with lower magnification ratios.

All standard deltameters are fitted with two adjustable tolerance pointers and two electric contacts. The tolerance pointers allow immediate checking of whether the dimension is within the specified limits, while the electrical contact points may be used to operate signal lamps,

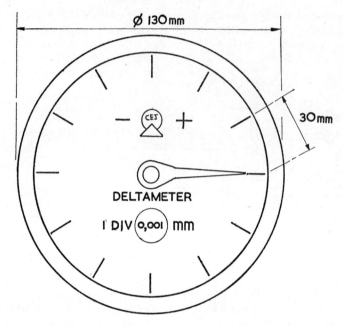

SYMMETRICAL SCALE

FIG. 5.15.—STANDARD DELTAMETER DIAL

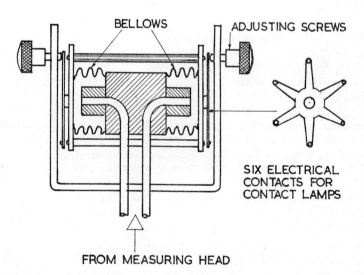

FIG. 5.16.—USE OF ELECTRICAL CONTACTS

alarm devices and sorting devices. Because of the use of air at fairly high pressure, causing large forces to operate on the bellows system within the indicating dial, up to six electrical contacts can be built in on each side of the instrument, and with a suitable low-tension 12-volt supply the deltameter can be set to sort workpieces into definite limit groups, as previously explained in 5.4.2.

Fig. 5.16 shows in simple principle how the variation of air pressure to the bellows results in the making of electrical contacts, with the contact settings easily achieved by rotation of the adjustable screw shown.

5.5.4. Application of liquicolumns

The liquicolumn principle of pneumatic gauging is ideally suited to the multi-dimension inspection technique, and has been pioneered and greatly developed by the Sigma Company. As a typical example of the versatility of this technique we may consider the inspection of a four-throw automobile engine crankshaft, a component representing a very high degree of complex machining to close limits of accuracy. Such a crankshaft is illustrated at Fig. 5.17A, and a simple outline of the semi-automatic liquicolumn machine is shown at Fig. 5.17B.

A total of thirty-three static and rotary dimensions are checked on this machine, using semi-skilled operatives, the whole checking operation

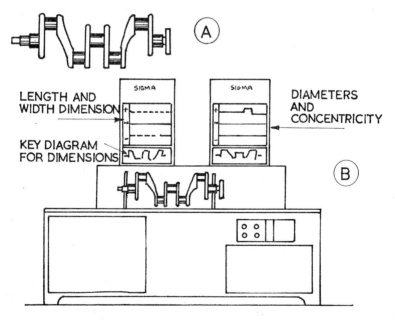

FIG. 5.17.—CRANKSHAFT INSPECTION

being completed in under one minute. In addition to the linear dimensions such as diameters and throw, rotation of the crankshaft makes it possible to check the non-linear functions of roundness and concentricity. Length and width dimensions are indicated on the liquicolumns on the left-hand side of the machine, and non-linear functions by those on the right.

A further advantage offered by this technique lies in the fact that the liquicolumn readings are retained on removal of the crankshaft from the machine; this allows an indication of dimensional drift, as the columns of liquid only move an amount equivalent to the difference in size between the successive crankshafts inserted in the machine. Once the instrument is set, using a master crankshaft, the checking operation is rapidly and efficiently performed, with segregation simply achieved on reference to the limit sizes clearly indicated on the liquicolumn scales. There is practically no limit to the type of inspection possible with these machines, and items such as ball races, roller bearings or gear shafts are readily inspected for linear dimensions and for squareness, eccentricity, lobing and taper.

Fully automatic machines are also available, the components being fed in through a hopper; for example, an automatic Sigma liquicolumn machine is capable of feeding, cleaning and checking the width and parallelism of face of ball races at the rate of 2 000 per hour.

Components of a more complex nature having a wide range of machining operations, for example a crankcase or crankcase cover, are readily checked using a battery of liquicolumn machines, the components being passed from one machine to the other in the minimum of time.

5.5.5. Application of Deltameters

The deltameter principle has been pioneered and brought to a high degree of perfection by the well-known firm of C. E. Johansson, of Eskilstuna, Sweden. It is of interest to know that a Swedish armourer inspector, Carl Johansson, was granted a British patent for his system of precision block gauges in 1902, and although regarded at that time as something of a novelty, his system of the precise determination of linear measurements by means of accurate block or slip gauges is now well established, and represents the basis of all measurements by comparison.

As we have seen, the great advantage of the deltameter principle is that a large-type dial is used, conveniently placed at some distance from the actual measuring head. This means that the technique is ideally suited for the determination of size **during the machining operation**. It must always be remembered that while a measuring device may immediately indicate an oversize dimension, the fact remains that the component is reject and unacceptable. Clearly, in many cases it is a great advantage to measure or check while the machining is in progress, and Fig. 5.18 illustrates in a simple manner a typical application. Here we see a deltameter used to give a continuous reading during the grinding of a precision shaft, and it is clear that the application of this technique provides the machine operator with a sure indication of whether he is machining the dimension within the limits given.

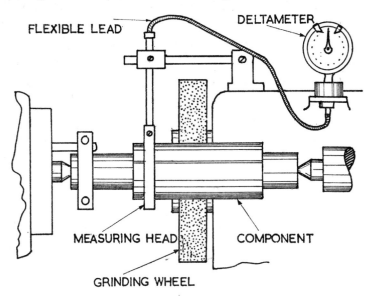

FIG. 5.18.—DIMENSIONAL CONTROL DURING GRINDING

Summary

It is an axiom of engineering manufacture that the application of new techniques in one field should be accompanied by similar developments in associated fields. For example, there is little to be gained by the introduction of high-efficiency machine tools capable of high rates of production if outdated, slow and unreliable inspection techniques are adopted to determine whether the machined dimensions are within the limits of acceptance.

It is true to state that except for relatively small batch production the use of limit gauges is now outdated, for a wide range of caliper gauges equipped with visual dials are now available; such gauges are capable of good accuracy, with the added advantage of indicating dimensional drift of the machined dimensions.

The application of such gauges to combination inspection techniques, that is to say the simultaneous gauging of several dimensions, follows as a logical development, and several efficient devices are available as standard units, readily converted to suit particular applications.

Perhaps it should be appreciated that the inspection of both internal and external screw threads may be carried out using screw-thread gauges, with several types available for external threads.

The need for rapid and efficient inspection of the many machined components has led to the introduction of compressed-air, or in other words pneumatic gauging. We have seen that two main types of pneumatic gauging are in use:

    (i) the Solex system, using liquicolumns;
    (ii) the Johansson deltameter, using large-diameter dials.

The Solex system operates on the rate of escape of air from a pre-fixed jet, changes in the escape rate leading to variations in height of a liquicolumn, while the deltameter principle relies on linear movement of the measuring plunger to vary the amount of air pressure conveyed to a sensitive bellows located in the dial. Both systems can be adapted to operate signal lamps, sorting devices or audible alarm systems, and there is practically no limit to the application of these techniques for the automatic or semi-automatic inspection of complex machined components. In many cases measuring stations incorporating either of the above-mentioned techniques can be placed integral with the machining process; for example, a transfer line used to machine the cylinder block of an automobile engine may have two or more inspection stations included in it. These inspection stations not only check previously machined dimensions but are able to give visible or audible indication should a dimension be outside the limits of acceptability, and in some cases automatically stop the transfer line, thus preventing further production of reject components.

We have seen, too, that automatic measuring or inspection devices may now be fitted to the actual machine tool producing the component; by this technique the operator is able to have complete control over the dimension to be machined. It must be kept in mind at all times that while inspection may reveal a faulty dimension, the part is still reject, and there is the added possibility that the machine tool may have produced a large number of reject components before the fault was detected.

EXERCISE 5

1 The component illustrated at Fig. 5.19 is to be produced at the rate of 500 per week. Describe a suitable inspection technique for this component, listing the equipment required.

2 Make a neat sketch of a dial snap gauge, explaining the advantages offered by the use of this gauge.

3 Explain what is meant by 'Taylor's principle' with respect to the gauging of engineering components.

Give, with reasons, **two** non-linear functions that cannot be detected by simple limit gauges.

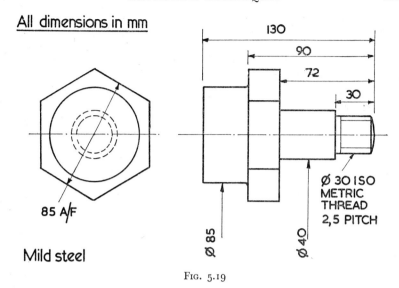

All dimensions in mm

85 A/F

Mild steel

130

90

72

30

Ø 30 ISO
METRIC
THREAD
2,5 PITCH

Ø 85

Ø 40

FIG. 5.19

4 Name the three elements of a screw thread that determine its accuracy. Sketch the limit gauges required to maintain dimensional control over large batches of M25 × 2 external ISO bolts machined at a capstan lathe.

5 With the aid of a multi-dimension component, explain the principle of the combination inspection technique using sensitive dial indicators.

State **two** advantages offered by the application of the above inspection technique.

6 Explain in some detail how machined components may be divided into tolerance grades for purposes of selective assembly.

What advantages are to be gained by the use of signal lamps?

7 With a neat diagram, show how restriction of air escape from an orifice results in linear displacement of a liquicolumn.

8 Explain the essential difference in principle between high- and low-pressure air-gauging systems. With a neat diagram show how linear movement of a measuring plunger as used in the high-pressure system results in changes of air pressure to the recording dial.

9 Sketch a typical component well suited to the application of the Solex system of pneumatic gauging on a semi-automatic basis. Explain the method adopted to set the liquicolumns to zero, and give a reason why the liquicolumns are arranged to retain their readings on removal of the component.

10 Explain why the Johansson deltameter system of high-pressure pneumatic gauging is eminently suitable for the measurement or inspection of machined dimensions during the actual metal-removal process.

6

SURFACE FINISH AND MACHINE-TOOL ALIGNMENTS

6.1. Introduction

The inherent ability of any machine tool to produce a given geometric surface depends in the first instance on the geometrical accuracy of the movements and alignments of the separate elements that make up the complete tool. For example, Fig. 6.1 shows in a simple manner the essential alignments between the worktable and wheelhead of a universal grinding machine when grinding a cylindrical surface. Clearly a great deal of metal-to-metal contact takes place during the grinding operation; for example, we may consider the following movements:

(i) rotation of the grinding-wheel spindle on its bearings;
(ii) rotation of the workpiece;
(iii) reciprocal traverse of the worktable;
(iv) infeed of the wheelhead.

All these movements call for conditions of precise alignment, and these alignments are achieved with the use of bearing surfaces and guideways. In other words, the bearing surfaces of the worktable must be plane surfaces, probably arranged as shown in Fig. 6.2A, and it is now clear that if a truly cylindrical surface is to be ground the centre line of the revolving workpiece must be parallel with the centre line of the grinding wheel in both horizontal and vertical planes and at any position of the worktable and wheelhead. This geometric alignment is simply illustrated at Fig. 6.2B; any deviation from these conditions must affect the accuracy of the cylindrical surface produced.

At the same time it is important that the grinding machine be able to produce accurate work over a period of time; that is to say it must have a reasonably long useful life. This brings us to the important aspect of surface finish. It has long been recognised that the useful life of moving parts is directly proportional to the quality of the surface finish of the mating surfaces; thus the alignments of machine tools are certain to be affected should the quality of the surface finish of the machined bearing surfaces fall below acceptable values.

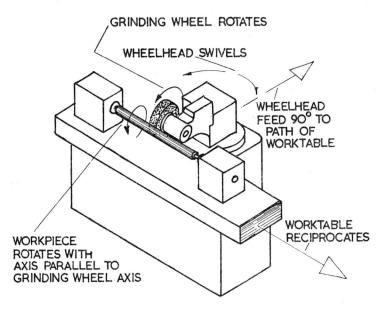

FIG. 6.1.—ALIGNMENTS OF MACHINE-TOOL ELEMENTS

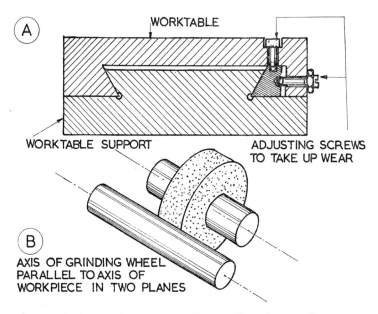

FIG. 6.2.—USE AND ADJUSTMENT OF BEARING SURFACES AND GUIDEWAYS

6.2. The elements of surface finish

In order to have a clear picture of the elements or factors that make up the surface finish of a machined face, we may consider in the first place a perfect plane surface as shown at Fig. 6.3A. No matter in which direction a cross-sectional cut is taken, the top profile representing the true plane surface appears as shown in the circles, which represent a highly magnified view of the section. The horizontal straight line represents the perfect surface, free from any roughness or waviness.

Let us now consider machining the top surface using a single-point cutting tool, as may be done by facing at the lathe, shaping, planing or fly-cutting at a vertical milling machine. Fig. 6.3B shows a somewhat exaggerated picture of the cutting action and the surface produced. We may consider the surface produced by the cutting tool to have a particular texture, made up from the following elements:

(i) roughness;
(ii) waviness;
(iii) lay.

6.2.1. Roughness

We see from Fig. 6.3B that the surface roughness is occasioned by the feed of the tool or worktable, the profile of the tool nose, and the actual cutting or shearing action of the tool upon the metal. Clearly the coarser the feed, the deeper the cut, and the more pointed the tool-nose profile, the greater will be the surface roughness. Provided, however, sufficient metal remains for a finishing operation, carried out with a finishing tool at a greatly reduced depth of cut, the roughness of a machined surface is of little account. Roughing operations are an essential part of machining when the primary object is the maximum amount of metal removal.

6.2.2. Waviness

There are two kinds of waviness likely in the machined surface shown at Fig. 6.3B. Firstly we have the intentional waviness produced by a combination of the tool profile and feed. This is shown at Fig. 6.3C. Considerable magnification is needed, but in a vertical direction only. For example, Fig. 6.3C shows a turned surface with a magnification of 200 times vertically and 20 times horizontally. Assuming the depth of cut to be about 0·05 mm with a feed of 0·13 mm/rev, then if the same magnification were used both vertically and horizontally, representation of the waviness of a turned bar 250 mm long would require a strip of paper 50 metres long!

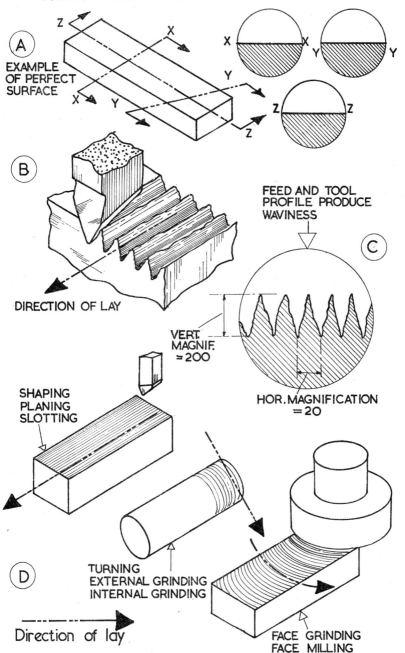

A
EXAMPLE
OF PERFECT
SURFACE

B
DIRECTION OF LAY

FEED AND TOOL
PROFILE PRODUCE
WAVINESS

C

VERT.
MAGNIF.
=200

HOR. MAGNIFICATION
=20

SHAPING
PLANING
SLOTTING

TURNING
EXTERNAL GRINDING
INTERNAL GRINDING

D

Direction of lay

FACE GRINDING
FACE MILLING

FIG. 6.3.—ELEMENTS OF SURFACE FINISH

This means that enlarged or magnified views of a machined surface are difficult to interpret, for the vertical scale may have a magnification of up to 100 000 times for a very well-finished or lapped surface, while the horizontal scale may have a magnification of only 100 times.

The second kind of waviness present in our machined surface may be considered as unintentional. This waviness may lie along the direction of machining, or the lay as it is more commonly called, and a further unintentional waviness may result from incorrect or faulty geometrical movements of the machine tool itself. The waviness along the lay is caused by the shearing action of the cutting tool together with vibration, leading to the familiar machining phenomenon known as **chatter.**

6.2.3. Lay

The term lay refers to the direction of machining, and it is essential to ensure that all determinations of roughness or surface finish are made at 90° to the lay of the machined surface. Fig. 6.3D illustrates simple examples of the lay of surfaces produced by different methods of machining.

6.3. Simple methods of determining roughness

The time-honoured method of determining surface roughness consists in lightly running one's finger or hand over the surface under test; indeed there are few men who have not, at some time or another, used this technique to determine whether or not a shave is necessary. For average workshop standards of machining the application of the 'feel' technique is well established, with several excellent roughness standards available. Such a roughness standard is simply illustrated at Fig. 6.4, with a total of twenty-four different grades of roughness available. As may be seen, the composite standard is rectangular in shape, with each separate roughness surface clearly indicated. A dark, hard-wearing plastic material is used, and the technique consists, not in visual use of the standard but in passing one's fingernail lightly over the machined surface under test, and then over the surface imprinted on the standard, as shown in the diagram. Better results are obtained by this feel technique because visual examination is affected by the actual metal or material under test. For example, a bright material appears to have a better finish than a dull material, or a polished surface than an unpolished or matt surface. Alternative sets of roughness standards are available, either cylindrical or rectangular and manufactured from metal. In all cases the surface standards just described give the machining processes together with the appropriate roughness number, thus allowing a machine operator to have a relatively simple check should the workpiece drawing specify a certain roughness number.

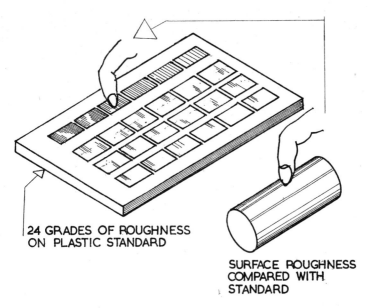

24 GRADES OF ROUGHNESS
ON PLASTIC STANDARD

SURFACE ROUGHNESS
COMPARED WITH
STANDARD

FIG. 6.4.—STANDARD FEEL TEST FOR SURFACE ROUGHNESS

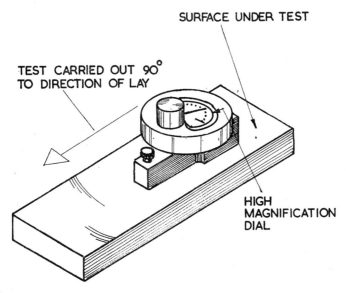

SURFACE UNDER TEST

TEST CARRIED OUT 90°
TO DIRECTION OF LAY

HIGH
MAGNIFICATION
DIAL

FIG. 6.5.—DIRECT READING SURFACE ROUGHNESS INDICATOR

A more precise method of determining surface roughness is possible with the use of a surface-finish indicator. Manufactured by the well-known firm of C. E. Johansson, this little instrument can be adapted to a wide range of surface measurements by means of suitable accessories. As may be seen in the diagram at Fig. 6.5, the unit consists of a high-magnification dial, the pointer of which greatly amplifies vertical displacements of a diamond-tipped stylus located in a hole in the leading support or skid. The faces of these skids are tipped with tungsten carbide to promote a long and accurate life, and the diamond-tipped stylus presses on the surface under test with a force of about 0·01 newtons.

Slow movement of the instrument along the surface under test results in variation of the pointer, with readings to within 0·000 12 mm. For the surface measurement of cylindrical bars or machined holes, attachments are available whereby a special feeding device is utilised to give uniformity to the traverse of the stylus. Note that in the simple example given in Fig. 6.5, the movement of the surface-finish indicator is at 90° to the lay.

6.4. Graphical representation of surface finish

A graphical representation of a machined surface is shown at Fig. 6.3c. A practical method of obtaining such a graph or profile was developed by G. A. Tomlinson of the National Physical Laboratory in 1939, and the device is remarkable for its simplicity and ease of operation. Reference to Fig. 6.6 will give a simple appreciation of its construction. Basically, the device amplifies very small vertical movements or displacements of a diamond-tipped stylus relative to a datum or skid as both are moved slowly over the surface under test. This principle is illustrated at Fig. 6.6A, and is common to most surface measuring instruments that record a graph or profile by direct methods.

Movement of the stylus is achieved as shown at Fig. 6.6B. The stylus is supported at the bottom by a thin steel strip, and at the top by a light spring; vertical movement causes slight rotation of the cylindrical bar shown as B. This bar is able to roll on the two cylinders shown as D, and a light arm attached to bar B terminates in a pointed scriber which traces a profile on a rotatable smoked-glass disc. There is no magnification of the horizontal movement of the stylus, and the vertical magnification of the stylus displacement is in the region of 160.

Further magnification of the traced profile is achieved by optical projection of the smoked plate on to a screen with a magnification of 100. This provides an image of the trace with a vertical magnification of 16 000 and a horizontal magnification of 100, while a photograph of this image provides a permanent record of the profile of the surface finish.

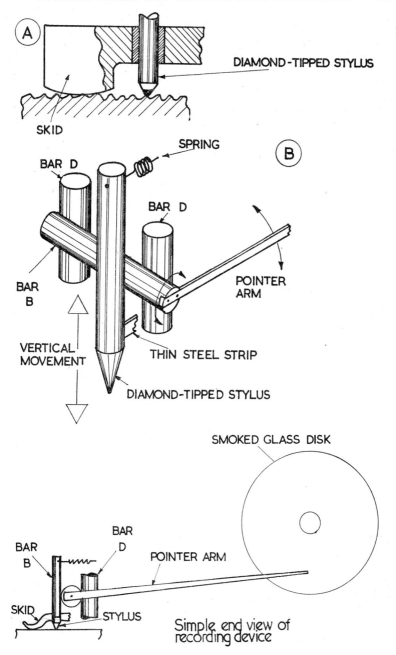

A

DIAMOND-TIPPED STYLUS

SKID

B

SPRING

BAR D

BAR D

BAR B

POINTER ARM

VERTICAL MOVEMENT

THIN STEEL STRIP

DIAMOND-TIPPED STYLUS

SMOKED GLASS DISK

BAR D

BAR B

POINTER ARM

SKID

STYLUS

Simple end view of recording device

FIG. 6.6.—PRINCIPLE OF THE TOMLINSON SURFACE ROUGHNESS RECORDER

6.4.1. The measurement of surface finish

The availability of a permanent profile of the surface finish led to the introduction of a measure of surface finish or roughness of a machined surface. In Great Britain the surface roughness is given an index number, which is the average height and depth of the profile curve with respect to a mean line passing through the profile; in other words, it is the average deviation of the profile curve above and below the mean line without

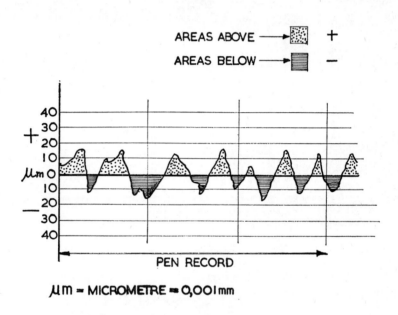

FIG. 6.7.—MEASUREMENT OF SURFACE ROUGHNESS

regard for positive or minus deviation. This is shown at Fig. 6.7, and mathematically the index or surface roughness number is obtained by dividing the sum of the areas by the vertical magnification and the length of the pen record.

The position of the mean line must be such that the areas above the line are equal to the areas below the line, although for all practical purposes it is sufficient if these areas are within 5% of the actual position.

The unit used is the micrometre = 0·001 mm indicated by the abbreviation μm, for example 6·3 μm.

6.4.2. The Talysurf measuring instrument

It should be clear at this stage that the determination of surface roughness involves a mathematical problem of considerable magnitude. For example the value for μ is given by the following formula:

$$\mu = \frac{1}{VL} \int \frac{Lc}{Oc} \sqrt{y^2 dx}$$

where V = vertical magnification

L = length of pen record

c = mean line

The complexity of the above calculations has inevitably led to the introduction of measuring instruments capable of automatically computing the surface roughness under test, and as, for most practical purposes, there is little real difference between the British and American standards, the same instrument may be used for both. For this sort of work the Talysurf is eminently suitable.

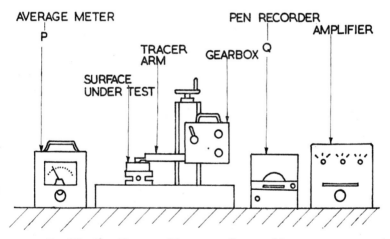

FIG. 6·8.—THE TALYSURF METHOD OF SURFACE MEASUREMENT

Essentially the Talysurf employs a diamond-tipped stylus, the radius of which will not exceed 0·0025 mm; this stylus is drawn slowly and automatically across the surface under test. Displacements of the stylus as it rides over the crests and hollows of the machined surface are amplified electrically and the instrument shown as P in Fig. 6.8, known as an average meter, gives a reading of the centre line average number suitable for the British system. The instrument indicated as Q provides both a reading and pen record of the surface profile; the length of stylus traverse is about 0·4 mm, with a stroke time of 3 seconds. The vertical magnification can be varied in steps from 1 000 to 50 000 by means of a simple switching arrangement, while horizontal traverse of the stylus is obtained by means of a gearbox, as shown at Fig. 6.8; the horizontal magnification being 20 or 100.

Note the tracer arm attached to the gearbox shown in Fig. 6.8. If it is required to detect waviness the tracer arm is used, providing a straight-line movement under automatic traverse from the gearbox. Under this con-

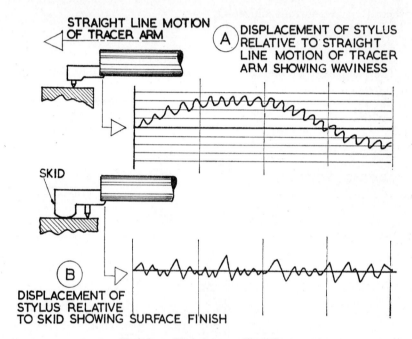

FIG. 6.9.—WAVINESS AND ROUGHNESS

dition, the vertical displacement of the stylus is relative to the straight-line motion of the tracer arm, and waviness of fairly low wavelength will be recorded as shown at Fig. 6.9A. If the surface roughness only is required the device shown at Fig. 6.9B is employed, whereby the vertical displacement of the stylus is relative to the skid. Clearly the bearing surface of the skid needs to be large enough to smooth out the effects of undulations or waviness on the machined surface.

6.5. Interpretation of profile charts

Considerable care needs to be given to the study of a profile chart which records the surface finish or roughness of a machined surface.

Fig. 6.10A shows a typical Talysurf chart representing a reamed finish. Clearly the profile is greatly exaggerated, for a reamer produces a well-finished or semi-polished hole, and the effect of a different ratio of magnification, that is to say a high vertical magnification and a low horizontal magnification, is to give a much distorted picture of the surface texture.

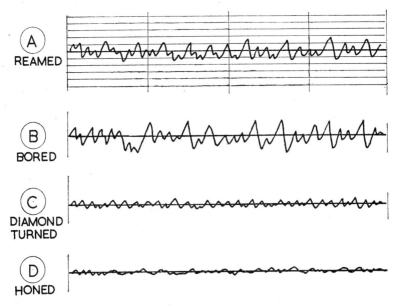

FIG. 6.10.—PROFILE CHARTS OF MACHINED SURFACES

Provided, however, the profiles are used for comparative purposes, they do give some measure of surface-finish assessment as shown in Fig. 6.10B, C and D. We have seen that the British system of surface-finish measurement makes use of the centre line average value (CLA); the average height and depth of the crests and hollows from a mean true plane are calculated and the resulting number is the surface roughness of the machined surface, the units used being micrometres.

Some idea of the difficulties involved in surface-finish assessment is given by Fig. 6.11. At A we see the perfect surface, at B a surface with a waviness of, say, a depth of 25 μm (0·025 mm). Clearly the deviation from the mean true plane over a full wavelength does not exceed 25 μm, and the surface would be regarded as reasonably smooth and flat. Fig. 6.11c shows a surface with a wavelength of much less frequency but the same depth or variation from the perfect surface. Although there is no increase in deviation from the mean true plane, the surface finish or roughness appears much worse, and would be considered as fairly poor.

Now, as we have seen, the roughness of a machined surface is related to the average deviation of the machined surface from a mean true plane, but it is clear from the simple examples given in Fig. 6.11 that the wavelength of the surface variations has an important effect on the surface finish. In other words, it is likely that a machined surface has a roughness of very short wavelength superimposed on a waviness of much longer

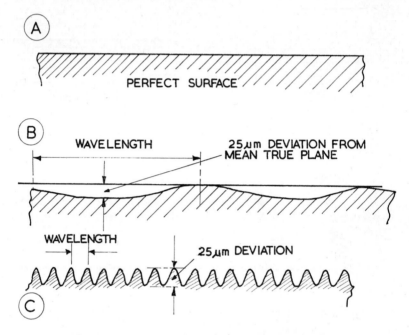

FIG. 6.11.—EFFECT OF LONG AND SHORT WAVELENGTHS

wavelength; the roughness being caused by the feed and depth of cut of the cutting tool, and the waviness introduced by out-of-straightness of the bearing surfaces or guideways of the machine tool used to produce the surface. This condition is illustrated at Fig. 6.12, and represents a very simple example of two wavelengths present on a machined surface. In actual machining practice, however, it is possible for four different wavelengths to be present, and not all in the same plane. For example, a turned surface will have a very short wavelength imposed by the shearing action of the cutting tool, and a longer wavelength introduced by the tool feed. These first two affect the roughness, as we have seen, but it is certain that another longer wavelength will be introduced by a combination of vibration in both workpiece and machine tool. In addition a longer wavelength will be present if there are any errors in the straightness or flatness of bearing surfaces or guideways, such errors resulting from damage, wear and tear, or poor adjustment of gib strips. It should be clear at this stage that the whole subject of surface measurement is relatively complex, and that the centre line average value needs to be interpreted with the greatest of care.

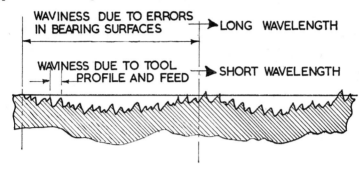

FIG. 6.12.—TYPICAL PROFILE OF MACHINED SURFACE

6.6. Surface roughness and machining methods

The surface roughness is determined by the method of machining the surface, although in each case the actual finish is affected by the rigidity of the tool and work set-up, and the condition of the machine tool employed. The chart illustrated at Fig. 6.13 gives an indication of the surface

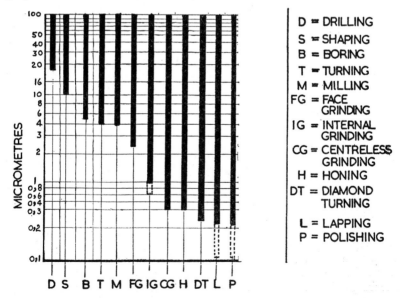

FIG. 6.13.—SURFACE ROUGHNESS AND MACHINING METHODS

roughness that can be expected from the actual machining method employed.

6.7. Surface finish and useful life of moving parts

The useful life of any machine tool can be defined as that period of use during which the machine tool is capable of producing work to within acceptable limits of accuracy. We have seen that in general waviness of a machined surface may be caused by out-of-straightness of machine-tool guideways or bearing surfaces, together with play in machine-tool spindles.

Clearly, constant usage of a machine tool under cutting conditions must lead to wear of the bearing surfaces, leading to the production of inaccurate work, and it is true to state that the greater the surface roughness the more rapid will be the wear.

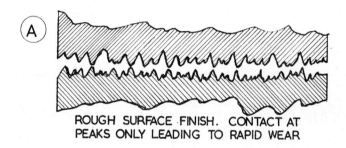

ROUGH SURFACE FINISH. CONTACT AT PEAKS ONLY LEADING TO RAPID WEAR

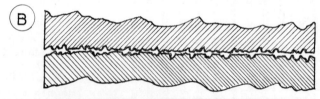

GOOD SURFACE FINISH. CLOSE CONTACT GIVING LONG ACCURATE LIFE

FIG. 6.14.—EFFECT OF SURFACE ROUGHNESS ON USEFUL LIFE OF MOVING PARTS

This is simply illustrated at Fig. 6.14A, where we see two surfaces of poor finish in sliding contact. The relatively high depths and peaks of the machined surfaces mean that contact is made only at the tips of the peaks, and on first assembly the quality of fit may appear to be of high order. The sliding action, however, must result in rapid abrasion or knocking off of the high points, with the result that play or slackness soon develops.

On the other hand, as Fig. 6.14B shows, two mating surfaces of good surface finish allow closer contact of the surfaces, with a much longer expectation of life. When machined surfaces are required to be produced to certain degrees of finish or roughness this must be indicated on the component drawing; Fig. 6.15 gives a typical example of the system used. The diameter on the left must have a roughness number not exceeding 32, while that on the right must have a roughness number between 8 and 16.

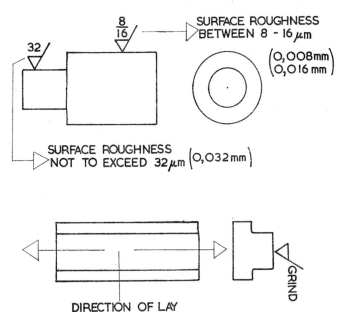

Fig. 6.15.—Methods of Indicating Surface Roughness and Direction of Lay

If it is required to specify the direction of lay, this may be indicated on the drawing as shown at Fig. 6.15, and it is permissible also to specify the required process, as shown in the diagram, where we see that the surface is to be produced by grinding. Wherever possible the recommended adopted values should be used; these are as follows in micrometres:

0·025   0·050   0·1   0·2   0·4   0·8   1·6   3·2   6·3   12·5   25

Sampling lengths, that is to say the amounts of traverse of the diamond-tipped stylus over the machined surface under test, are laid down by BS 1134, and are as follows in millimetres:

0·08   0·25   0·8   2·5   8·0   25·0

For fine surfaces the sampling length of 0·8 mm is most used; the higher values are for the more conventional machining methods such as milling or turning.

6.8. Machine-tool alignments

By machine-tool alignments we mean the geometrical relationship between the various elements inherent in all machine tools. It must be appreciated at all times that a machine tool is primarily a surface-producing device, and all surfaces must of necessity be of a geometrical nature.

While the quality of surface finish possessed by machine-tool elements has a direct influence on the life of the machine tool, it is also very necessary that these elements possess also the required degree of accuracy of alignment.

In most cases the production or machining of a given geometric surface is achieved through a combination of work–tool movements. In other words, the machined surface is generated, and the accuracy of the surface depends on the accuracy of the mating elements present in the machine tool. These basic alignments are common to most machine tools, and may be summarised as follows:

(i) straightness and flatness of guideways and bearing surfaces;
(ii) perpendicularity of guideways to other guideways or bearing surfaces;
(iii) float and true running of spindles;
(iv) parallelism of spindle axis to guideways or bearing surfaces;
(v) alignment of spindle to guideways or bearing surfaces.

At Fig. 6.16 we see simple representations of all the above basic alignments, and it may be worthwhile to have a closer look at each in turn, for it is most important that we fully appreciate and understand the geometrical alignment involved before attempting to check it.

6.8.1. Straightness and flatness of guideways and bearing surfaces

At Fig. 6.16A we see part of a bed for a centre lathe. Note the use of separated inverted Vs for saddle and tailstock guiding and of separate bearing surfaces for saddle and tailstock support. Clearly both bearing surfaces need to have the quality of flatness, or, in other words, they should follow a mean true plane as closely as possible. This means that a definite alignment exists between the plane surfaces P and Q, in addition to the fact that both P and Q need to be plane or flat surfaces.

On the other hand, the guideways shown as R and S are used to guide the saddle and tailstock respectively, and both these guideways must possess the quality of straightness in the first instance.

In addition to straightness both guideways need to be in accurate alignment, that is to say they must be parallel to each other in both the horizontal and vertical plane. It should be clear at this stage that the alignments of even the bed of a simple centre lathe present some problems both in interpretation and checking.

6.8.2. Perpendicularity of guideways to other guideways or bearing surfaces

The above condition or element is simply illustrated at Fig. 6.16B, where we see the body of a simple shaping machine. Clearly the bearing surfaces for the shaping-machine ram must be not only flat but also at 90° to the bearing surfaces used to obtain vertical movement of the worktable support. The latter bearing surfaces need also to be flat and parallel in the vertical plane.

6.8.3. Float and true running of spindles

Fig. 6.16c shows a simple spindle intended for a centre lathe. By axial float of this spindle we mean the out-of-squareness of the location face shown as F with the axis of the spindle. This must not be confused with endplay, which is movement along the spindle axis occasioned by clearance between the bearing surfaces of the spindle. Many spindles are now fitted with preloaded bearings, and a spindle fitted in this way will have no endplay. Under cutting conditions, however, the thrust of the cutting tool cancels out the preloading or tightness of the spindle, whereupon the spindle rotates freely.

True running of the spindle means complete absence of any tendency of the spindle to bend or distort under the influence of the pressure exerted by the cutting tool, in addition to true running when not under load.

6.8.4. Parallelism of spindle with guideways or bearing surfaces

A good example of this condition is clearly seen on reference back to Fig. 6.16A. We may consider the centre line as a true extension of the spindle axis, and the generation of a true cylindrical surface is possible only when the centre line of the rotating work is parallel in both horizontal and vertical planes with the guideways and bearing surfaces.

6.8.5. Alignment of spindle with guideways or bearing surfaces

Fig. 6.17A shows a typical application of this condition. The axis of the vertical spindle needs to be in true alignment with the guideways and bearing surfaces carrying the worktable. In this case, as we see, the application is to a vertical milling machine, and the alignment required is

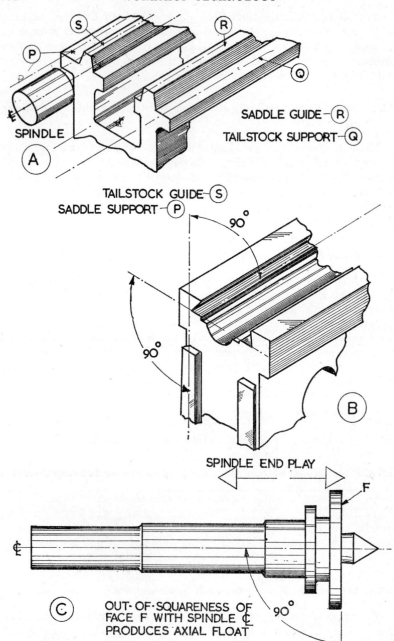

SADDLE GUIDE — R
TAILSTOCK SUPPORT — Q

SPINDLE

A

TAILSTOCK GUIDE — S
SADDLE SUPPORT — P

90°

90°

B

SPINDLE END PLAY

C

OUT-OF-SQUARENESS OF
FACE F WITH SPINDLE ₵
PRODUCES AXIAL FLOAT

90°

FIG. 6.16.—MACHINE-TOOL ALIGNMENTS

that the axis of the spindle be at 90° to the path of the worktable. Any error from this alignment of 90° means that the bottom face of, say, a shell-end mill will machine a non-flat or slightly oval surface, as shown in the diagram at Fig. 6.17B.

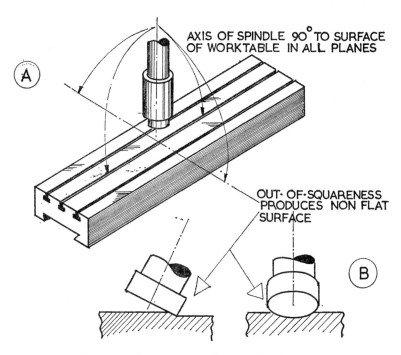

FIG. 6.17.—IMPORTANCE OF SPINDLE AXIS ACCURACY

The examples given above may be considered as fairly representative, but a little thought will soon bring an appreciation of the fact that the same kind of alignments as those shown at Fig. 6.16 are needed in machine tools such as:

(i) all types of milling machines;
(ii) all types of grinding machines;
(iii) capstan, turret and automatic lathes;
(iv) shaping and planing machines.

Now that we are familiar with the basic alignments of machine tools, and the interdependence of dimensional accuracy of a machined component with these basic alignments, we may with profit turn our attention to the important matter of alignment testing.

6.9. Alignment testing

Before any of the basic alignments discussed above are checked, it is necessary first to ensure that the machine tool has not been distorted owing to faulty or careless installation. For example, it is certain that a workshop floor is not a plane or flat surface, for the spreading and levelling of concrete is not a precision job, with the result that a concrete floor may have relatively serious deviation from a mean true plane. The effect of this deviation is most marked if we consider what happens when a centre lathe is secured to the workshop floor using the familiar grouting bolts shown in Fig. 6.18A.

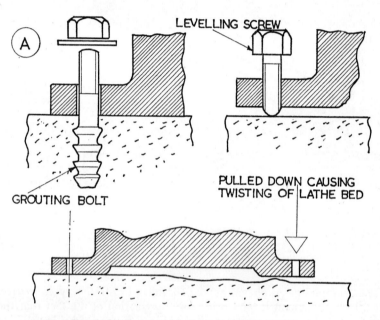

FIG. 6.18.—BOLTING AND LEVELLING MACHINE TOOLS

It is clear that if the centre lathe is simply bolted down, then any out-of-flatness of the workshop floor is certain to result in bending or twisting of the lathe bed, and as a relatively small centre lathe of 200 mm above centres will have a bed length of about 2 metres, such twisting of the bed must have a serious effect on the accuracy of the machined surfaces. In other words, misalignment of the guideways and bearing surfaces is certain to take place, with the result that the path of the tool is no longer parallel with the spindle axis, and a true cylindrical surface cannot be produced.

Method of obtaining correct alignment when installing machine tools

The whole object of correct installation is to ensure that all horizontal faces lie on a true horizontal plane and all vertical faces on a true vertical plane. If this is done, and the machine tool is secured to the floor so that the above conditions are maintained, the basic geometry adopted when actually machining and assembling the lathe or machine tool has been repeated, and the original accuracy preserved.

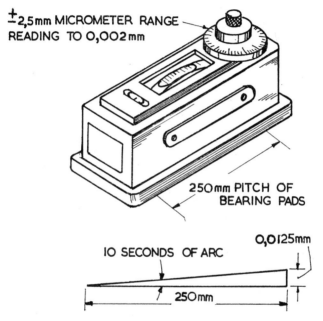

FIG. 6.19.—LINEAR READING ADJUSTABLE BLOCK LEVEL

To install a machine tool, a good or high-precision spirit level is absolutely necessary. Such a level is illustrated at Fig. 6.19, and may be described as linear-reading adjustable block level. Note the micrometer which enables direct linear readings to be made in terms of bubble displacement, though for the purposes of machine-tool installation this is not strictly necessary.

The accuracy of this level is indicated by the simple diagram at Fig. 6.19, where it may be seen that a displacement of 0·0125 mm results in a bubble movement of one division. Because the base of the level is 250 mm, the angle of tilt is equivalent to 10 seconds of arc, as shown on the diagram. We shall have further use for this level when checking the flatness or straightness of bearing surfaces later in this chapter.

To return now to the correct installation of our centre lathe, or for that matter of any other machine tool, reference to Fig. 6.20 should make the picture clear. Here we see a simple view of the bed of our centre lathe; the headstock, tailstock and saddle are omitted for clarity.

In actual practice the saddle is taken to mid-point along the bed before the levelling takes place. The spirit level is first placed at position X as shown in the diagram, and with a simple though rigid bridge another

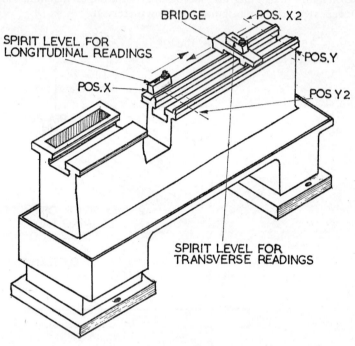

FIG. 6.20.—USE OF SPIRIT LEVEL WHEN INSTALLING CENTRE LATHE

level is placed as shown at Y. Taking the position at X, the bubble is set to zero and then moved down to the position at X2. A zero reading is required also at this position, and it is certain that adjustment needs to be made using either of the devices shown at Fig. 6.18. At the same time an eye needs to be kept on the spirit level at position Y, for we need the same condition here, namely a zero reading of the bubble from position Y to position Y2.

The insertion of wedges or shim may be used to effect slight lifting or lowering of the lathe corners as required, or rotation of the levelling screws may be employed. Provided that there is no appreciable bubble movement from zero when the two levels are moved to the positions indicated, the lathe may be secured to the floor; the usual method is to run a slurry of concrete around the base of the bed.

In general, slight movement of the bubble is permissible, provided such movement does not exceed about one-half of a division from position to position. With a bubble division equivalent to 0·0125 mm per 250 mm base, the levelling accuracy is about 0·025 mm per metre. A similar procedure is adopted for the installation of machine tools such as milling machines, grinding machines, capstan and automatic lathes; provided the levelling accuracy is held below about 0·025 mm per metre, the installation is acceptable. Note that the whole procedure is greatly simplified or speeded up if two spirit levels are used simultaneously, as lifting the corner of a bed must affect both transverse and longitudinal readings.

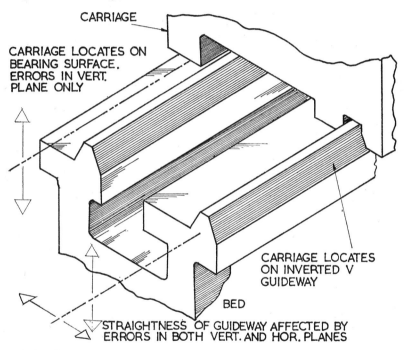

FIG. 6.21—ELEMENTS OF STRAIGHTNESS AND FLATNESS IN BED OF CENTRE LATHE

6.9.1. Testing for straightness and flatness

Before dealing with the testing techniques required for the determination of straightness and flatness it is important to have a clear appreciation of the difference between those two alignments. Consider the simple machine bed illustrated at Fig. 6.21. The purpose of this bed is to provide positive guidance or location for the carriage shown. Now the inverted V shown on the right is a guideway; it provides a straight-line

G

path for the carriage, preventing movement to left or right. Clearly the weight of the carriage helps to ensure close contact of the bearing surface of the carriage against the faces of the inverted V; thus we have complete restriction of movement except in a straight-line path along the inverted V. We need, however, additional support to the carriage, and this is achieved by using the bearing surface shown. It is customary to place the bearing surface as far as possible from the guideway in order to promote a more stable guiding arrangement.

Now the straightness of the guideway is affected by errors in both vertical and horizontal planes, while the bearing surface, being of fairly narrow section, is affected by errors in the vertical plane only. These faults are simply indicated in the diagram, but clearly testing for straightness is more complicated than testing for flatness.

Straightness

In order to test the straightness of the inverted V in the horizontal plane it will be necessary to use an autocollimator and a reflector suitably located on a V carriage. The principle and method of reading the autocollimator is dealt with in Chapter 4, section 4.13.2, where there is a

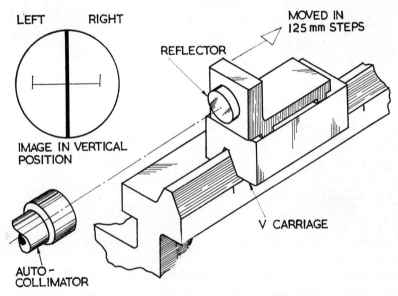

FIG. 6.22.—TESTING STRAIGHTNESS OF GUIDEWAY

simplified account of the technique adopted. It will be convenient at this stage to deal more fully with the actual technique for arriving at the true error from straightness in the horizontal plane. Fig. 6.22 shows the set-up required. Note that the reflector is mounted on a carriage which locates only on the sloping sides of the inverted V. The autocollimator is rotated to a fixed stop so that the reflected image is in a vertical position, and care needs to be taken to ensure that the axis of the collimator is in true alignment with the V; that is to say the reflected image of the vertical cross-wire for any position of the carriage along the V remains in our field of view.

We may now step off along the V in 125 mm intervals, giving us ten positions for a 1·5 metre length of V. The accuracy of the autocollimator is 30 seconds of arc for a 0·018 mm tilt of the reflector, or one second of arc is equivalent to a displacement of 0·0006 mm.

With the reflector carriage in position 1, and the straddle wires enclosing the reflected image, the reading is taken from the micrometer drum, care being exercised to ensure that the autocollimator is securely set on a rigid tripod or other suitable support about 1 metre from the end of the V.

The method of entering the readings is shown in the table, and the following information will make clear the purpose of the seven columns used.

(i)	(ii)		(iii)	(iv)	(v)	(vi)	(vii)
Position	Autocollimator reading		Diff. from (ii)	Linear displacement	Cumulative linear displacement	Adjustment to zero	Error
			0	0	0	0	0
1	1	30	0	0	0	+ 12·6	+ 12·6
2	1	36	− 6	− 3·6	− 3·6	+ 25·2	+ 21·6
3	1	40	− 10	− 6·0	− 9·6	+ 37·8	+ 28·2
4	1	48	− 18	− 10·8	− 20·4	+ 50·4	+ 30
5	1	52	− 22	− 13·2	− 33·6	+ 63·0	+ 29·4
6	1	54	− 24	− 14·4	− 48·0	+ 75·6	+ 27
7	1	58	− 28	− 16·8	− 64·8	+ 88·2	+ 23·4
8	2	0	− 30	− 18·0	− 82·8	+ 100·8	+ 18
9	2	4	− 34	− 20·4	− 103·2	+ 113·4	+ 10·2
10	2	8	− 38	− 22·8	− 126	+ 126	0
	Min.	Sec.	Sec.	Units = μm = 0·001 mm			

Note.—Image movement to the right shown as —ve, indicating deviation of the V to the left.

COLUMN (II.)

Here we enter the autocollimator reading.

COLUMN (III.)

Here we enter the difference in the reading from the original or zero reading at position 1. Movement of the image to the right is given a negative sign; this means that the V deviates to the left as viewed from the autocollimator. Note that the units are seconds.

COLUMN (IV)

In this column we convert the angular tilt to linear displacement, knowing that 1 second of arc is equivalent to a linear displacement of 0·0006 mm. As the image has constantly moved to the right all displacements are given a negative sign.

COLUMN (V)

This column gives the cumulative displacement from the original reading, that is to say the total displacement of each position from the original setting or reading. We may now plot these readings as shown in the graph illustrated at Fig. 6.23, with reflector position along the

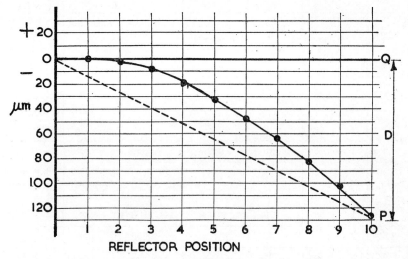

FIG. 6.23.—GRAPHICAL REPRESENTATION OF GUIDEWAY STRAIGHTNESS

horizontal axis of the graph and displacement in micrometres on the vertical axis. Now the straightness of the inverted V in the horizontal plane can be represented by the broken line drawn from the first to the last position on the graph, while the out-of-straightness is shown by the deviation of the plotted curve from this line.

A somewhat clearer picture is obtained if the straight line OP is brought to a horizontal position, that is to say by adjusting or lifting point P to Q; this is done in the following manner.

COLUMN (VI)

To bring point P to zero it is necessary to add distance D, that is to say 126 units (each unit = 1 micrometre); this is shown in column (vi), position 10. By simple proportion, the amount to be added to position 9 to bring it to zero is nine-tenths of 126 μm, eight-tenths of 126 μm to bring position 8 to zero, and so on. These adjustments are entered in column (vi).

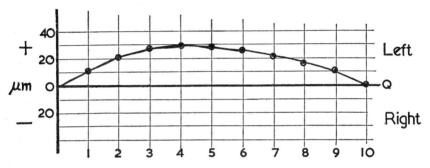

FIG. 6.24.—SHOWING DEVIATION FROM A STRAIGHT LINE

COLUMN (VII)

This column gives the actual deviation of the inverted V under test from a straight line. The amount of deviation at any position is the algebraic difference between columns (v) and (vi), and the figures in this column allows direct plotting of the graph shown in Fig. 6.24. Note that a positive displacement indicates deviation or out-of-straightness to the left when viewed from the autocollimator position or the front end of the V. This graph of course gives a much exaggerated picture of the actual out-of-straightness of the V, for we need to remember that the horizontal scale covers a distance of 1·5 metres while the vertical scale is in micrometres. The maximum error from a straight line is 30 μm at position 4, and we may regard this is a reasonable standard of accuracy, as an error of 0·02 mm per metre is considered as an acceptable tolerance for out-of-straightness of machine-tool guideways.

Flatness

Exactly the same procedure may be adopted for flatness testing, except that the autocollimator is rotated through 90°, bringing the reflected image horizontal, thus checking out-of-straightness in the vertical plane.

Another method is to make use of the spirit level illustrated at Fig. 6.19; Fig. 6.25 shows a typical application of the spirit-level technique when determining the flatness of a bearing surface. Once again, the spirit level is stepped off along the bearing surface, at intervals equal to the base of the level. Tilts of the level at particular positions are corrected by rotating the micrometer until the bubble is relevelled. Linear variations in heights at these positions are read off on the micrometer drum direct to 0·002 mm and a table is constructed in the same manner as when using the auto-collimator, thus allowing the plotting of a graph showing the out-of-flatness of the bearing surface.

The following table shows a typical set of readings using a linear-

(i)	(ii)	(iii)	(iv)	(v)	(vi)
Position	Micrometer reading	Linear displacement per position	Cumulative displacement	Adjustment to zero	Error
		0	0	0	0
1	8	0	0	− 1·6	− 1·6
2	10	+ 4	+ 4	− 3·2	+ 0·8
3	11	+ 2	+ 6	− 4·8	+ 1·2
4	12	+ 2	+ 8	− 6·4	+ 1·6
5	11	− 2	+ 6	− 8	− 2
6	11	0	+ 6	− 9·6	− 3
7	13	+ 4	+ 10	− 11·2	− 1·2
8	14	+ 2	+ 12	− 12·8	− 0·8
9	15	+ 2	+ 14	− 14·4	− 0·4
10	16	+ 2	+ 16	− 16	0
			Units = μm = 0·001 mm		

Note.—1 division on micrometer = 0·002 mm.

reading adjustable spirit level having a sensitivity of 0·0125 mm per 10 seconds of arc tilt. With a spirit level of this type the operation of testing for flatness is greatly simplified; Fig. 6.26 shows the graphs plotted from

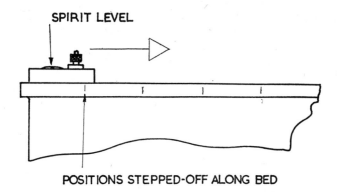

FIG. 6.25.—FLATNESS TESTING WITH SPIRIT LEVEL

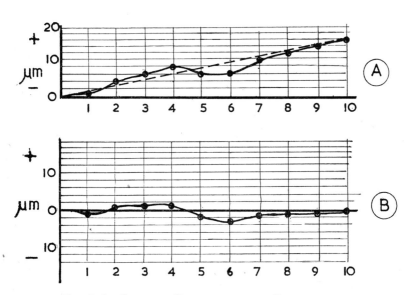

FIG. 6.26.—GRAPHICAL REPRESENTATION OF OUT-OF-FLATNESS

the table. At A we see the plotting of the cumulative displacement, while at B we see the graph produced by forcing the last position to zero. It is clear that the flatness of the surface under test is of a high order; the greatest error is at position 6, where the surface is 0·003 mm below the true surface.

Note that the cumulative displacements are calculated algebraically, with due regard for positive or negative values.

Use of bridging pieces

In many cases it is necessary to test that one guideway or bearing surface is straight and flat in relation to another. In this event a bridging piece is required and Fig. 6.27 shows a simple example of a suitable bridging piece. With the linear-reading adjustable spirit level readings are taken at

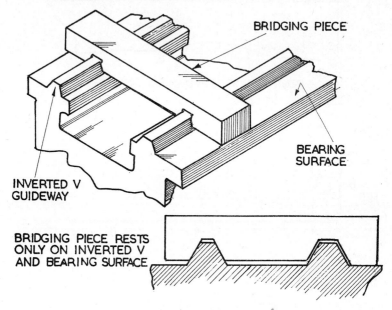

FIG. 6·27.—USE OF BRIDGING PIECE

stepped intervals along the bed of the machine tool under test, and in this way any out-of-straightness of one bearing surface to another is readily plotted and shown on a graph. Such a graph reveals what is known as 'cross-wind', in other words the effect produced when the two bearing surfaces have different errors in straightness and flatness, or lie in non-parallel planes.

6.9.2. Testing for perpendicularity of guideways or bearing surfaces

By perpendicularity of guideways we mean the 90° relationship between, say, the worktable and the column of a vertical milling machine.

As we have seen, it is a geometrical condition that the axis of the spindle be truly at 90° to the worktable surface at any position of the head or table; the necessary alignment is simply shown at Fig. 6.28. Note that

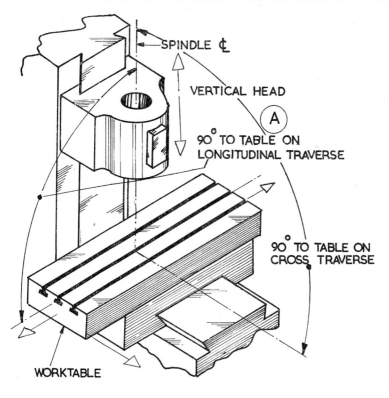

SPINDLE ℄

VERTICAL HEAD

Ⓐ

90° TO TABLE ON
LONGITUDINAL TRAVERSE

90° TO TABLE ON
CROSS TRAVERSE

WORKTABLE

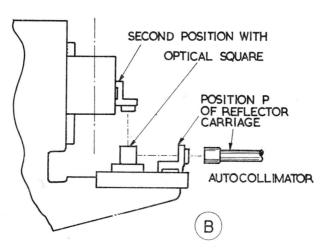

SECOND POSITION WITH
OPTICAL SQUARE

POSITION P
OF REFLECTOR
CARRIAGE

AUTOCOLLIMATOR

Ⓑ

FIG. 6.28.—ALIGNMENT OF SPINDLE WITH WORKTABLE

the 90° alignment needs to be checked in **two** planes, as shown in the diagram; once again we may use an autocollimator or precision spirit level. In the case of the autocollimator the correct technique may be seen by reference back to Chapter 4, Fig. 4.25A, where we see the application of an optical square. This square is a most precise piece of equipment, capable of turning a ray of light through 90°, and its application is further illustrated at Fig. 6.28B.

Note that if it is assumed that the worktable traverses a true path and that the guideways carrying the vertical head are truly flat also, then the determination of the 90° alignment is a relatively simple matter, and may be carried out as shown at Fig. 6.28B.

A zero reading is taken at position P; the reflector is now secured to the vertical head and an optical square placed as shown in the diagram. If the worktable surface is truly at 90° to the datum face on the vertical head there will be no change in the reading; in other words the deviation from 90° will be zero.

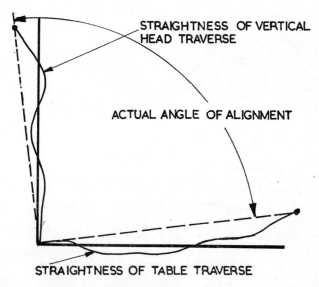

FIG. 6.29.—GRAPHICAL REPRESENTATION OF STRAIGHTNESS AND ANGULAR ERROR

If it is required to determine the accuracy of the 90° alignment at any position of the table, then the procedure is as follows:

    (i) Plot a graph of worktable travel by moving the table at steps equal to the base of the reflector carriage.

    (ii) With the vertical head in the lowest position, and the worktable in the first position of travel check, plot a graph of vertical head travel, using an optical square and moving the head at the same steps as the worktable.

At Fig. 6.29 we see the resultant graph; care must be taken to ensure that any error is in the correct direction. The profile along the horizontal axis represents the straightness of the worktable travel, while that along the vertical axis represents the straightness of the vertical head travel. The angle between the dotted lines joining the first and last positions represents the actual alignment between the worktable and vertical head.

6.9.3. Float and true running of spindles

Several machine tools produce machined surfaces by a combination of a rotating cutting tool and feed of the workpiece; typical examples include milling machines, boring machines and grinding machines. At the same time a wide variety of lathes, comprising centre, capstan, turret and automatic types, produce machined surfaces by rotation of the workpiece in conjunction with feed of a suitable cutting tool. In all the above machine tools, an accurate well-running spindle is an essential factor in the production of high-finish surfaces to close dimensional accuracy; such a spindle needs to retain this high degree of accuracy irrespective of the speed of rotation, depth of cut or cutting rate of the tool. For this reason testing of spindles must be carried out at the normal working temperature of the spindle; in other words, the spindle is run for a short period before the commencement of the test.

The test for axial slip is simply illustrated at Fig. 6.30, together with the conditions leading to axial slip. As may be seen, axial slip or float is caused by the non-parallelism of the thrust faces leading to slight linear movement or float of the spindle on rotation. This is easily detected with a sensitive dial indicator; it is important that the plunger axis lies on the spindle axis, as shown in the diagram.

By true running of a machine-tool spindle we mean its concentricity of rotation. Because, for example, in all types of lathes, workholding devices such as chucks locate on the spindle, or collet chucks in a taper machined in the spindle, any out-of-true running of the spindle must result in a similar fault in the workholding device, and hence in the workpiece.

Fig. 6.31 shows a typical method of testing the true running or concentricity of a taper in a machine-tool spindle, in this case on a centre lathe, although a similar technique is used for, say, a horizontal miller or jig borer. Note the use of a precision test bar located in the taper in the spindle, together with a sensitive dial indicator which must be capable of indicating to within 0·002 mm. The true running of external diameters or tapers which may be used for chuck location is also tested with a sensitive dial indicator as shown in Fig. 6.31.

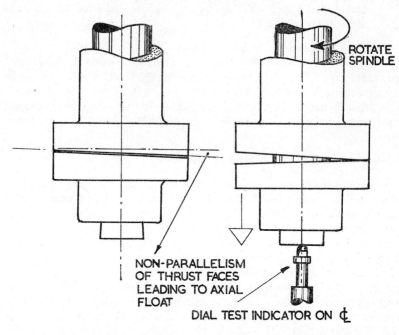

FIG. 6.30.—TESTING FOR AXIAL SLIP OF MACHINE-TOOL SPINDLE

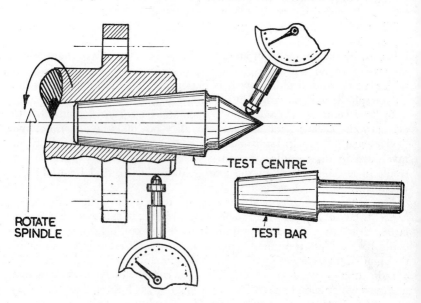

FIG. 6.31.—TESTING FOR TRUE RUNNING OF SPINDLE

In general, the tolerance permissible on machine-tool spindles with regard to axial slip and out-of-true running seldom exceeds 0·01 mm for machine tools of average quality, that is to say standard milling machines while in the case of more precise machine tools such as grinding machines, toolroom lathes and jig borers the tolerance is not likely to exceed 0·005 mm.

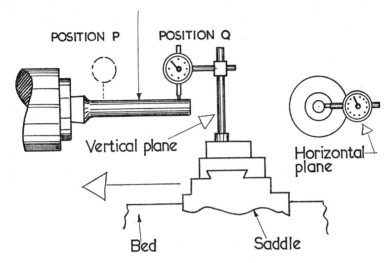

FIG. 6.32.—TESTING SPINDLE ALIGNMENT WITH GUIDEWAYS

6.9.4. Testing parallelism of spindle axis with guideways

Once again a precision test mandrel is required for this test, and Fig. 6.32 shows a set-up applicable to a centre or capstan lathe. Note that the length of the test bar is such that any error or out-of-true running of the taper in the spindle must be considerably magnified at the extreme end of the test bar. As stated, no more than 0·01 mm is permissible at point P, while the maximum deviation from true at point Q should not exceed 0·025 mm for standard machine tools.

With a sensitive dial indicator mounted on the saddle, a zero reading is taken at the extreme end of the test bar, and movement of the saddle along the bed of the lathe should not cause a deviation from zero of more than 0·04 mm per metre. Note that the test must be carried out in two planes, the horizontal and the vertical; the front elevation shows the test as applied to the vertical plane, and the plane to the horizontal.

It must be remembered that tolerances applicable to certain machine-tool elements may be directional in character; that is to say the tolerance is permitted in one direction only. The reason for this is that certain machine-tool elements are subject to deflection and wear under the influence of the weight of workholding devices, or of the forces exerted by the cutting tool. For example, the lathe spindle shown under test in Fig. 6.32 has to support a chuck or faceplate which will tend to give a downward deflection to the spindle. Thus the tolerance on the spindle is positive towards the tailstock; that is to say a slight upward slope from the headstock is permitted.

A slight deviation towards the tool position in the horizontal plane is also permitted; thus the tool pressure will tend to bring the spindle closer to its true running position.

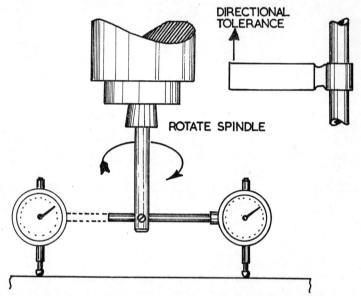

FIG. 6.33.—TESTING ALIGNMENT OF DRILLING M/C SPINDLE

6.9.5. Testing spindle alignment

Perhaps the simplest example of the need for precise spindle alignment is given by the geometry required from all drilling machines: namely, that the axis of the drilling spindle is at 90° to the worktable in all planes, and maintains this accuracy at any position of the spindle or worktable. Fig. 6.33 shows the technique adopted; once again a directional tolerance is in operation, as may be seen from the diagram. A slight deviation is permitted upwards; thus the weight of the workpiece together with the downward thrust of the drill tends to bring the table to its true alignment. Clearly if the table were permitted a minus tolerance, that is to say a slight sag or droop from the column, then the weight of the workpiece plus the downward thrust of the drill would tend to increase the alignment error further.

6.10. Performance testing

It is customary for the purchaser of a machine tool to lay down the minimum standard of performance expected from it. In this way agreement is reached between the manufacturer and the purchaser as to exactly the sort of accuracy the machine tool is capable of under actual working conditions. A performance test, therefore, may be considered as an acceptance test, and typical tests include the following:

(i) facing test for a centre lathe;
(ii) parallel turning test for a centre lathe;
(iv) facing test for horizontal boring machine;
(v) parallel grinding test for surface grinding machine.

In general, test pieces are machined under prescribed cutting conditions, that is to say the depth of cut, cutting speeds and feed rates are agreed upon, together with the type and quality of the cutting tool used.

Summary

We have seen in this chapter the importance of both surface finish and machine-tool geometry. The surface finish of a machined component is more aptly described as the surface roughness; the lower the surface roughness number, the closer the machined surface approaches a true plane. The degree of roughness is given a numerical assessment or preferred CLA (centre–line–average) value, the unit μm (micrometre) being used. Several methods of determining surface roughness are available, ranging from simple test pieces allowing direct comparison to highly sophisticated devices which not only give a profile of the surface under test but also integrate the readings to give a direct assessment of the surface roughness number.

The importance of a good surface finish with respect to the moving or sliding parts of machine-tool elements cannot be over-emphasised. The useful life of any machine tool, that is to say its ability to produce accurate or acceptable work, is in direct proportion to the quality of the surface finish present on the machined dimensions, and where a specified surface roughness is required it is necessary to indicate on the drawing the values within which the surface roughness must fall.

Finally we have seen some of the methods and principles adopted for the checking of machine-tool alignments. These basic alignments are common to most machine tools and are mainly concerned with the straightness, flatness and perpendicularity of guideways and bearing surfaces, together with float, true-running and parallelism of machine-tool spindles. In addition to the above tests, which are designed to test the inherent geometry of the machine tool, certain dynamic testing is needed. By dynamic testing we mean the determination of the actual performance of the machine tool under typical working or cutting conditions. This type of test ensures that the machine tool is capable of producing work to within the limits required, and that the machine-tool elements do not deviate or deflect under the influence of the forces set up during the machining operation.

EXERCISE 6

1 With the aid of neat sketches, illustrate the following elements associated with a surface produced by a planing machine:

    (i) roughness;
    (ii) waviness;
    (iii) lay.

2 Explain what is meant by the 'lay' of a machined surface, and with simple diagrams show the direction of lay for each of the following machining operations:

    (i) facing at a capstan lathe;
    (ii) grinding a flat surface at a surface grinding machine;
    (iii) milling a flat surface using an inserted-tooth face milling cutter.

3 Describe a typical method of determining the surface roughness of a ground surface by **either** of the following methods:

    (i) direct comparison with roughness standards using the 'fingernail' technique;
    (ii) use of a direct-reading surface-finish indicator.

4 Explain what is meant by the centre line average method of surface-finish assessment.

5 Show by means of simple diagrams how the following are indicated on an engineering drawing:

    (i) surface roughness not to exceed 16 μm;
    (ii) surface roughness to lie between 8 and 16 μm;
    (iii) direction of lay.

6 Describe in some detail a method of determining the flatness of the narrow bearing surface shown as S in Fig. 6.34A.

7 Using a linear-reading adjustable spirit level, outline a suitable method of determining the parallelism of the two bearing surfaces shown at Fig. 6.34B.

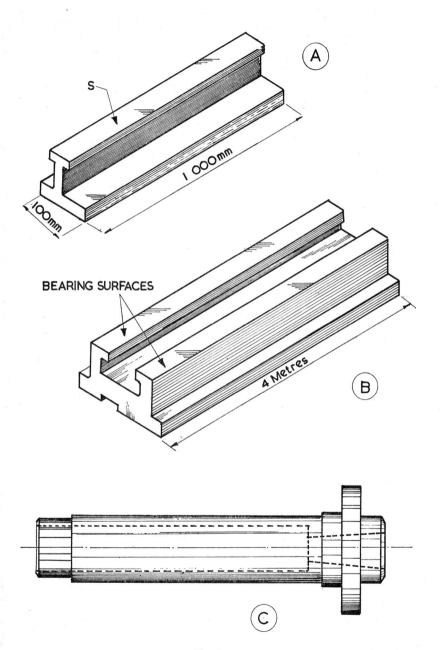

S

A

1 000 mm

100 mm

BEARING SURFACES

4 Metres

B

C

FIG. 6.34.

8 Explain the meaning of axial slip with regard to the spindle of a turret lathe, and describe a method of determining such axial slip.

9 Fig. 6.34c shows in simple detail the spindle of a centre lathe. Describe methods of testing the following:

(i) true running of the spindle;
(ii) parallelism of the spindle with the bed of the lathe.

10 Explain what is meant by a dynamic test on a machine tool, and with an example of your own choice describe a typical dynamic test, outlining its purposes.

7
GRINDING

7.1. Introduction to grinding

We have seen in the previous chapter the importance of accurately machined surfaces possessing a high degree of surface finish. The grinding process, whereby a rotating grinding wheel is presented to the workpiece, is of vital importance in all aspects of engineering manufacture, especially where fine tolerances are required. In addition the grinding process lends itself readily to the machining of materials in the hard state; for example the sharpening of, say, a high-speed milling cutter is not possible unless a suitable grinding wheel is used.

In general the grinding process is restricted to those machining operations that may be classified as finishing operations, for the use of grinding wheels is not suitable for heavy metal-removal conditions. In order to give an indication of the scope of the process we may consider the following typical production examples, and it may then be appreciated that, in terms of speed of output and ability to maintain close tolerances, the grinding process has few equals.

7.2. Typical grinding examples

Fig. 7.1A shows the die of a press tool. This die needs periodic grinding of its top face in order to maintain a sharp edge on the shearing faces. This is a typical example of surface grinding and would be carried out in a toolroom, using a **surface** grinding machine. Total grinding time should not exceed about 3 minutes.

Fig. 7.1B shows a shaft with three ground external diameters. This job would be carried out on an **external** grinding machine on a production basis, with an output of 60 shafts per hour readily achieved.

Fig. 7.1c shows the outer race of a ball-bearing. An **internal** grinding machine is used to machine the inner diameter, with a machining time of 17 seconds.

Fig. 7.1D shows a steel tube used as part of the rear-axle assembly of a modern motor car. A **centreless** grinding machine is used to grind the external diameter indicated on the diagram, with a production rate of 100 per hour.

The examples overleaf give only a small indication of the scope and speed

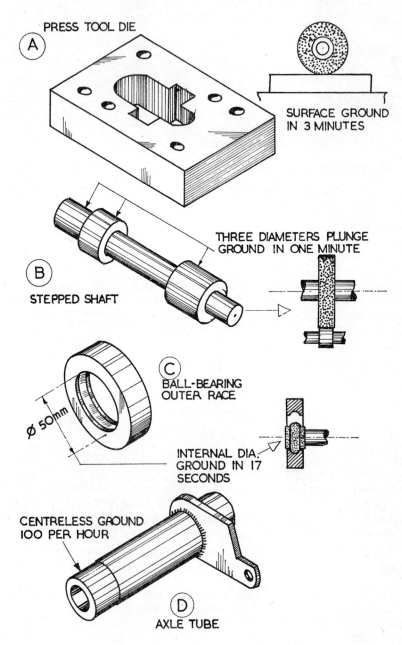

A PRESS TOOL DIE

SURFACE GROUND
IN 3 MINUTES

B STEPPED SHAFT

THREE DIAMETERS PLUNGE
GROUND IN ONE MINUTE

C BALL-BEARING
OUTER RACE

Ø 50mm

INTERNAL DIA.
GROUND IN 17
SECONDS

CENTRELESS GROUND
100 PER HOUR

D AXLE TUBE

FIG. 7.1.—TYPICAL GRINDING EXAMPLES

of the grinding process, and it needs to be remembered that for each of the above examples a tolerance of plus and minus two micrometres can be held under production conditions. Similar tolerances are also possible on most other types of grinding machine. The following list gives a further indication of the wide adoption of the grinding process in all types of engineering manufacture:

    (i) universal grinder;
    (ii) thread grinder;
    (iii) profile grinder;
    (iv) tool and cutter grinder;
    (v) gear grinder;
    (vi) chucking grinder;
    (vii) plunge grinder;
    (viii) automatic crankpin grinder.

Although the above list presents a formidable array of current grinding machines it is by no means complete; there are several other types, including special-purpose types specifically designed for given grinding operations. Clearly it is not possible in one chapter to cover the basic requirements and operating principles of all the grinding machines mentioned, but in general all the surfaces ground result from the familiar principle of generation. We may now turn our attention to the main types of grinding machine in general use.

7.3. Types of grinding machines

We may conveniently separate the main types of grinding machines as follows:

    (i) surface;
    (ii) cylindrical;
    (iii) centreless.

While the centreless grinding machine may be considered as a special adaptation involving the application of a control wheel and work rest, all other grinding machines, such as chucking, plunge, gear and cutter grinders, can be considered as improved versions of either surface or cylindrical machines, with special provisions for workholding and feeding.

7.4. Surface grinding machines

As the name suggests, the primary use of surface grinding machines is the grinding of flat or plane surfaces. The principles adopted to generate the plane surface are similar in many respects to those found in both horizontal and vertical milling machines; thus we find that surface grinding machines may be classified as follows:

(i) Horizontal-spindle types;
(ii) vertical-spindle types.

The principles underlying horizontal-spindle type surface grinders are simply illustrated at Fig. 7.2, where we see that there are **two** techniques in use. At A we see the familiar horizontal surface grinder with recipro-

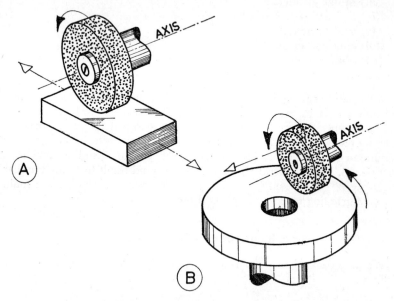

FIG. 7.2.—HORIZONTAL-SPINDLE GRINDING TECHNIQUES

cating table, the plane surface being generated by a combination of work feed and wheel feed. This type of machine is ideal for the grinding of medium-sized plane surfaces such as those found in tool and die work, and in the hands of a skilled toolroom grinder it is capable of carrying out a remarkable variety of grinding operations. Such operations include spline, gauge and form grinding, and it is clear that this type of machine is an essential feature of any toolroom or maintenance department.

At Fig. 7.2B we see a horizontal-spindle surface grinding machine with a rotary table. Once again a plane surface is generated by a combination of work and grinding-wheel movements, and as may be appreciated this type of machine is most suitable for grinding the surfaces of circular discs.

Large discs may be placed reasonably concentrically on the magnetic table, while small-diameter discs may be conveniently arranged in concentric circles on the table. Clearly this type of horizontal-spindle machine is not as versatile as the previous type; but nevertheless it is a useful machine when considerable numbers of circular dies, discs or saws need regrinding.

At Fig. 7.3 we see that there are also two types of vertical-spindle surface grinding machines. Their principles are identical with those of horizontal-spindle machines; one type has a reciprocating and the other a rotary worktable.

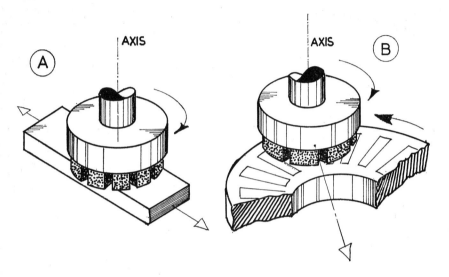

FIG. 7.3.—VERTICAL-SPINDLE GRINDING TECHNIQUES

The type shown at A is best suited for the grinding of relatively large surface areas, such as those found on large-capacity press tools; this type of machine is sometimes referred to as a plough grinder. Of rigid construction and massive proportions, it makes use of special segmented large-diameter grinding wheels, giving excellent rates of metal removal together with good surface finish.

The second type of vertical-spindle surface grinding machine is simply illustrated at Fig. 7.3B. This machine has a rotary table, and is ideal for mass-production grinding of fairly small components spaced out on the magnetic table. Once again these machines are of very robust construction, and excellent metal-removal rates are possible, with direct grinding of well-finished surfaces from black or forged stock, thus eliminating the need for a preliminary machining operation.

7.4.1. Magnetic chucks

The workholding devices invariably used for surface grinding machines are magnetic chucks. These chucks are eminently suited for holding plane surfaces of good finish, with no possibility of damage such as often results when work is held or gripped by hardened steel jaws. The magnetic chucks may be rectangular or circular in design; the circular type being best suited for surface grinding machines equipped with a rotary table, as shown in Figs. 7.2 and 7.3. The magnetic forces required to hold the work in close contact with the chuck surface are either supplied by permanent magnets or induced by an electric current. Whichever method is adopted the operating principle is much the same; it is simply illustrated at Fig. 7.4A. In the OFF position the magnetic forces or flux are not present

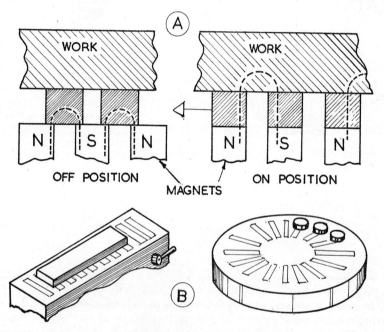

FIG. 7.4.—MAGNETIC WORKHOLDING TECHNIQUES

in the electrically operated type, while in the non-electrical or permanent-magnet type movable pole pieces allow the magnetic forces to pass from pole to pole as shown in the diagram. In the ON position the magnetic flux passes through the workpiece as shown at Fig. 7.4A, and it is of importance that the surface of the magnetic chuck be kept in good condition and free from burrs or scratches. At Fig. 7.4B we see typical applications of both rectangular- and circular-type magnetic chucks.

7.5. Shapes of grinding wheels

In order to cover the very comprehensive range of grinding operations an equally wide range of grinding-wheel shapes are available, but in general terms the actual shape of the grinding wheel depends on whether it is peripheral-cutting or face-cutting. In surface-grinding machines, we have seen that when the wheel axis is horizontal the grinding wheel

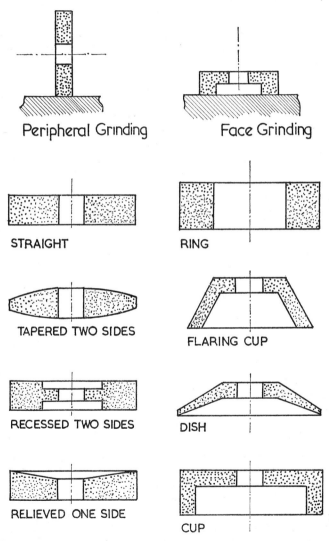

FIG. 7.5.—GRINDING WHEEL SHAPES

must cut on its periphery, as can be found by reference back to Fig. 7.2; when the grinding-wheel axis is vertical the cutting action is at the bottom face of the grinding wheel.

Except in special cases, then, we may classify grinding wheels as either peripheral-cutting or face-cutting. Fig. 7.5 gives an indication of the types of grinding wheel available for general-purpose work.

In addition to the shapes or sections shown, certain grinding operations require wheels with a shaped periphery; for example, both inner and outer races for ball-bearings require a grinding wheel having a spherical radius on the periphery, as shown at Fig. 7.6A. International standards are now in force giving a wide range of shaped peripheries, and typical examples are shown at Fig. 7.6B.

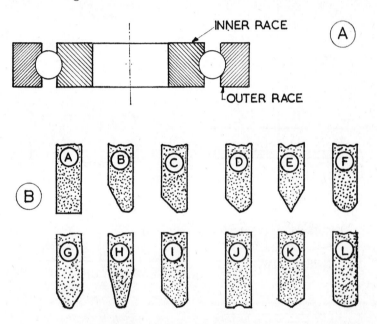

FIG. 7.6.—GRINDING WHEEL PROFILES

7.6. Testing and mounting of grinding wheels

The cutting action of all grinding wheels depends on a very high peripheral speed of the cutting face of the wheel; in other words the grinding-wheel spindle must rotate at a high speed. These high rotational speeds common to all grinding operations represent a continued source of danger to the machine operator, and this means that very careful control needs to be maintained over both the manufacture of the grinding wheel and its mounting on the spindle.

All grinding wheels of over 150 mm diameter are tested by the manufacturer at 50% above the maximum recommended working speed; thus
provided the maximum speed is not severely exceeded during the working
life of the wheel there is no danger of burst or shattered wheels. Bursting
of a grinding wheel is brought about by the centrifugal force set up at
high rotational speeds, with the value of the centrifugal force proportionate
to the imbalance of the wheel. For most commercial work a new grinding

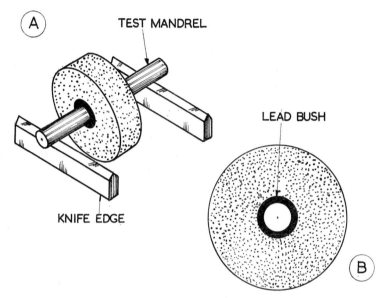

FIG. 7.7.—WHEEL BALANCING ON TWO KNIFE-EDGES

wheel is quite safe to use, owing to the high degree of balance and quality
achieved by precisely controlled manufacturing techniques, but certain
high-precision grinding operations demand the use of an accurately
balanced wheel. The principle of wheel balancing is simply illustrated
at Fig. 7.7A. Any imbalance in the wheel causes it to come to rest
repeatedly in the same position, that is to say with the heavy part under-
neath. Clearly the knife-edges used need to be parallel, with both lying
on a truly horizontal plane. Imbalance may be rectified by light scraping
of the lead bush or by painting the light side of the wheel with a special
heavy paint. A well-balanced wheel is indicated by the fact that it comes
to rest in different positions on the knife-edges.

   In the interests of safety it is important that the grinding wheel be a
good slide fit on the mandrel used for testing, and also that the wheel
be a good slide fit on the spindle of the grinding machine. In no circumstances must force be used to get the wheel on to the spindle, and any
tightness may be removed by careful scraping of the lead bush, as shown

in Fig. 7.7B. It is also good practice to give the grinding wheel a light tap with a metal bar before assembly; a sound wheel gives forth a ringing note, while a faulty or cracked wheel has a dull sound. A faulty wheel

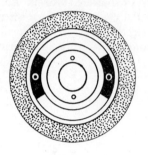

LOCK WHEEL ON SPINDLE
FIX BALANCE WEIGHTS
DIAMETRICALLY OPPOSITE
DRESS WHEEL

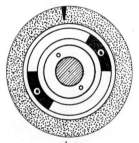

REMOVE WHEEL
SET-UP ON KNIFE EDGE
ROLL AND MARK TOP WHEN
WHEEL COMES TO REST

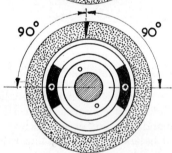

MOVE BALANCE WEIGHTS
90° FROM MARK AND
DIAMETRICALLY OPPOSITE

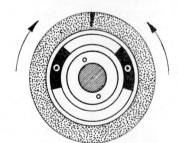

RE-ROLL AND MOVE BALANCE
WEIGHTS APPROXIMATELY 3mm
AT A TIME UNTIL WHEEL
BALANCES. MOVE WEIGHTS
TOWARDS MARK

LOCK WHEEL BACK ON SPINDLE
AND RE-DRESS

FIG. 7.8.—WHEEL BALANCING WITH BALANCE WEIGHTS

must be broken up immediately to prevent any chance of its being used at a later date.

Most precision grinding machines make use of a collet device for holding the wheel; this principle is simply illustrated at Fig. 7.8. The correct procedure for this type of wheel mounting is as follows:

(i) Remove balance weights and true-up wheel with a diamond.
(ii) Remove collet from grinding wheel, mount on an arbor, and setting on a pair of knife-edges adjust balance weights until wheel is truly balanced.
(iii) Reset collet to grinding machine and true-up wheel.

This technique is simply illustrated at Fig. 7.8.

7.7. Dressing and truing grinding wheels

The operation of removing metal particles or dulled abrasive grains from the cutting face of a grinding wheel is known as dressing the wheel. This operation is invariably carried out with a diamond mounted in a suitable holder in the case of precision-grinding machines, or with a piece of abrasive or special wheel dresser in the case of hand or pedestal grinding machines. All the above methods are shown at Fig. 7.9; it is clear that

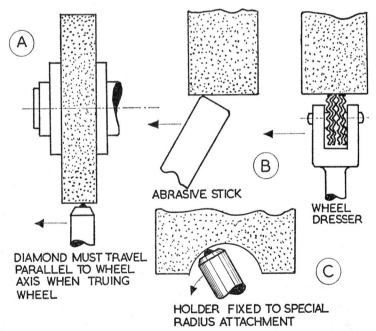

A

ABRASIVE STICK

B

WHEEL DRESSER

DIAMOND MUST TRAVEL PARALLEL TO WHEEL AXIS WHEN TRUING WHEEL

HOLDER FIXED TO SPECIAL RADIUS ATTACHMENT

C

FIG. 7.9.—METHODS OF WHEEL DRESSING AND TRUING

if a diamond is used as shown at A, then the traverse of the diamond across the face of the wheel not only cleans or dresses the wheel but also imparts a geometrical condition. In other words, if the wheel is intended to grind a cylindrical surface it is essential that the path traversed by the diamond be truly parallel with the wheel axis in both horizontal and vertical planes. Any deviation of the path of the diamond from these geometrical conditions must result in a non-cylindrical condition of the grinding wheel; in other words, the wheel will not be dressed true. Thus we see that wheel truing consists in the use of a diamond to ensure that the cutting face of the wheel possesses the necessary geometry. For example, if a grinding wheel is required to grind a radius, then it will be necessary from time to time to retrue the wheel, using a diamond mounted in a special radius-truing device, as shown at Fig. 7.9c.

7.8. Cutting action of a grinding wheel

A grinding wheel is essentially a multi-point self-sharpening cutting tool. In order to appreciate the cutting action of a grinding wheel we may consider Fig. 7.10, where we see an enlarged view of a small portion

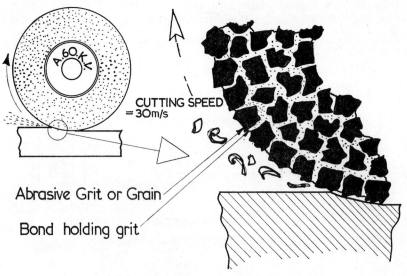

CUTTING SPEED = 30m/s

Abrasive Grit or Grain

Bond holding grit

FIG. 7.10.—CUTTING ACTION OF GRINDING WHEEL

of the wheel at the actual moment of metal removal. The cutting points of the wheel are provided by the very large number of cutting particles; these are more commonly referred to as 'grit' or 'grain'. This is an abrasive; that is to say it is a hard material, well capable of cutting or abrading hardened steel. If the grinding wheel has a peripheral speed of

30 metres per second, as shown in the diagram, the friction set up by the high velocity of the grit results in an elevated local temperature of the workpiece at the point of wheel–work contact. Whereupon the impact of the grit abrades or shears small metal particles from the workpiece. The so-called sparks are therefore particles of metal at relatively high temperature sheared from the parent metal, but accompanying the metal particles are small fragments of the actual grit or abrasive grains.

Clearly a type of glue or bond is needed to hold the abrasive grit together, and the tenacity with which the bond holds the grit determines the hardness of the grinding wheel. An ideal bond is one which retains the abrasive grit as long as it presents a sharp edge to the metal, but releases the grit when the edge becomes dulled or blunt. The ability of the bond to retain the grit is known as the **grade** of the wheel; a **soft** wheel is one where the grit is easily broken away, while a **hard** wheel is one where the grit can be broken away only with difficulty.

The spacing of the grit within the bond is known as the **structure** of the wheel; in other words, it is the proportion of the grit to the bond. A wheel with wide grit spacing is said to have an **open** structure, while a wheel with close grit spacing is said to have a **close** structure.

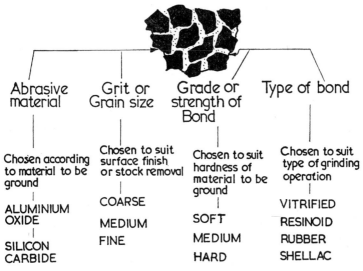

Abrasive material	Grit or Grain size	Grade or strength of Bond	Type of bond
Chosen according to material to be ground	Chosen to suit surface finish or stock removal	Chosen to suit hardness of material to be ground	Chosen to suit type of grinding operation
ALUMINIUM OXIDE	COARSE		VITRIFIED
	MEDIUM	SOFT	RESINOID
SILICON CARBIDE	FINE	MEDIUM	RUBBER
		HARD	SHELLAC

FIG. 7.11.—GRINDING-WHEEL ELEMENTS

We may, then, consider a grinding wheel as a combination of abrasive grit, grade and structure. Fig. 7.11 illustrates in a simple manner the effect and availability of the above elements. Clearly if we are to make the correct choice of a grinding wheel for a specific operation we need to have available a large variety of grinding wheels correctly classified with regard to the type of abrasive, grit or grain size, grade of bond and type of bond. Such classification needs to be clearly indicated on the wheel to ensure that the correct type of wheel is used for the nature of the grinding operation and the material to be ground.

7.9. Classification of grinding wheels

All grinding wheels are classified according to the marking system set out in BS 4481 : Part 1 : 1969. This marking system utilises symbols which indicate the following grinding-wheel elements:

   (i) type of abrasive;
  (ii) size of grain;
 (iii) grade;
 (iv) type of bond;
  (v) any special characteristic, e.g. structure or exact type of bond.

The table shown below gives a complete picture of grinding-wheel classification, and we may use the grinding wheel indicated in Fig. 7.10 to show the application of the system. The wheel is marked thus:

A 60 K V

We see from the table that the letter A denotes that the abrasive used is aluminium oxide. In order that we may appreciate the correct choice of an abrasive we may consider the main types of abrasive and their uses.

7.9.1. Types and uses of abrasives

Aluminium oxide

Given the letter A, aluminium oxide is sometimes known as bauxite. It is produced by fusing the soft clay-like mineral bauxite in electric furnaces, and crushing after cooling, with great care exercised on the resultant particle shape. Its hard, tough nature makes it eminently suitable for grinding metals of high tensile strength such as the carbon steels.

White bauxite

This is a refined form of bauxite, having a higher percentage of aluminium oxide than a wheel carrying the symbol A. More brittle than plain bauxite, a white bauxite wheel has good cool-cutting properties, making it very suitable for grinding operations on hardened steels. This type of grinding wheel, therefore, is well suited for all tool- and cutter-grinding operations.

Silicon carbide

This is a very hard though brittle abrasive, produced by the chemical interaction of high-carbon coke and pure silicon sand in an electric furnace, with small amounts of salt and sawdust added to assist the chemical process. Silicon carbide is harder than aluminium oxide, but lacks the toughness of the latter; thus its use is best restricted to low-tensile-strength materials such as cast iron and non-ferrous metals. It is also much used for grinding materials such as glass, marble, granite and porcelain.

Abrasive	Letter	Grain size	Grade	Bond type	Suffix
Aluminium	A	COARSE	SOFT	V	
oxide		8	E	VITRIFIED	
(Bauxite)		10	F		
		12	G	S	
White	WA	14	H	SILICATE	
bauxite		16	I		
		24		R	
Silicon	C		MEDIUM SOFT	RUBBER	
carbide		MEDIUM	J		
		30	K	B	
Other types	BC	36	L	RESINOID	
of silicon		46		(synthetic resin)	
carbide		54	MEDIUM		
		60	M	BF	
			N	RESINOID	
Bauxite	MA	FINE	O	(reinforced)	
combination		70	P		
		80		E	
		100	HARD	SHELLAC	
		120	Q		
		150	R	Mg	
		180	S	MAGNESIA	
		VERY FINE	VERY HARD		
		220	T		
		240	U		
		280	V		
		320	W		
		400	X		
		500	Y		
		600	Z		

A special symbol to denote structure, grit combination and exact type of bond employed

TABLE 7·1. Marking system for grinding wheels.

7.9.2. Grit or grain size

The grit or grain size refers to the actual size of the abrasive particles. The size of the grit is determined by passing it through a sieve with a definite number of meshes per unit length. For example, a grit size of 30 is considered as medium, and a grit size of 100 is considered as fine. The

H

larger the grit size the rougher will be the surface finish, although the metal-removing properties will be good. In general it may be seen that the finer the grain the better is the surface finish produced, as there are more cutting points available; for example, the heavy roughing of chilled cast iron can be achieved with a grit size of 36, while fine grinding of a chilled-cast-iron roll requires a grinding wheel with a grit size of 320, and if a mirror finish is required a grit size of 500 must be used.

7.9.3. Grade or bond strength

The grade of a grinding wheel is denoted by capital letters, as shown in the preceding table. This is the hardness of a wheel; that is to say the grade is a measure of the ability of the bond to prevent breakage of the grit during the grinding operation. Thus a soft wheel is one from which the abrasive grit is easily broken, while a hard wheel is one from which the grit is broken away only with difficulty. It needs to be remembered that the grade or hardness of a grinding wheel has nothing to do with the hardness of the abrasive; a wheel manufactured from a very hard abrasive but having a grade of H is considered as a soft wheel. Typical examples of the use of wheels with a grade of H would be for the finish grinding of plug and gap gauges. In other words, soft wheels are used for hard materials; a hard metal tends quickly to blunt or dull the abrasive grit, and if the wheel is to have an efficient grinding action it is necessary that the dulled or blunt grit is broken away from that part of the wheel in contact with the work, enabling new sharp grit to continue with the removal of metal. This is the self-sharpening capacity of a grinding wheel; namely the use of a bond having the strength to retain sharp grit, but unable to retain grit which has dulled or blunted. As may be seen from the preceding table, the grades of wheel range (for practical purposes) from E, which is very soft, to Z, which is very hard. In general hard materials require wheels with soft grades, while soft materials need hard-grade wheels.

7.9.4. Type of bond

Referring back to the table showing the marking system for grinding wheels we see that there are four main types of bond in use:

(i) vitrified;
(ii) resinoid;
(iii) rubber;
(iv) shellac.

Vitrified bond

Most grinding wheels are given a vitrified bond. The method of manufacture consists in mixing the abrasive with carefully controlled amounts of clay and fusible materials and pressing in moulds according to the shape of wheel required, with subsequent drying and kilning. The vitrified-bond wheel is reasonably robust and well able to stand up to normal usage.

Resinoid bond

When a higher factor of safety is required a resinoid-bond wheel is preferred. Resinoid-bond wheels combine the free-cutting properties of the vitrified wheel with the safety of a shellac- or rubber-bond wheel. Because of the higher speeds possible with resinoid wheels, rapid stock removal is made possible, and it is normal practice to run these wheels at surface speeds of between 45 and 48 metres per second.

A typical application of resinoid wheels is the fettling of steel and iron castings, where rapid metal removal combined with maximum safety are essential factors. Thin resinoid wheels are also used for cutting off metal bars and tubes and for granite and marble.

Rubber bond

When considerable elasticity is required rubber-bond wheels are used. Three typical examples are:

(i) very thin wheels for cutting off metal bars;
(ii) control wheels for centreless grinding machines;
(iii) wheels for producing a very fine finish on cylindrical grinding machines.

Shellac bond

Very similar to rubber-bond wheels, shellac wheels have a high safety factor. For grinding applications such as cutting off damaged portions of hardened cutting tools like taps or drills, shellac wheels are ideal.

7.9.5. Structure of grinding wheels

By structure we mean the relative spacing of the grit and the proportion of grit to bond. An open-structure wheel, that is to say a wheel with grit widely spaced, is better suited for good stock removal with less consideration for the quality of the surface finish. Such a wheel is much improved with regard to its cool-cutting properties by the introduction of artificial pores or voids during manufacture. At Fig. 7.12A we see a small section of an open-structure wheel; note the wide spacing of the grit and the presence of small voids in the bond. The spacing of the grit is classified on a scale ranging from dense to open; a very close-spaced or dense grit is given the numeral 1, and a very open or widely spaced grit the numeral 15. Such a structure is illustrated at Fig. 7.12A, while at Fig. 7.12B we see a dense structure. A dense-structure wheel is much preferred for hard brittle materials and for grinding operations that demand long wheel life; for example, the grinding of threads or special profiles. The close spacing of the grit together with the absence of voids promotes a long life for the grinding wheel and a good surface finish on the workpiece.

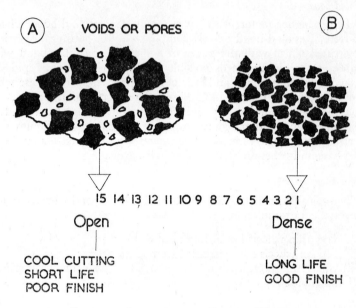

FIG. 7.12.—STRUCTURE OF A GRINDING WHEEL

The diameters of the pores are also controlled by grinding-wheel manufacturers, with 0 indicating a very small and 10 a very large pore size. This information is usually included as a suffix to the grinding-wheel marking, with porous wheels given the letters P or Y followed by the pore-size numeral.

7.10. Examples of grinding wheels

Perhaps a few simple examples of grinding-wheel selection will help to develop an appreciation of the marking system and of the importance of the correct choice of wheel according to the operation at hand.

Fettling

Fig. 7.13A shows a simple fettling operation on a portable grinding machine. The wheel shape is straight, and the periphery is used. For low-speed grinding a suitable wheel is C24SV, and for high-speed grinding C16RB. The low-speed wheel is used for roughing off the surplus metal,

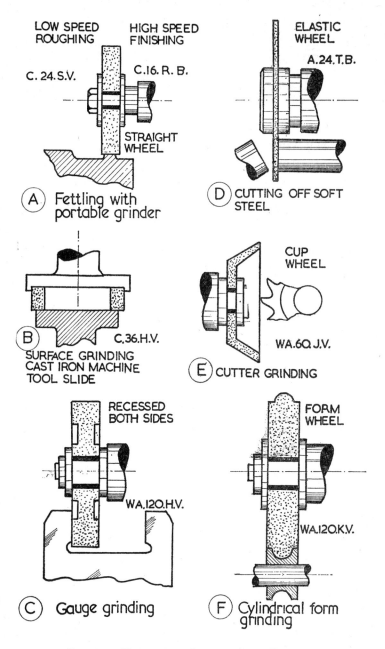

LOW SPEED ROUGHING HIGH SPEED FINISHING

C. 24. S.V. C.16. R. B.

STRAIGHT WHEEL

(A) Fettling with portable grinder

ELASTIC WHEEL

A.24.T.B.

(D) CUTTING OFF SOFT STEEL

(B) SURFACE GRINDING CAST IRON MACHINE TOOL SLIDE C.36.H.V.

CUP WHEEL

WA.6Q.J.V.

(E) CUTTER GRINDING

RECESSED BOTH SIDES

WA.120.H.V.

(C) Gauge grinding

FORM WHEEL

WA.120.K.V.

(F) Cylindrical form grinding

FIG. 7.13.—EXAMPLES OF GRINDING-WHEEL SELECTION

while the high-speed wheel is used for rapid finishing. We may sum-marise both wheels as follows:

Low-speed (C24SV). The abrasive is silicon carbide, quite suitable for a low-tensile strength metal such as cast iron. The grit size is 24; this is a coarse grade, as may be expected for a roughing operation where fast stock removal is the primary consideration. The grade or hardness of the wheel is S; as can be seen from the table this is a fairly hard wheel, but one quite suitable for a low-tensile strength metal like cast iron. The symbol V tells us that the bond is of the vitrified type, well able to stand up to normal working conditions.

High-speed (C16RB). Once again the abrasive is silicon carbide, but the grit size is now slightly coarser, to improve the free-cutting qualities of the wheel. The grade is now R, very similar to the roughing wheel only very slightly softer. The most significant change is in the type of bond. The symbol B tells us that it is now resinoid, not vitrified; the adoption of this bond allows a higher grinding speed with no undue risk to the operator. Note that the wheels specified above are applicable only to portable grinding machines; floor or swing-frame grinders require different wheels, as recommended by the manufacturer.

Surface grinding

Fig. 7.13B shows the use of a cylindrical grinding wheel for surface grinding the top face of a machine-tool slide. Note that the face of the wheel is used, and not the periphery as in the previous example of fettling.

The wheel for this job is C36HV. The abrasive therefore is silicon carbide, best suited for a low-tensile-strength metal such as cast iron.

The grit size is 36, which can be considered as medium, while the grade of the wheel is H. This is a relatively soft wheel, advisable where a fairly large work–wheel contact area exists, as is the case in face grinding. The bond is of the vitrified type, providing a rigid wheel which is usually mounted to a backplate by flowing molten sulphur or shellac between the wheel and the mounting-plate flange; a very firm bond is achieved on solidification of the sulphur or shellac.

Gap-gauge grinding

Fig. 7.13c shows in simple manner the technique adopted when grinding gap gauges. In order to ensure parallelism of the ground sides it is essential to grind them at the same setting, and this means that both sides of the grinding wheel need to be used. In general it is not considered good practice to use the side of a grinding wheel, but this class of work demands the services of a highly skilled craftsman who will possess the necessary skill and experience to use the sides of a grinding wheel with no undue risk. Note that the grinding wheel used is a straight wheel, recessed both sides. The purpose of the recess is to reduce the area of contact between the wheel and the work, thus reducing the possibility of overheating and distortion of the workpiece.

A suitable wheel for this operation is WA120HV. We are now grinding hardened tool steel, therefore the abrasive of the wheel needs to be tough as well as hard. As we have seen, the best abrasive for this kind of work is aluminium oxide or bauxite, with a white bauxite wheel preferred for hardened steel. As may be expected, the symbols WA indicate that a white bauxite is used. Now the gap gauge is to be used for precision checking; thus a high surface finish is required on the ground gauging faces. This means that a small grit size is needed, for the finer the grit the better the surface finish, as more cutting points are in contact. We see that the grit size is 120; this can be considered as approaching very fine.

As we are grinding a hardened tool steel it is imperative that the grit, which is likely to dull quickly, breaks away fairly easily from the bond, and this means that a fairly soft grade is called for. In other words, a hard material needs a soft wheel, remembering that 'soft' refers to the grade of the wheel and not to the abrasive. The wheel, as we see from Fig. 7.13c is grade H, a fairly soft grade.

Once again a rigid wheel is needed, free from all tendency to bend or deflect during the grinding operation; the symbol V tells us that the bond is vitrified.

Cutting off

Fig. 7.13D shows a typical cutting-off operation for the high-speed production of short lengths of mild-steel bar. The grinding wheel used is commonly known as an **elastic** wheel, the term indicating that the wheel possesses a good degree of flexibility.

We see that the wheel is marked A24TB. The abrasive is aluminium oxide, the common choice for mild or soft steel, a reasonably strong metal. The grit size is 24, fairly coarse but providing ample swarf clearance and suitable for good stock removal with less consideration for surface finish. The grade of the bond is given by the symbol T, and it is clear that this is a very hard wheel, which means that the grit is only broken away from the bond with difficulty; thus the wheel tends to have a long life.

The bond is of the resinoid type, as indicated by the symbol B. The use of a resinoid bond ensures that the wheel has ample flexibility to suit its narrow section and gives a high degree of safety.

Cutter grinding

Fig. 7.13E shows a typical application of cutter grinding, the operation consisting of regrinding the teeth of a milling cutter. Note the use of a cup grinding wheel, giving a fairly small area of contact, thus preventing overheating of the cutting edge of the cutter during the grinding operation.

We see that the cutter is marked WA60JV. Once again, for hardened tool steel such as a milling cutter a white bauxite wheel is used, slightly more brittle than a plain bauxite wheel and thus possessing cooler cutting properties. The grit size is 60, which may be considered as fine, giving a good surface finish to the cutting edges of the milling cutter.

The grade is J, medium soft, to ensure breaking away of the grit; this maintains a sharp face to the grinding wheel, very necessary for grinding high-speed steel in a hardened condition, the material from which the milling cutter is made. The vitrified bond ensures a strong, rigid wheel.

Cylindrical form grinding

Fig. 7.13F shows a simple example of form grinding using a cylindrical grinding machine. Clearly the form on the grinding wheel needs to be precisely produced by either diamond forming or wheel crushing, and it is also important that the grinding wheel is capable of maintaining its accurate form or profile, or more time is likely to be spent in forming the grinding wheel than in grinding workpieces. The wheel chosen is WA120KV. As the radiused form is to be ground on hardened steel components, a white bauxite wheel is used. The grit size is very fine, with the number 120, the very large number of grains promoting long life of the grinding wheel together with a good surface finish on the component. The grade or hardness of the wheel is K, medium-soft, to meet the hardness of the material to be ground. Finally the bond, as may be expected, is vitrified, giving a rigid, robust wheel.

The above examples give only a small indication of the range of grinding wheels available. At all times the best plan is to consult the actual grinding-wheel manufacturer, who is well able to recommend the best type of grinding wheel for any specific operation.

7.11. Factors affecting correct choice of grinding wheels

It is of interest to consider some of the factors that influence the correct choice of a grinding wheel for a specific operation. In general we may list the following factors in the order shown:

   (i) material to be ground;
  (ii) amount of material to be removed;
 (iii) quality of finish required;
 (iv) area of contact;
  (v) condition of grinding machine;
 (vi) cutting speed.

7.11.1. Material

In general, the harder the material the softer the grade of the wheel. All low-tensile materials such as non-ferrous metals and cast and chilled iron should be ground with a silicon-carbide wheel, while the carbon steels and alloy steels in the unhardened state should be ground with a bauxite wheel. All steels in the hardened condition should be ground with a white bauxite wheel.

7.11.2. Amount of material to be removed

If a large amount of material needs to be removed, grinding may be considered as a roughing operation; a coarse-grain wheel is needed, having the necessary open structure improved by the inclusion of voids or pores. For a finishing operation, where the amount of metal removed is small and a better finish is required, a fine-grain wheel is needed.

7.11.3. Quality of finish

When a good surface finish is needed a fine grain must be used, with a shellac bond. Such wheels are suitable only for small amounts of metal removal; therefore production times with them are likely to be excessive. The finer the grit size the better the surface finish; a very high degree of surface finish can be expected from a grinding wheel having a grit size of 600. The average size of the grit would be about 0·05 micrometres across; in effect it is a form of very fine powder or flour. For certain applications diamond wheels can be used, the grit in this case consisting of very fine diamond powder no less than 1 micrometre across. Such a wheel can be used to grind very hard surfaces such as tungsten-carbide tips, producing at the same time an excellent surface finish.

7.11.4. Area of contact

The amount of contact between the workpiece and the grinding wheel, that is to say the area of contact, has an important bearing on the choice of a grinding wheel. As we have seen, most grinding techniques fall under one of two headings:

(i) peripheral grinding;
(ii) face grinding.

In peripheral grinding, as for example in surface grinding with a straight wheel, only line contact exists between the wheel and the workpiece. This is simply illustrated at Fig. 7.14; it can be seen that the area of contact is very small. The area of contact is mainly determined by the depth of cut, which in most cases is of the order of a few hundredths of a millimetre only. The plane surface is generated by the summation of table movement and wheelhead feed, in much the same manner as when shaping or planing a flat surface.

Because of the relatively small contact area, a fine grit and hard bond are the best combination. The small area of contact means that fewer cutting points are in contact with the work; hence the disruptive forces acting on the grit have a high value and a hard grade is needed to prevent excessive wheel wear. The number of grains in contact with the work can be increased by ensuring a fine grit size, with consequent improvement of the surface finish.

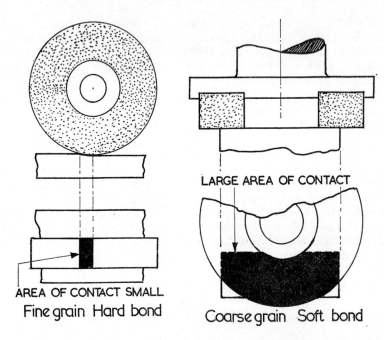

LARGE AREA OF CONTACT

AREA OF CONTACT SMALL
Fine grain Hard bond

Coarse grain Soft bond

FIG. 7.14.—EFFECT OF CONTACT AREA ON GRAIN AND BOND

The area of contact when cutting with the face of a cylindrical or cup wheel is fairly large, as can be seen on reference to Fig. 7.14. This means that a very large number of cutting points are in contact with the work; hence the disruptive force acting on the grit is of a low order as there are so many grains to share it. A soft grade is now required, together with a coarse grit size, giving a good open structure with ample swarf clearance and cool-cutting properties.

7.11.5. Condition of grinding machine

As with any other machine tool, the condition of the grinding machine has an important effect on the quality and accuracy of the ground surface. Loose bearings, lack of rigidity and unbalanced wheels are the prime causes of chatter and uneven wheel wear, while vibrations caused by external sources may also affect the quality of the ground surface. In general, a grinding machine in poor condition produces better work with a wheel having a harder grade than that normally chosen for the particular operation in hand, while a slightly softer grade than normal can be used by a grinding machine in first-class condition.

7.11.6. Cutting speed

The cutting speed at which a grinding wheel should be operated is always stated with the marking system, and is the speed the manufacturer considers most suitable. As with most other cutting tools certain operations are given ideal or recommended cutting speeds, derived from long practical experience, and in common with other metal-removal procedures cutting speeds are given in metres per second. The cutting speed for a grinding operation is the peripheral speed of the grinding wheel in relation to the workpiece, and clearly this cutting speed must be proportional to the diameter of the grinding wheel. Before dealing with the connection between cutting speed and wheel diameter, it will be of interest to have at hand the following table, which recommends suitable cutting speeds for a wide range of grinding operations:

Operation	Cutting speed in metres per second
Cylindrical grinding	25 – 30
Crankshaft grinding	25 – 33
Surface grinding (cup and cylindrical wheels)	20 – 25
Surface grinding (peripheral wheels)	22 – 28
Tool and cutter grinding	25
Fettling	25 – 30
Cutting off	45 – 80

TABLE 7.2. Cutting speeds for grinding operations.

The above table gives the recommended peripheral or surface speed of the grinding wheel, and as grinding wheels are available in various diameters it becomes necessary to express surface speed in terms of wheel diameter and spindle speed. Before dealing with the procedure required for calculating spindle speeds, it must be mentioned that incorrect speeds have a material effect on the cutting action. If the spindle speed is too high the wheel becomes apparently harder, that is to say the grit is more difficult to dislodge, while if the wheel runs at too low a speed it appears softer and wears away more quickly.

This means that a grinding wheel may be made harder by increasing the spindle speed, while on the other hand a hard wheel may be made softer by running at a lower spindle speed. By the same token, a peripheral cutting wheel suffers a reduction in diameter in proportion to the amount of wear taking place; thus as the diameter decreases so does the cutting speed, so that the wheel appears too soft for the operation in hand. The remedy in this case is to increase the spindle speed, if this is possible on the type of grinding machine being used.

We see now the necessity for calculation of spindle speed in terms of cutting or surface speed, and the following section indicates a speedy and simple approach to this problem.

7.12. Calculations on spindle speeds and cutting speeds

Perhaps the simplest method of calculating spindle speed given the cutting speed is to use a table of circumferences, and such a table follows, where circumferences for wheels ranging from 25 to 1 000 mm are given. Remember that quite small-diameter wheels are used for the cylindrical grinding of internal holes, while large 'plough'-type surface grinding machines commonly use grinding wheels of 600 mm diameter. Let us consider a very simple problem involving the correct choice of a spindle speed given the diameter of the wheel and the cutting speed.

EXAMPLE 1

A 250 mm diameter grinding wheel is to be used for cylindrical grinding at a cutting or surface speed of 25 metres per second. Calculate the revs per second of the grinding-machine spindle. Using the table given opposite, we find that a 250 mm diameter wheel has a circumference of 0·8 metres. To find the spindle speed we divide surface speed by circumference:

$$\text{Spindle speed} = \frac{\text{surface speed}}{\text{circumference}}$$

$$= \frac{25}{0\cdot8}$$

$$= 31\cdot25 \text{ rev/s}$$

Wheel diameter (mm)	Circumference (m)	Wheel diameter (mm)	Circumference (m)
25	0·08	525	1·68
50	0·16	550	1·76
75	0·24	575	1·84
100	0·32	600	1·92
125	0·4	625	2·00
150	0·48	650	2·08
175	0·56	675	2·16
200	0·64	700	2·24
225	0·72	725	2·32
250	0·80	750	2·40
300	0·96	800	2·56
350	1·12	850	2·72
375	1·20	875	2·80
400	1·28	900	2·88
450	1·44	950	3·04
500	1·60	1 000	3·20

TABLE 7.3. Table of circumferences.

EXAMPLE 2

A cup wheel of white bauxite has worn down to 100 mm diameter. If it is to be used at a surface speed of 25 metres per second for re-grinding a milling cutter, calculate the spindle speed of the cutter grinding machine.

From Table 7.3, the circumference of a 100 mm diameter wheel is 0·32m.

$$\text{Spindle speed} = \frac{\text{surface speed}}{\text{circumference}}$$
$$= \frac{25}{0·32}$$
$$= 78·1 \quad \text{rev/s}$$

We may also use the circumference table in reverse—that is to say to find the surface speed of a grinding wheel of given diameter.

EXAMPLE 3

Calculate the surface speed of a 250 mm diameter grinding wheel rotating at 25 rev/s. From Table 7.3, the circumference of a 250 mm diameter wheel is 0·8 metres.

Surface speed = circumference in metres multiplied by rev/s
$$= 0·8 \times 25$$
$$= 20 \text{ metres per second}$$

It is unlikely, of course, that a grinding-machine spindle can be set to revolve at precisely the calculated speed; the nearest available speed must be used.

7.12.1. Use of a speed table

The table below provides a rapid and precise method of achieving the sort of answers obtained from the circumference table without any need for calculation for grinding wheels up to 250 mm diameter, and with only simple additions for wheels in excess of 250 mm diameter.

Wheel diameter (mm)	Surface speed in metres per second					
	20	25	30	33	45	48
25	254·6	318·2	381·9	413·8	572·9	604·3
50	127·3	159·1	191·0	206·9	286·5	302·1
75	84·9	106·1	127·3	137·9	191·0	301·7
100	63·7	79·6	95·5	103·4	143·2	151·1
125	50·9	63·7	76·4	82·8	114·6	120·9
150	42·4	53·0	63·7	69·0	95·5	100·9
175	36·4	45·5	54·6	59·1	81·8	86·4
200	31·8	39·8	47·7	51·7	71·6	75·5
250	25·5	31·8	38·2	41·4	57·3	60·5
	revs per second					

TABLE 7.4. Grinding wheel speed/diameter table.

The following simple examples will serve to illustrate the use of the table.

EXAMPLE 1

A grinding machine spindle is set to run at 45 revs per second, and a wheel is to be selected for grinding mild steel at a surface speed of 30 metres per second. Using Table 7.4 select the correct-diameter wheel. Choosing the column headed 30 metres per second we move down until we reach the speed of 47·7 revs per second. This is the nearest speed to 45 metres per second, and moving across to the left-hand column we see that the correct diameter wheel is 200 mm.

EXAMPLE 2

A cutting-off grinding machine has a top spindle speed of 200 revs per second. Find the surface speed of a 250 mm diameter wheel fitted to this machine.

Moving along the bottom line we may choose the nearest factor of 200, for example multiplying 25·5 by 8 gives 204, hence if we multiply the surface speed at the top of the column containing 25·5 by 8 we arrive at an approximate value of the surface speed. Hence, approximate surface speed:

$$20 \times 8 = 160 \text{ metres per second}$$

7.13. Calculations of pulley speeds and diameters

There are still a large number of grinding machines in use having the simple driving arrangement shown at Fig. 7.15. Clearly, as we have

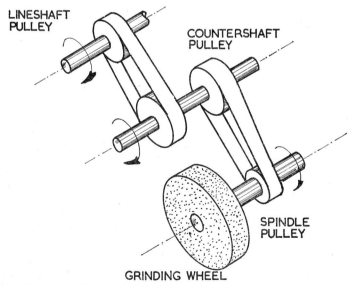

LINESHAFT
PULLEY

COUNTERSHAFT
PULLEY

SPINDLE
PULLEY

GRINDING WHEEL

FIG. 7.15.—DRIVING ARRANGEMENT OF A GRINDING-WHEEL SPINDLE

seen from the preceding tables on surface speeds and wheel diameters, it is often necessary to change spindle speeds to suit different-diameter wheels or different surface speeds or to compensate for loss in diameter as the grinding wheel wears. The following easy rules will simplify the problem of changing the belt position or the pulleys themselves to suit different grinding conditions.

In general, one of three calculations is likely to be required:

   (i) Finding the speed of the countershaft for a given spindle speed.

  (ii) Finding the diameter of the countershaft pulley, given the spindle speed and spindle pulley diameter.

 (iii) Finding the diameter of the pulley on the lineshaft, given the revs per second of the lineshaft and countershaft and the pulley diameter on the countershaft.

Reference to Fig. 7.15 shows the main elements involved in the above calculations, and the following simple examples will serve to illustrate the correct approach to the solution of these problems.

EXAMPLE 1

A grinding-wheel spindle has a pulley of 200 mm diameter and rotates at 20 revs per second. If the pulley on the countershaft is of 500 mm diameter, calculate the revs per second of the countershaft.

The rule here is simple. Multiply the revs per second of the grinding wheel spindle by the diameter of its pulley, then divide the product by the diameter of the countershaft pulley.

$$\text{Revs per second of countershaft pulley} = \frac{20 \times 200}{500}$$

$$= 8 \text{ rev/s}$$

EXAMPLE 2

A grinding-wheel spindle is to run at 30 revs/per second with a pulley of 150 mm diameter. If the countershaft rotates at 15 revs per second, calculate the diameter of the countershaft pulley.

The rule here is to multiply the revs per second of the grinding-wheel spindle by the diameter of its pulley, then divide the product by the revs per second of the countershaft.

$$\text{Diameter of countershaft pulley} = \frac{30 \times 150}{15}$$

$$= 300 \text{ mm diameter}$$

EXAMPLE 3

A lineshaft rotates at 4 revs per second and is to drive the countershaft at 20 revs per second. If the pulley on the countershaft is of 200 mm diameter, calculate the diameter of the pulley required on the lineshaft.

In this case we need to multiply the revs per second of the countershaft by the diameter of its pulley, then divide the product by the revs per second of the lineshaft.

$$\text{Diameter of pulley on lineshaft} = \frac{20 \times 200}{4}$$

$$= 1\ 000 \text{ mm diameter}$$

7.14. Wheel faults arising from incorrect conditions

The non-appliance of correct surface or grinding-wheel spindle speeds results in a marked deterioration of both the cutting properties of the wheel and the quality of the ground surface. This is owing to two well-known wheel conditions called glazing and loading.

Glazing

This term describes the condition in which a grinding wheel has a glazed or shiny surface. It results from the inability of the dulled or blunt grit to break away from the bond, and the effect on the ground surface is overheating or burning, with consequent distortion and poor finish. The remedy here is to use a softer wheel; that is, to choose a wheel with a grade lower down the alphabet. Alternatively, the grinding-wheel spindle revs per second can be reduced by the use of a larger-diameter pulley on the grinding-wheel spindle or a smaller pulley on the countershaft.

Loading

A loaded wheel is one which retains particles of metal on its surface; such particles interfere with the cutting action of the wheel, leading to excess friction and overheating of the ground surface. Loading may be caused by using a wheel of too hard a bond, or by excessive depths of cut, and the remedy is to choose a wheel with a softer bond or increase the spindle speed. Both loaded and glazed wheels are restored to normal by dressing with a diamond, but repeated dressing reduces the useful life of the wheel, increases unproductive time and leads to difficulty in holding close tolerances.

7.15. Use of coolants

If a grinding coolant is used it is essential that a copious flow be directed on to the work. The purpose of a coolant is to prevent excessive rise in temperature of the ground surface, while an additional advantage is the immediate washing away or removal of the swarf and dislodged grit. It is essential that the coolant be thoroughly cleaned or filtered before it is returned to the grinding location, as dirty or contaminated coolant tends to increase the possibility of a loaded wheel as well as having an adverse effect on the surface finish of the ground work. A widely used grinding coolant consists of a mixture of water, carbonate of soda and a little oil, although there are many special coolants designed for specific grinding operations. It is advisable to seek the aid of the grinding-wheel manufacturer in order to ensure that the best possible coolant is employed for the job in hand.

It is a mistake to allow coolant to flow on to a stationary grinding wheel, as the wheel will become heavy at its saturated part, and this is likely to produce an unbalanced condition, which may be a serious matter if the grinding wheel is used at a high spindle speed.

7.16. Horizontal-spindle surface grinding

We have seen in 7.4 the principles underlying the two main types of surface grinding machine, and Fig. 7.3 shows two typical applications of surface grinding. Probably the simplest of all grinding operations is surface grinding with a reciprocating motion of the table and a horizontal axis of the grinding-wheel spindle.

The horizontal-spindle grinder is undoubtedly the most versatile of the surface grinding machines, as both the periphery and the face of the grinding wheel can be used. If the face of the wheel is to be used a recessed wheel is essential, to reduce the area of contact between the wheel and workpiece; an excessive contact area results in overheating of the ground surface.

When the periphery of the wheel is used, as shown at Fig. 7.16A, care needs to be taken with the rate of traverse of the wheel across the workpiece as shown at the end elevation. Best grinding results are obtained when the rate of traverse is about two-thirds of the width of the wheel for each stroke of the table. This ensures that the wheel wear is even; that is to say that the periphery remains flat. If the traverse is less than one-half of the wheel width the wheel will wear at its edges and a convex peripheral face will result.

The horizontal-spindle surface grinder finds its widest application in high-class toolroom grinding; its wide open front allows easy access to the work set-up and checking as the grinding proceeds. The open table permits the use of the usual range of accessories, such as angle plates, V blocks, sine-bar settings and toolmaker's vices, and with equipment of this nature a wide range of grinding operations are possible.

As previously stated, both the periphery and the face of the grinding wheel can be used, but it is vital that the wheel is dressed in the manner shown at Fig. 7.16B before the finishing cuts are taken. The periphery of the wheel is first dressed with the diamond holder firmly held to the magnetic chuck, the diamond lying below the centre line of the wheel. Light cuts are taken, with horizontal infeed of the workhead to true the wheel periphery, while a special holder, capable of presenting the diamond at 90° to the previous position, enables the side of the wheel to be dressed as shown at Fig. 7.16B. Vertical downfeed of the grinding head is employed to dress the side of the wheel, and in this way the geometrical

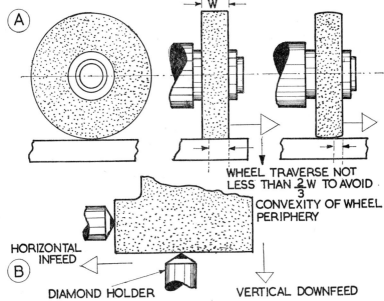

FIG. 7.16.—FEEDING AND DRESSING PERIPHERAL WHEELS

alignments of the grinding machine are transferred to the wheel, resulting in a corresponding high degree of 90° accuracy between adjacent surfaces ground at the same setting.

Some typical examples of the class and scope of work possible with a horizontal-spindle surface grinder are illustrated at Fig. 7.17, each set-up demanding a high degree of skill from the craftsman.

Fig. 7.17A

The diagram shows the use of a surface grinder when grinding a die insert to a precise angle. Note the use of a precision angle plate, sine bar and workshop slip gauges. The accuracy of the angle shown will be of a high order and certainly within $\pm$ 15 seconds of arc. Alternatively, the set-up may be achieved with angle gauges wrung together to the required angle.

Fig. 7.17B

The resurfacing or regrinding of both punches and dies is carried out on a surface grinder. At Fig. 7.17B we see a typical set-up involving the regrinding of two punches.

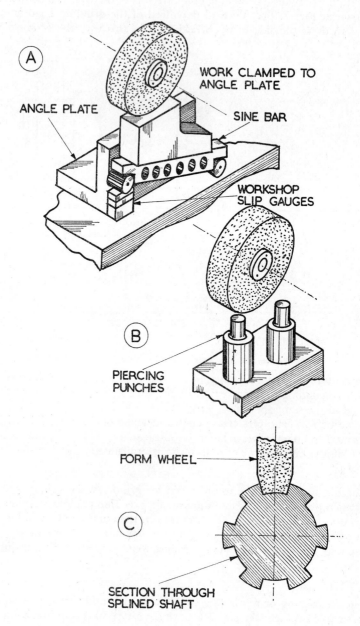

(A)   WORK CLAMPED TO ANGLE PLATE

ANGLE PLATE   SINE BAR

WORKSHOP SLIP GAUGES

(B)

PIERCING PUNCHES

FORM WHEEL

(C)

SECTION THROUGH SPLINED SHAFT

Fig. 7.17.—Examples of Surface Grinding

Fig. 7.17c

Spline grinding is a good example of the use of a formed wheel on a surface grinder. Fig. 7.17c shows an end view of the grinding operation, with six equi-spaced splines to be ground. The set-up is somewhat difficult, for the centre line of the splined shaft must be truly at 90° to the grinding wheel axis, with the shaft centre directly below the wheel centre. A dividing head is needed to index the shaft six times; each spline is rough ground first time around, then finish ground after dressing the grinding wheel.

7.17. Cylindrical grinding

In the same way that surface grinding follows closely the milling technique, so does cylindrical grinding follow the turning technique. Cylindrical grinding consists of the generation of a cylindrical surface by rotation of the workpiece about its axis together with traversing of the workpiece across a rotating grinding wheel. This principle is simply illustrated at Fig. 7.18A, where we see the process of external grinding, while at B we see internal cylindrical grinding.

If a grinding machine is capable of both techniques it is known as a

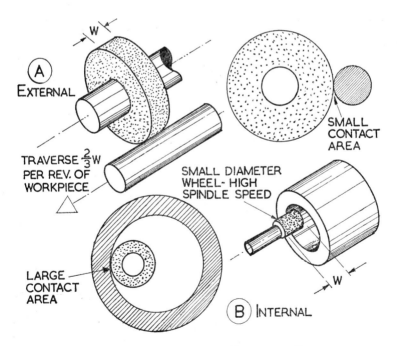

Fig. 7.18.—Contact Area when Cylindrical Grinding

universal grinder, and this is the type of machine best suited for tool and jig work. It follows that a universal grinder is an essential piece of equipment in any toolroom, requiring a highly skilled craftsman for its efficient operation.

Note that in external cylindrical grinding as shown at Fig. 7.18A a fairly large-diameter grinding wheel is used, with the result that the area of contact between wheel and workpiece is relatively small. On the other hand, internal grinding must involve the use of a small-diameter grinding wheel, with the possibility of a fairly large area of contact, as shown at Fig. 7.18B. This means that all internal grinding involves very high spindle speeds to compensate for the small diameter of the grinding wheels; speeds up to 500 revs per second are now commonplace.

The rate of traverse of the worktable is also shown at Fig. 7.18. Note that as in surface grinding the rate of traverse of the workpiece which travels with the table must exceed two-thirds of the grinding-wheel width per revolution of the workpiece. This ensures even wearing of the wheel surface. It is clear that the wider the wheel the greater is the rate of metal removal.

7.17.1. Plain cylindrical grinding machines

Plain cylindrical grinding machines are mainly used for production work. They are designed to maintain high production rates with accurate size repetition, and essential features include a robust, rigid construction incorporating the following items:

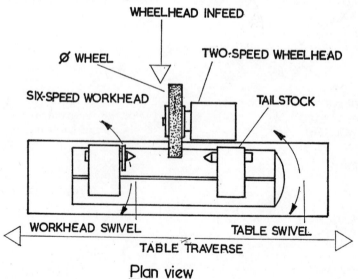

Fig. 7.19.—Plain Cylindrical Grinding Machine

Worktable

A simple plan view is shown at Fig. 7.19, and it may be seen that the table is capable of a small swivel angle of about 20°, thus permitting the production grinding of slow tapers using the automatic traverse. A wide range of traverse speeds are available, ranging from about 1 mm to 5 000 mm per second. The table is equipped with precision T slots for the swift and accurate location of accessories.

Wheelhead

The wheelhead of a cylindrical grinding machine represents a very high standard of engineering precision. Not only must the wheelhead spindle be free from deflection and play, but the wheelhead sliding arrangement which provides infeed must also provide precise and sensitive movement if consistent accuracy is to be maintained on the ground diameters. Wheelhead spindles are made from nitrided steel, are of large diameter, and run in rigid-type pre-adjusted bearings lubricated by filtered oil supplied by a pump. To ensure high production rates, large-diameter grinding wheels are mounted on the spindle, and wheels of up to 600 mm diameter are in common use. In many cases, automatic diamond truing devices are fitted, allowing rapid and accurate dressing or truing of the wheel.

In addition, control of the ground diameter may be automatically achieved by the use of an electronic automatic sizing attachment which stops the machine when the required diameter has been reached. This device permits production grinding of batches of components to tolerances on diameter within 0·001 mm. Yet another modern technique consists of grinding diameters to match given bores. This is sometimes known as **match grinding,** and involves the following technique. The bore to which the ground diameter is to match or mate is measured automatically by an electronic measuring device, which in turn controls the electronic device governing the amount of infeed of the wheelhead. In this way the diameter ground is always within a given tolerance of the bore with which it is to mate, thus ensuring a remarkably high-quality fit.

Workhead

The purpose of the workhead is to provide both support and rotation of the work to be ground. Located on the worktable, the workhead is easily moved and locked at any position of the table, and it is capable also of swivelling and locking at any required angle. Both chucks and centres may be used to hold the workpiece, and a range of workspeeds are available. An electric motor is used to provide rotation, and most cylindrical grinders have about six speeds, ranging from, say, 1 to 5 revs per second, to accommodate work of different diameters.

Tailstock

The tailstock serves a purpose identical with that of its counterpart on the centre lathe. Intended to support long work, it is readily locked at any position of the table, and its work-supporting ability may be assisted by the inclusion of a work support or steady, placed in opposition to the grinding wheel and clamped to the worktable.

7.17.2. Plunge grinding

Plain cylindrical grinding machines may be used for the technique known as plunge grinding. This method is preferred when the diameter to be ground is of relatively short length, as shown at Fig. 7.20A. The

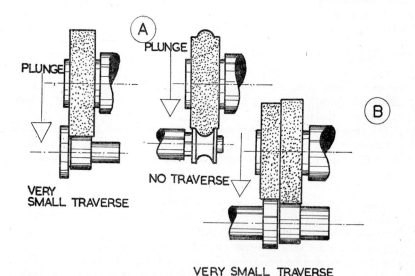

FIG. 7.20.—PLUNGE GRINDING TECHNIQUES

grinding wheel is now fed or plunged directly into the work with very small traverse of the worktable. Without slight oscillation of the table the technique of plunge grinding suffers from the defect that any faults or imperfections on the surface of the grinding wheel are transmitted to the workpiece. Note that for the second example of plunge grinding shown at Fig. 7.20A no traverse of the worktable is permissible.

At Fig. 7.20B we see a further adaptation of plunge grinding, where two diameters are ground simultaneously; once again slight oscillation or very small table traverse is permissible.

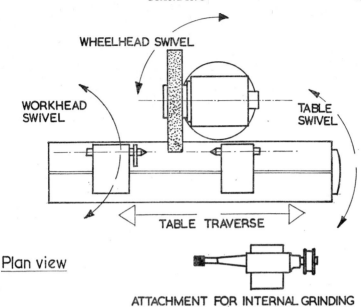

WHEELHEAD SWIVEL

WORKHEAD SWIVEL

TABLE SWIVEL

TABLE TRAVERSE

Plan view

ATTACHMENT FOR INTERNAL GRINDING

FIG. 7.21.—UNIVERSAL GRINDING MACHINE

7.17.3. Universal grinding machines

Fig. 7.21 shows a simplified plan of a universal grinding machine. This machine is capable of wheelhead swivel and also of the fitting of an internal-grinding attachment; thus the range is considerably enlarged. In order to show the range of grinding operations possible we may consider the simplified examples shown at Fig. 7.22.

A. Taper grinding with worktable swivelled for traverse grinding

The illustration shows taper grinding with the work mounted between centres. The taper is obtained by swivel of the worktable, thus allowing the use of traverse.

B. Taper grinding with wheelhead swivelled

In this example the work is held in a four-jaw chuck, the taper being obtained by swivelling the wheelhead to the angle required. No traverse is permissible. This method is suitable for grinding fast tapers, for which insufficient swivel of the worktable is available.

C. Face grinding a large-diameter component with workhead swivelled

The component is now held in a faceplate, with the workhead swivelled through 90°.

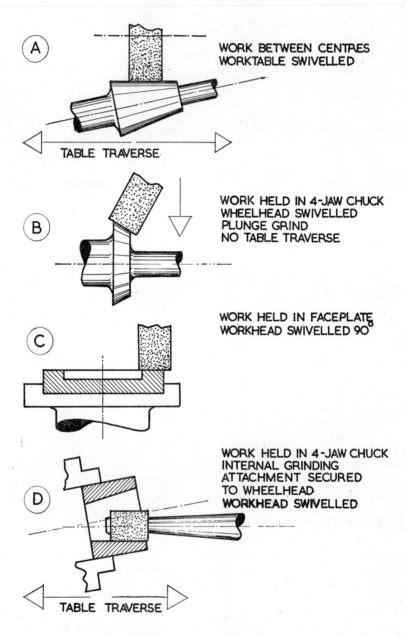

A — WORK BETWEEN CENTRES
WORKTABLE SWIVELLED

TABLE TRAVERSE

B — WORK HELD IN 4-JAW CHUCK
WHEELHEAD SWIVELLED
PLUNGE GRIND
NO TABLE TRAVERSE

C — WORK HELD IN FACEPLATE
WORKHEAD SWIVELLED 90°

D — WORK HELD IN 4-JAW CHUCK
INTERNAL GRINDING
ATTACHMENT SECURED
TO WHEELHEAD
WORKHEAD SWIVELLED

TABLE TRAVERSE

FIG. 7.22.—EXAMPLES OF UNIVERSAL GRINDING

D. Internal taper grinding with wheelhead swivelled

The internal grinding attachment is secured to the wheelhead, and the workhead is swivelled to the angle required. The work is mounted in a three- or four-jaw chuck and table traverse is used.

The above simple examples show clearly the versatility of the universal cylindrical grinding machine; in general surface finishes down to 0·1 micrometres are readily achieved.

7.18. Centreless grinding

All the grinding techniques so far described require mounting or chucking of each individual workpiece, with consequent loss of machining time. This drawback has led to the introduction of the centreless grinding technique, whereby accurate location of the workpiece is achieved without the aid of centres.

In other words the workpieces require no preliminary setting or location, and can be fed to the grinding station by gravity feed from hoppers or other loading devices. This is a great advantage when production grinding cylindrical components; modern machines are equipped for fully automatic operation, and include built-in wheel-truing devices and electronic control of the ground diameters. The principles underlying the grinding operations are similar to those used for normal cylindrical grinding and include:

(i) through-feed grinding;
(ii) plunge or infeed grinding.

At Fig. 7.23 we see the basic principle of centreless grinding. It may be noted that the work is supported on a workrest, which is given an extremely hard working surface.

The large-diameter wheel is the grinding wheel proper, grinding the surface of the workpiece, which is held between the workrest and the control wheel. The cutting action of the grinding wheel forces the workpiece down on the workrest, while the grinding pressure of the wheelhead forces the work in the direction of the control wheel. This control wheel takes no part in grinding or metal removal, although it is an abrasive wheel with a rubberised bond. It has two main purposes:

(i) to provide revolution of the workpiece;
(ii) to provide feed of the work.

The control wheel has a relatively low surface speed, between 0·25 and 1 metre per second, and this is transmitted to the workpiece by friction drive, owing to the wedging action shown in Fig. 7.24A. Note that the axis of the control wheel falls below the axis of the grinding wheel, and, in addition, the axis of the control wheel is slightly inclined, as shown in

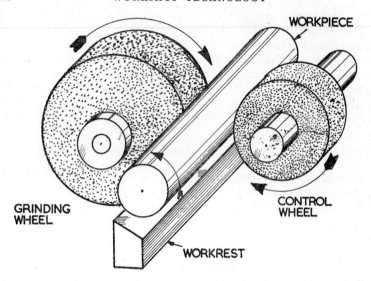

FIG. 7.23.—PRINCIPLES OF CENTRELESS GRINDING

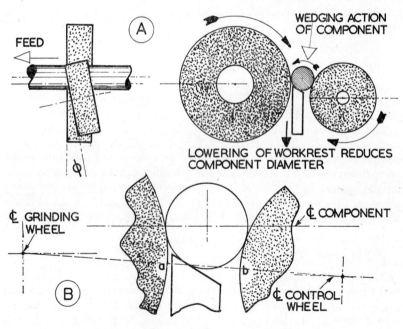

FIG. 7.24.—INCLINATION AND POSITION OF CONTROL WHEEL

the end elevation at Fig. 7.24. The value of this angle of inclination determines the rate of traverse of the workpiece between the wheels; the greater the angle, the faster the rate of traverse.

To calculate the rate of traverse given the surface speed of the control wheel and the angle of inclination, the following formula may be used:

Rate of traverse = surface speed of control wheel ×
$$\text{sine of the angle of inclination}$$

or $$F = S \sin \phi$$

where F = feed of workpiece in metres per second

S = surface speed of control wheel in metres per second

ϕ = inclination of control wheel

For example, if the control wheel has a surface speed of 0·25 metres per second, and is inclined at an angle of 1°, then,

$$F = S \sin \phi$$
$$F = 0\text{·}25 \times \text{·}0175$$
$$F = 0\text{·}004 \text{ metres per second}$$

Thus assuming a continuous feed of small cylindrical shafts 50 mm long through the grinding station, the production rate per hour is simply calculated as follows:

$$\text{Production rate per hour} = \frac{1\,000\,F \times 3\,600}{L}$$

where F = feed in metres per second

L = length of component in millimetres

$$\text{Hence production rate per hour} = \frac{1\,000 \times 0\text{·}004 \times 3\,600}{50}$$

$$= 288 \text{ per hour}$$

At Fig. 7.24B we see that the diameter of the ground workpiece depends on the position of the workpiece from a line joining the centres of the grinding wheel and the control wheel. Thus, as these centres are fixed, the smallest diameter that can be ground is represented by the distance ab. It follows, therefore, that lowering of the workrest results in a reduction in the diameter of the ground work, but if the centre of the workpiece approaches too closely to the line ab there is a risk of producing lobed diameters. This effect is caused when a high spot on the surface of the workpiece meets point b on the control wheel. If the centre of the workpiece lies along ab it will be pushed against the grinding wheel, with the result that a concave surface will be ground opposite to the high spot. To avoid this defect the centre of the workpiece is set well above the centres of the grinding and control wheels; thus a high spot meeting the control wheel will not produce a concave surface on its opposite side, and the high spot will tend to be removed when it meets the grinding wheel.

7.18.1. Examples of centreless grinding

Perhaps the following typical examples of centreless grinding on a production basis will give some idea of the high degree of efficiency obtainable from this process.

Fig. 7.25A

This is a good example of the through-feed grinding technique. The component is a hardened silver-steel shaft 40 mm long and of 3 mm diameter. The diameter of the grinding wheel is 300 mm and its width is 75 mm, while the control wheel has a diameter of 180 mm and a width of 75 mm. The components are fed automatically from a hopper, and the production rate for this job can reach 3 850 per hour. As shown in the diagram, a top plate is used to prevent the chatter likely to arise when relatively slender or small-diameter work is ground.

Fig. 7.25B

Here we see an example of plunge grinding, in this case the finish-grinding of a valve stem for an internal-combustion engine. A 500-mm-diameter grinding wheel having a width of 120 mm is used for this operation, while the control wheel has a diameter of 300 mm and a width of 120 mm. The valve stems are both loaded and ejected automatically, with the rate of loading and ejection controlled by a variable timing device. About 0·08 mm is removed and the production rate is 500 per hour to a tolerance of 0·02 mm.

Fig. 7.25c

This is yet another example of the plunge-grinding technique, carried out using a centreless grinding machine. Both the spherical radius and the tapered diameter are ground simultaneously, with about 0·02 mm removed on the spherical radius and about 0·02 mm on the taper. The profile is ground to a tolerance of 0·025 mm, with a special rotary indexing magazine used for loading and grinding. The production rate can reach 500 components per hour.

Fig. 7.25D

This example represents a typical application of the centreless grinding technique to the mass-production of ground shafts having relatively large diameters and lengths. Three diameters are to be ground on the component shown in the diagram, the tolerance on diameter is to be 0·12 mm and the roundness tolerance 0·025 mm. The centreless grinding machine

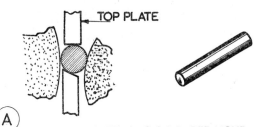

TOP PLATE

A THROUGH FEED AT 3 000 PER HOUR

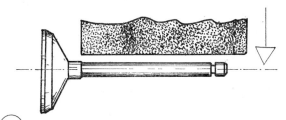

B PLUNGE GROUND AT 500 PER HOUR

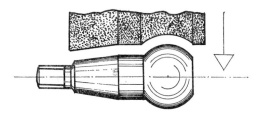

C PLUNGE GROUND AT 500 PER HOUR

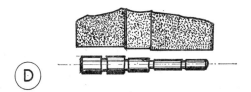

PLUNGE GROUND AT 240 PER HOUR

FIG. 7.25.—EXAMPLES OF CENTRELESS GRINDING

used for this type of work is fully automatic in operation, turning out the component at the rate of 240 per hour, and equally capable of centreless grinding shafts up to 200 mm in diameter and 300 mm long.

Summary

It is a mistake to regard the grinding process as a means of machining hard metals or cutting tools. The ultimate aim of all machining methods is the production of components having an acceptable surface finish, with dimensions within the tolerances laid down, and the grinding process is now well established for this kind of work.

We have seen in this chapter the basic principles of grinding, together with a representative selection of grinding examples, and it can be stated that, with regard to accuracy of dimensions and quality of surface finish, the grinding process has few equals in the art of engineering manufacture. The selection of grinding wheels requires a great deal of care and thought, and at all times the manufacturer's advice should be sought as to the best type of wheel to suit the operation in hand. At the same time the correct surface speed must be applied, for too fast a speed leads to reduction of the cutting forces, with the result that the wheel is unable to lose the dulled or blunted grit, and loading or glazing of the wheel surface follows, with deterioration of the ground surface. Similarly, too low a spindle speed has the effect of softening the wheel, with rapid wear and much production time lost in redressing or retruing the wheel.

We have seen, too, that in general the grinding process follows very closely the milling process with regard to the geometry of the metal-removal technique. The introduction of centreless grinding allows the mass-production of a wide range of engineering components to close limits of accuracy at high production rates. Modern grinding machines are equipped with many automatic devices, including hydraulic form dressing of the grinding wheel for profiled components, automatic control of wheelhead infeed, and automatic loading and ejection of components. While grinding machines of this type are essential for the high production of a large number of engineering components, we must not forget that the toolroom-type open surface grinder is still an indispensable machine tool, essential for the production and maintenance of the punches and dies used in press tools. We also need cutter grinding machines and jig grinding machines, both of which demand a high degree of skill and knowledge from the craftsmen who operate them.

Finally, by the very nature of their operation, all grinding machines pose serious problems with regard to the safety and welfare of the personnel responsible for their operation, for high spindle speeds are inevitable, with the consequent risk of burst or shattered wheels. This means that the use of safe wheel and pulley diameters needs to be stressed, with such information on permanent display. The products of the grinding operation, that is to say the dust and swarf, must be ducted away from the machine, so that there is no possibility of inhalation by the grinding-shop personnel, and an efficient method of ventilation must be installed and inspected at regular intervals.

Eye protection of grinding-machine operators must be rigidly enforced at all times, either by individual protection with the aid of glasses or goggles, or by suitable transparent screens fitted to the grinding machines.

EXERCISE 7

1 With neat sketches illustrate a typical application of any three of the following grinding machines:

    (i) a surface grinding machine;
    (ii) a cylindrical grinding machine;
   (iii) a cutter grinding machine;
   (iv) a centreless grinding machine.

2 Explain why face-grinding-type surface grinding machines are preferred for the production grinding of batches of small components. Sketch the essential working movements of a face-grinding machine with a rotary table and horizontal spindle.

3 Give reasons and suggest suitable remedies for the following grinding faults:

    (i) excessive wheel wear when surface grinding;
    (ii) periphery of wheel wearing convex;
   (iii) overheating or discoloration of the ground surface.

4 Describe the effects of operating an unbalanced grinding wheel. Describe a method of ensuring that a grinding wheel is balanced before proceeding to surface-grind a die.

5 Outline in some detail the standard marking scheme for grinding wheels and suggest suitable wheels for the following operations:

    (i) cutter grinding a hardened milling cutter;
    (ii) cutting off short lengths of steel bar;
   (iii) face grinding mild-steel discs;
   (iv) finish grinding a hardened plug gauge.

6 List four main factors that influence the correct choice of a grinding wheel.

7 Show, by means of neat diagrams, the self-sharpening action of a grinding wheel. What is the difference between the following:

    (i) loading and glazing;
    (ii) wheel dressing and wheel truing?

I

8 Make a neat plan view of a plain cylindrical grinding machine, showing clearly the main features and movements required for plain cylindrical grinding.

9 With neat diagrams illustrate how the following grinding operations are carried out, using a universal grinding machine:

   (i) grinding an internal taper;
  (ii) grinding a slow external taper under automatic traverse;
 (iii) plunge grinding a short fast taper.

10 With a neat diagram illustrate the principle of centreless grinding, showing clearly how the following features are achieved:

   (i) avoidance of lobed work;
  (ii) rotation of the workpiece;
 (iii) reduction in the diameter of the workpiece;
 (iv) feed of the workpiece.

8
SPECIALISED PRODUCTION TECHNIQUES

8.1. Introduction

In this chapter we shall be concerned with the more specialised production techniques, including the production of fine surfaces, jig boring, spark erosion and the testing of welded joints. All the above techniques now regularly play an important part in the manufacture of engineering components, and can no longer be considered as the ultimate in modern manufacturing methods. Indeed, it was pointed out in the preface to Volume 1 of this series that the production of surfaces by metal removal represented a wasteful process, and great attention is now being applied to the production of engineering components by metal forming. Metal-forming techniques include all types of casting, hot and cold extrusion (including impact extrusion) and hot and cold forging.

Although the above processes are outside the recommended syllabus for the Technicians' course, most are in wide use in our manufacturing industries at the present time, and the student at this stage of his studies should be aware of them. The examples shown in Fig. 8.1 are intended to give a simple appreciation of these new processes, and should be read, not for the purpose of examination passing but as a source of interest in the ever-expanding art of engineering manufacture.

Fig. 8.1A. Cold extrusion

Sometimes referred to as impact extrusion, this process was simply described in Volume 2 in connection with the mass-reproduction of thin-walled containers in aluminium. At the present time, however, the process has been extended for the production in mild steel of relatively complicated components, and Fig. 8.1A shows a typical example. This component is produced while it is in the cold state, to excellent surface finish and close dimensional accuracy. The only machining operation is the trimming of the edge as shown. Clearly the amount of waste metal is at a minimum for the following features are all produced during the impact or cold extrusion process:

(i) internal and outside diameters;
(ii) parallel knurling;
(iii) hexagonal form;
(iv) internal splines.

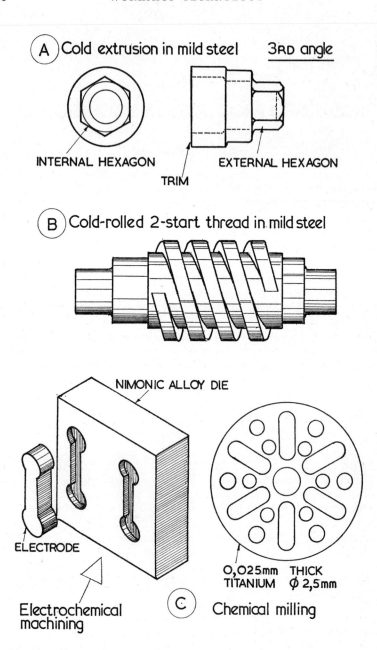

A Cold extrusion in mild steel   3RD angle

INTERNAL HEXAGON   EXTERNAL HEXAGON

TRIM

B Cold-rolled 2-start thread in mild steel

NIMONIC ALLOY DIE

ELECTRODE

Electrochemical machining

C Chemical milling

0,025mm THICK
TITANIUM Ø 2,5mm

FIG. 8.1.—EXAMPLES OF MODERN PRODUCTION TECHNIQUES

In addition, owing to the work-hardening set up by cold working the tensile strength of the mild steel increases, thus making the component stronger and more reliable, and this use of mild steel with the enhanced mechanical properties of a more expensive steel reduces cost considerably.

Fig. 8.1B. *Cold rolling*

Much ado is made about the production or machining of screw threads, both single and multi-start, but this somewhat complicated metal-removal technique finds little application in the commercial production of external screw threads. The cold rolling of screw threads extends back over a hundred years, and modern machines are capable of cold rolling threads to a high degree of accuracy and finish in a fraction of the time required for machining. This is clearly shown by reference to the example given in Fig. 8.1B, where we see a typical cold-rolled two-start thread. The blank is first machined to the effective diameter of the thread required, then highly polished thread rollers under hydraulic pressure force the metal to flow to the profile of the thread form. A smooth burnished finish results, with additional strength gained by grain-flow of the thread profile together with local work-hardening. The production of this two-start thread is completed in under one minute, while other thread-rolling machines are capable of producing threads on small components at the rate of several hundred components per minute.

Fig. 8.1c. *Electrochemical machining and chemical milling*

Electrochemical machining is now standard procedure in the manufacture of specialised components for the jet engine, an assembly demanding the use of difficult-to-machine metals such as titanium and nimonic alloys. Essentially the principle consists in the reproduction of a shaped electrode in the component. Considerable amperage is required, with a conductive solution enabling the passage of the high-amperage current to reproduce the shape of the electrode on the workpiece. The electrodes are fed into the workpiece, and there is practically no limit to the profiles or contours that can be produced by this process. At Fig. 8.1c we see a simple diagram outlining the essentials of the process.

Chemical milling provides an alternative method to the press-tool operations of blanking and piercing, and is especially suited to the manufacture of intricate components in very-thin-gauge metal. Basically the process consists in photo-etching the profile of the component on the metal sheet from which it is to be made. The metal sheet is first treated with a chemical resist which ensures the retention of the wanted parts, but allows a subsequent acid bath to remove the unwanted parts. Thus the component illustrated at Fig. 8.1c, made from titanium of 0·025 mm thickness and only 2·5 mm diameter, is speedily and most accurately produced by chemical milling. It should be clear that the manufacture of this tiny component would prove a most difficult and perhaps impossible task if attempted by any more conventional method.

It is hoped that the above simple examples of new developments in engineering manufacture will give an indication of the constant attempts made by engineers to seek and utilise new techniques and processes to meet the needs of an ever-increasing technological demand for new materials and intricacy of component shape or size. We may now, however, return to the more conventional methods of obtaining fine surface finishes.

8.2. The lapping process

We have seen in an earlier chapter that the quality of surface finish is measured by the average height of the peaks and valleys from a mean line passing through the profile of the machined surface. Because the grinding process must involve the traverse of the workpiece and the infeed of the grinding wheel, a geometrical pattern must be present on the ground

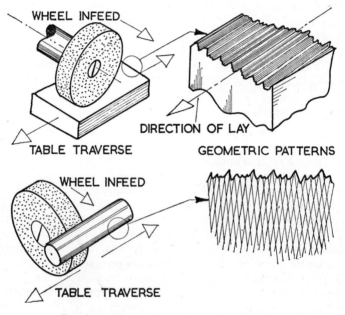

Fig. 8.2.—Surface Patterns on Ground Work

surface, and the roughness needs to be measured across the lay of the machined surface. This aspect of grinding is simply illustrated at Fig. 8.2; it is clear that while a ground surface may appear smooth it still consists of an arrangement of peaks and valleys in a fixed geometrical pattern.

Lapping is essentially a surface-finishing process, involving the removal of peaks and the reduction of the depth of valleys, thus bringing the surface closer to the ideal of perfect flatness. In other words, lapping is carried out only on surfaces that have already been brought to a high degree of finish or flatness, for as stated it is a finishing process involving fairly small amounts of metal removal. The lapping process is shown at Fig. 8.3, and as can be seen involves the use of a suitable abrasive to

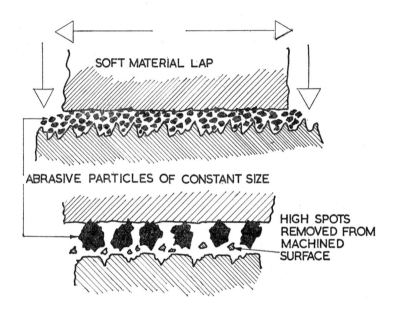

FIG. 8.3.—THE LAPPING PRINCIPLE

remove or reduce the high spots or peaks of the machined surface. If this is to be done effectively the first essential is to ensure that the size of the abrasive particles is constant; as in grinding wheels, the smaller the grain size the finer the resultant finish.

The abrasives used are similar to those employed in grinding-wheel manufacture: silicon carbide, aluminium oxide and diamond dust. To facilitate manipulation of the abrasive and to absorb fragments of metal removed by the lapping process, a light oil or other suitable lubricant is used. As lapping proceeds the paste made up of abrasive and lubricant becomes charged with metal particles which adversely affect the operation, at which point the lapping compound needs to be removed, the component thoroughly cleaned and a fresh charge of lapping compound used.

8.2.1. Lapping a true plane surface

The production of a true plane surface needs the application of a lapping process during the final stages of manufacture. A true plane surface is generated; that is to say three surfaces are needed, each of which is lapped in turn and in sequence to another, with the result that all errors of concavity or convexity are removed. This simple technique

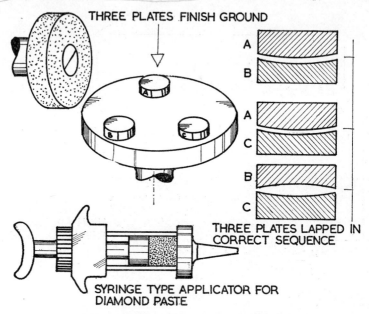

THREE PLATES FINISH GROUND

A

B

A

C

B

C

THREE PLATES LAPPED IN CORRECT SEQUENCE

SYRINGE TYPE APPLICATOR FOR DIAMOND PASTE

FIG. 8.4.—GENERATING A FLAT SURFACE

is illustrated at Fig. 8.4; it must be appreciated that every available precision method needs to be adopted to make the three surfaces as flat as possible before the final lapping process.

When the three small surface plates have been finish ground on their working surfaces they are lapped in the following sequence:

  (i) A to B;
  (ii) A to C;
  (iii) B to C.

The purpose of this is as follows. Let us assume that A has a slight convexity; lapping to B means that this convex surface of A will tend to produce the opposite effect on the surface of B, namely a concave surface. Similarly, lapping A to C produces a concave surface on C; in other words, the surface fault present on A has been transmitted in opposite to both B and C, as shown at Fig. 8.4. Hence if we now lap B and C to each other we are bringing opposite faults together and removing them. This lapping process is essentially a hand method, and flatness of the working faces only is achieved, the degree of finish being determined by the size of the abrasive used. It is customary to lap first, with a coarse abrasive, then after thorough cleaning to use a medium abrasive, and finally to finish with a very fine abrasive such as diamond paste. Diamond pastes are available in the syringe-type applicator shown at Fig. 8.4; a colour code identifies the grade or type of the paste, the finer grades having particles less than 1 micrometre in size.

Clearly the lapping of three plates to produce one is a tedious business, especially if we remember that it is essentially a hand process, and that (as in all lapping techniques) it is vital that the surface be as true as possible before commencing to lap. In this way the lapping process removes only the high peaks or geometrical pattern left by the previous machining operation. The process is much improved if the lap is made of a relatively soft material. Reference back to Fig. 8.3 shows that the abrasive grains tend to embed themselves in the softer material of the top lap, helping to keep the lapped surface free from abrasive.

8.2.2. Machine lapping

Modern lapping machines seldom make use of the grinding or lapping paste principle, as the problem of removal and replenishment of lapping paste is extremely difficult when relatively large areas require to be machine lapped. Instead the lapping paste is replaced by flat discs of extremely fine grit and soft grade. The principle is illustrated at Fig. 8.5, and it may be seen that the two circular laps lie in the same axial plane but rotate in opposite directions.

The components are constrained in a workholder which rotates with an eccentric motion as shown in the diagram, having the effect of moving each component across the faces of the laps. Once again the finish of the components will depend on the grit size of the abrasive used; such abrasives include aluminium oxide, silicon carbide and diamond dust. The parallelism of the lapped surfaces is a different matter, and if (as shown at Fig. 8.5) the axes of the laps are fixed, parallelism depends on the alignment of the laps. In other words, a very high degree of precision must exist with regard to the co-axiality of the lap centres. An alternative technique is to rely on the parallelism of the components as produced by the previous grinding operation and mount the top lap on a universal joint, thus allowing it to 'float' and hence follow the top surface provided by the components. This technique is illustrated at Fig. 8.6, where we see the production lapping of cylindrical components. In this application the top lap is floating; eight cylindrical components are given a random movement as they revolve between the faces of the laps by virtue of the eccentric rotation of the workholder.

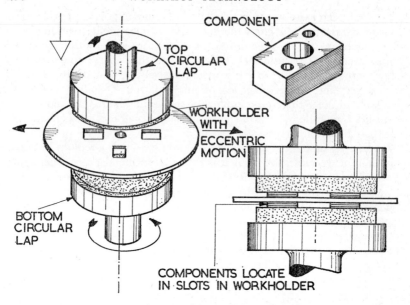

FIG. 8.5.—PRINCIPLE OF A LAPPING MACHINE

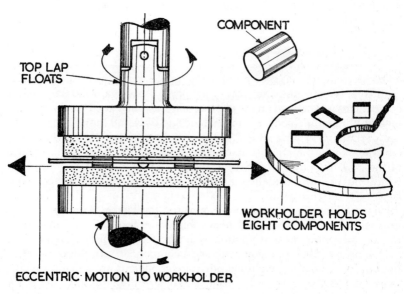

FIG. 8.6.—FLOATING HEAD LAPPING MACHINE

An alternative method of lapping an external cylindrical surface is shown at Fig. 8.7. The bar or workpiece is rotated in a centre lathe while the craftsman operates the lap by hand, traversing it slowly down the rotating bar. The body of the external lap may be made from hard wood, while the metal portion of the lap can be soft copper, lead, brass or grey cast iron. Note that the lap follows the axis of the component and will not cure or correct any geometrical misalignment of the shaft. The

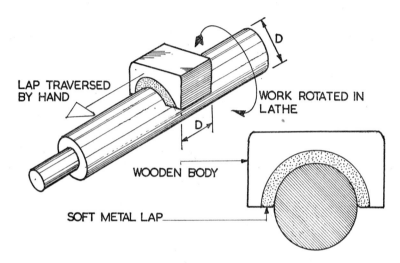

LAP TRAVERSED
BY HAND

WORK ROTATED IN
LATHE

WOODEN BODY

SOFT METAL LAP

Fig. 8.7.—Principle of External Cylindrical Lapping

purpose of lapping in this manner is the removal of the high peaks or crests left by the previous machining operation, and once again the quality of finish is determined by the grade of lapping paste. If diamond paste is used, cylindrical steel shafts in the hardened condition are readily brought to a high degree of finish in the minimum of time.

Cylindrical holes may also be lapped, but this is seldom carried out on a production basis, as the honing technique is preferred. A simple lap suitable for lapping out the odd hole can be seen at Fig. 8.8; it is very often applied in the manufacture of press tools, when heat treatment leads to a slight degree of shrinkage. Very light adjustment is possible by tapping the outer component up the slight taper machined on the body of the lap. This has the effect of opening out the outer copper lap; the process is greatly assisted by the slot cut diagonally across the copper lap, as shown in the diagram. This slot serves also the additional function of providing a reservoir or storage space for the lapping compound. In some cases the work is held by hand and fed gently to and fro on the revolving lap, in which case the lap follows the hole geometry, improving the surface finish by removal of the peaks and valleys left by the previous machining process. As in other lapping techniques the amount of metal removed is relatively small, and this has led to the adoption of the honing technique for the fine finishing of internal holes or bores.

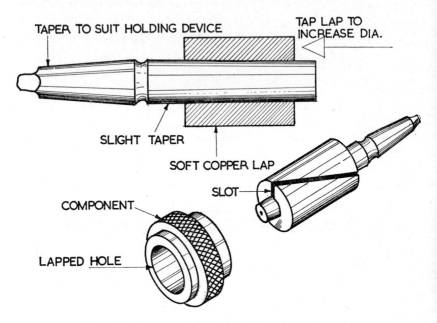

TAPER TO SUIT HOLDING DEVICE

TAP LAP TO INCREASE DIA.

SLIGHT TAPER

SOFT COPPER LAP

SLOT

COMPONENT

LAPPED HOLE

FIG. 8.8.—PRINCIPLE OF INTERNAL CYLINDRICAL LAPPING

8.3. Honing

When cylindrical holes or bores require a high degree of surface finish and accuracy, the honing process is certain to be adopted. The ever-increasing use of hydraulic power as a motivator of mechanical equipment has led to the need for cylindrical bores to be machined to close degrees of both accuracy and surface finish. This need is best appreciated by reference to Fig. 8.9, where we see the principle underlying the operation of a slave cylinder. Hydraulic oil from the master cylinder is forced under pressure into the slave cylinder, with the sole object of driving the piston in the direction of arrow Y; this piston operates perhaps a clutch or brake lever.

To ensure a leak-free system a plastic oil-resistant washer is used in the position shown in the diagram, the recess in front of the washer allowing the oil pressure to give an effective seal between the washer and the bore. Clearly the surface finish of the bore needs to be of a high order if a reliable and trouble-free life is to be expected from the assembly; a poor surface finish on the bore must result in rapid fraying or damage to the bearing face of the washer and hence in oil leaks, loss of pressure and malfunctioning of the assembly.

It is in precisely such conditions as these that the honing process is applied, the object being to achieve an acceptable surface finish together with close dimensional and geometrical accuracy. Several types of both horizontal and vertical honing machines are now available, capable of high production honing of both through and blind holes.

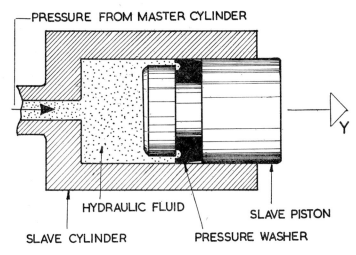

FIG. 8.9.—COMPONENT REQUIRING HONED INTERNAL DIAMETER APPLICATION OF AN INTERNAL HONE

8.3.1. The honing principle

Honing may be described as the application of abrasive sticks or hones under pressure against the surface to be honed. This principle is simply illustrated at Fig. 8.10A, where we see a plan view of a hone in a bored hole. Hones are generally equipped with three or six sticks arranged radially around the body of the hone. Provision must exist for withdrawing the sticks to insert the hone into the bore, then expanding the sticks as the honing operation commences, expansion ceasing when the desired size has been attained.

Both mechanical and hydraulic methods are used to bring about expansion of the abrasive sticks; in the production honing of large numbers of components, expansion and retraction of the sticks is completely under automatic control.

Unlike lapping, honing is capable of considerable stock removal, made possible by the use of long sticks which present a very large number of abrasive particles to the work surface, while their length also promotes correction of ovality or misalignment of the machined bore. This is shown at Fig. 8.10B, where it may be seen that slight waviness of the bored surface will be removed by the hone, but any serious misalignment will not be corrected.

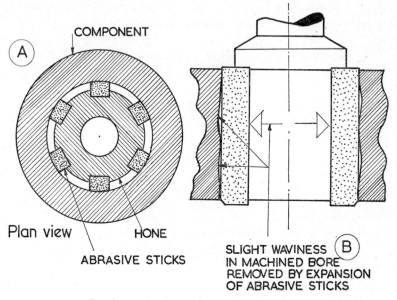

FIG. 8.10.—APPLICATION OF AN INTERNAL HONE

It is general practice to allow the hone to **float**, that is to follow the machined hole or bore. The quality of the surface finish is dependent on the grit size of the abrasive stick; the finer the grit the better the surface finish, as with grinding wheels. The usual abrasive materials are employed for the sticks, and excellent results are possible with metal-bonded diamond hones. Fig. 8.11 shows the basic technique adopted for honing cylinder liners on a production basis. The method is as follows:

A. A roughing six-stick honing head on rigid axis rough-hones a machined surface finish of about 2·5 micrometres to about 1·2 micrometres. Abrasive sticks are impregnated with diamond grit of 60/80 mesh.

B. The component is passed to a second honing machine, where a 120/140 mesh diamond grit finishing hone brings the bore of the cylinder liner to a surface finish of about 0·5 micrometres.

An appreciation of the superior qualities of diamond hones is afforded by the remarkable production runs achieved; a set of roughing and finishing hones is capable of producing upwards of 50 000 liners before requiring replacement.

Note that these liners are honed with a rigid honing head; that is to say the honing does not follow the bore, and therefore the hone corrects any fault set up in the previous boring operation. It is important that no particle of grit on the outside surface of the abrasive stick is ever allowed to repeat its previous path. This will happen if the hone is given

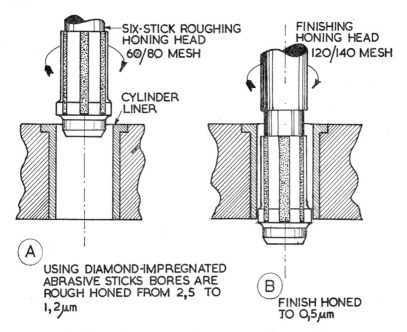

FIG. 8.11.—ROUGHING AND FINISHING WITH INTERNAL HONES

a constant movement up and down the bore in relationship to its rotation. The effect of this is to induce each particle of grit to cut its own individual helical path in the bore, leading to uneven wear of the abrasive sticks and the introduction of a helical pattern to the bore.

To avoid these undesirable effects the hone is given an end motion in addition to its rotation, the cutting particles following a figure-of-eight course and never repeating their original path.

The abrasive sticks are subject to the same considerations as grinding wheels with regard to correct choice and operating faults. Hard materials will require a hard but tough abrasive, while a more brittle abrasive can be used for softer materials. At the same time, incorrect cutting or surface speeds can lead to glazing or loading of the abrasive sticks and also to excessive wear.

8.3.2. External honing

External honing is sometimes referred to as superfinishing, and is adopted only when a high-quality finish is required. Two main techniques are in use, one applicable to work of fairly large diameter and the other to small-diameter work. The first method is shown at Fig. 8.12A,

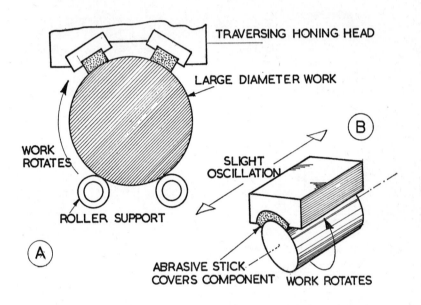

TRAVERSING HONING HEAD

LARGE DIAMETER WORK

WORK ROTATES

ROLLER SUPPORT

SLIGHT OSCILLATION

B

A

ABRASIVE STICK COVERS COMPONENT   WORK ROTATES

FIG. 8.12.—APPLICATION OF EXTERNAL HONES

where it may be seen that the work is mounted on a roller support. The honing head carries two abrasive sticks as shown, and reciprocates or traverses along the rotating workpiece. Once again the honing head is given an endways movement to prevent the abrasive sticks from honing a helical pattern on the surface of the workpiece.

At Fig. 8.12B we see the method adopted for smaller work, and this perhaps can be regarded as a true superfinishing process. In this technique the abrasive stick extends over the length of the work, and slight traverse or oscillation is permissible as in plunge grinding. A suitable coolant must be used if a mirror finish is required; the operation consists of the removal of the peaks and valleys left by previous machining. The rate of metal removal is very small, and it is essential that the best possible surface finish be obtained before any attempt is made to superfinish it.

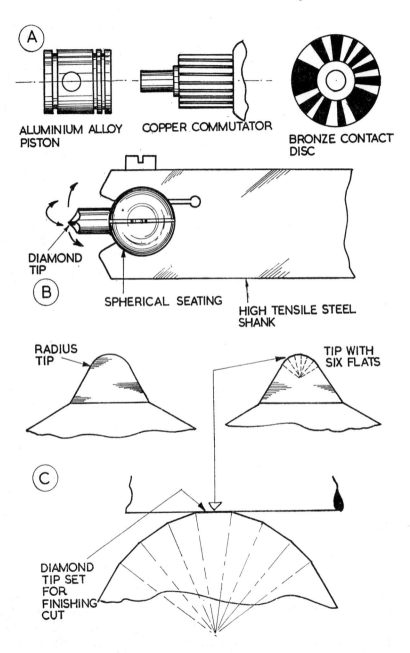

ALUMINIUM ALLOY
PISTON

COPPER COMMUTATOR

BRONZE CONTACT
DISC

DIAMOND
TIP

SPHERICAL SEATING

HIGH TENSILE STEEL
SHANK

RADIUS
TIP

TIP WITH
SIX FLATS

DIAMOND
TIP SET
FOR
FINISHING
CUT

Fig. 8.13.—Machining with Diamond-tipped Tools

8.4. Diamond turning and machining

When a superfine finish is required on a component made from a non-ferrous metal such as copper, brass, zinc, silver, gold or platinum a diamond tool is used. Suitable also for plastic and other synthetic materials, a diamond is capable of producing a mirror finish provided the proper precautions are taken with regard to the elimination of all vibrations arising from rotation of the workpiece or deflection under the cutting load. The fairly high tensile strength of most ferrous metals, together with chemical reaction and chip formation under high temperature contact conditions, makes them unsuitable for diamond machining; thus it is very seldom that steel is machined with a diamond-tipped tool.

Fig. 8.13A gives some typical examples of diamond turning; in each case a mirror finish is obtained. Note the design of the single-point cutting tool illustrated at Fig. 8.13B. The purpose of the spherical seating is to permit three-way adjustment of the diamond tips shown enlarged at Fig. 8.13c. Thus the radiused tip may be set to cut at any particular part of the profile, while the diamond-tipped tool used for finishing cuts must be set so that the flat portion of the diamond is parallel with the work axis.

Very high speeds are possible when diamond turning, but the machine tools used need to be extremely rigid and completely free from internal vibration of any kind. Light cuts of not more than 0·15 mm are the order of the day, with feeds not exceeding 0·02 mm per revolution of the workpiece. Provided the diamond tool is used with great care and under correct conditions, exceptionally long life is possible, although a reconditioning service is offered by the manufacturers.

8.4.1. Diamond burnishing

Unlike diamond turning, which removes material in the form of a chip, diamond burnishing does not involve any metal or material removal, and can therefore be readily applied to the ferrous metals such as mild and alloy steels. The process consists in the application of a rounded diamond to the revolving surface of the workpiece. Under light pressure, with traversing of the diamond-tipped tool, the peaks and irregularities are burnished or ironed out, with a work-hardened highly polished or burnished surface resulting. Not only will a burnished surface possess a superior finish, but it will also be more wear-resistant and much less likely to fracture or crack, owing to the enhanced strength and freedom from minute tool marks from which cracks or surface faults are likely to start. Fig. 8.14 illustrates the principle of diamond burnishing.

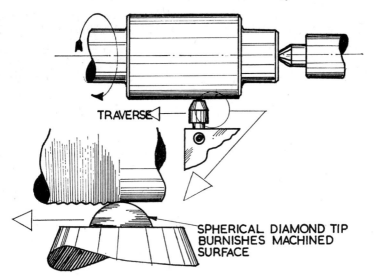

TRAVERSE

SPHERICAL DIAMOND TIP
BURNISHES MACHINED
SURFACE

FIG. 8.14.—BURNISHING WITH DIAMOND-TIPPED TOOL

8.5. Jig boring

Of all the machining operations carried out in the process of engineering manufacture, there is none as difficult as the machining of holes to accurate centre distances and diameters. The manufacture of all kinds of precision equipment such as machine tools, jigs and fixtures must

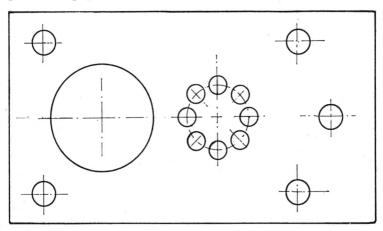

ALL TOLERANCES ± 0,005mm

FIG. 8.15.—COMPONENT REQUIRING JIG BORING

involve the accurate production of bored holes to close limits of accuracy, and for this kind of work the jig boring machine has no equal. Fig. 8.15 shows a typical example of the need for jig boring, and in this case the hole centres are held to a tolerance of plus and minus 5 micrometres.

8.5.1. Types of jig boring machine

Jig boring machines generally fall into two main types:

(i) cross-beam;
(ii) open-front.

The cross-beam type is simply illustrated at Fig. 8.16A, where it may be seen that the work spindle traverses along a rigid beam supported by two columns which enclose the table of the machine. This design promotes maximum rigidity, although the worktable is not as readily accessible as in the open-front type simply illustrated at Fig. 8.16B. For both types of machine the principle of co-ordinate positioning is adopted, and many ingenious devices are in use to ensure precise and positive movement of the worktable. Modern jig boring machines are capable of machining holes with centre distances to within 1 micrometre.

8.5.2. Principle of co-ordinate machining

By co-ordinate machining we mean the production of holes, faces or other machined profiles working from two datums at 90° to each other. We see on reference back to Fig. 8.16 that the cross-beam type of jig boring machine makes use of the following two movements:

(i) longitudinal movement of the worktable;
(ii) movement of work spindle at 90° to worktable movement.

On the other type of jig boring machine, namely the open-front machine, there is no cross movement of the work spindle; the positioning of the work is achieved by both longitudinal and cross movement of the worktable. In other words, for both types of jig boring machine rectangular co-ordinates are used to position the hole centres.

This principle is simply illustrated at Fig. 8.17, where we see a plan view of a casting fully dimensioned with rectangular co-ordinates. Face A and face B are the datum faces, and all dimensions proceed from these two faces, including the six holes on a pitch-circle diameter. Clearly the application of trigonometrical principles is needed to convert the circular spacing of the six holes to rectangular co-ordinates, but the adoption of this technique permits the whole of the machining to be carried out by precise movement or positioning of the workpiece by 90° movements of the worktable or spindle.

When the table movement is under the control of the operator it is

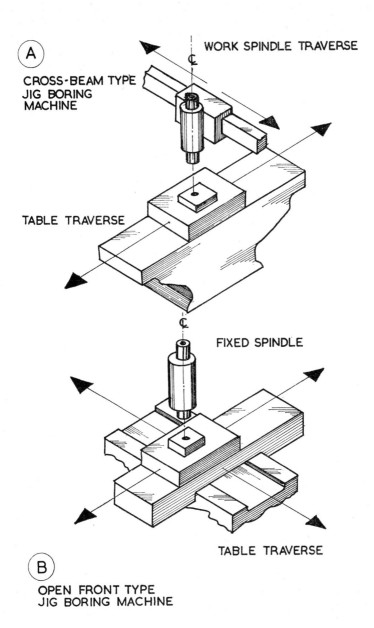

FIG. 8.16.—TYPES OF JIG-BORING MACHINES

said to be under manual control; in fact the table setting is achieved by the operator making use of either manual or optical devices. Most mechanical devices involve the use of precision rollers or slip gauges, together with dial indicators or micrometer heads reading to 2 micrometres. With optical devices, accurate engraved metal scales are attached

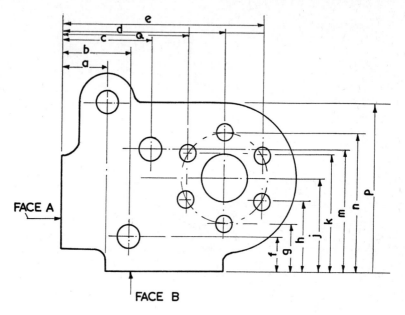

FIG. 8.17.—PRINCIPLE OF RECTANGULAR CO-ORDINATE DIMENSIONING

to the stationary slide members, allowing very positive positioning of the table by means of illuminated screens and micrometer thimbles. Jig boring machines operated under manual control are widely used for the machining of precision components such as dies used in press tools, plastic mouldings or pressure die castings, and jigs and fixtures required for the mass-production of machined components.

8.6. Numerical control of machine tools

The numerical control of machine tools is now established, by which the positioning of the worktable is achieved independently of the human element; that is to say the operator no longer has control over the movements of the workpiece or tool. Once again the principle of rectangular co-ordinates is used, and several machine tools are now available with numerical control on a three-axes system. This system is simply shown at Fig. 8.18, and it may be seen that the position of the drilled hole is achieved by automatic positioning along the X and Y axes, while the depth of the drilled hole is controlled by movement along the Z axis.

Using the principle shown, horizontal boring machines are now available capable of drilling, boring and milling using numerical control. Such machines are eminently suitable for batch or flow-line production, ensuring a high rate of production to close limits of accuracy.

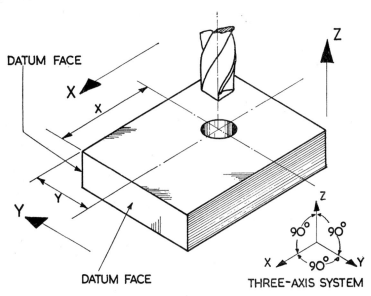

DATUM FACE

DATUM FACE   THREE-AXIS SYSTEM

Fig. 8.18.—Three-Axes System for Drilling a Hole by Numerical Control

Essentially the principle of numerical control consists in feeding information to the machine, generally by magnetic tape. This information is converted into linear movement of the table, with an extremely accurate degree of response, and in this way the milling of slots and faces and the drilling and boring of holes in relation to milled faces is achieved solely through the movement or positioning of the worktable in response to information fed to the machine. Clearly this information is reproduced in terms of rectangular co-ordinates, and it is also clear that this technique can be readily applied to most forms of metal removal and manipulation. For example, the production of turned parts on a centre or capstan lathe results from two rectangular co-ordinates, namely:

(i) traverse of the tool to give the length of the turned part;
(ii) infeed of the tool to give the diameter of the turned part.

This is simply shown at Fig. 8.19, and it is clear that if we are able to feed the necessary information to the centre lathe, thus controlling the tool movements both parallel with the work axis and at 90° to the axis, numerical control of the centre lathe is achieved, resulting in the fully automatic production of turned components. Numerically controlled centre lathes are now available, invaluable for the mass-production of the larger-type machined component.

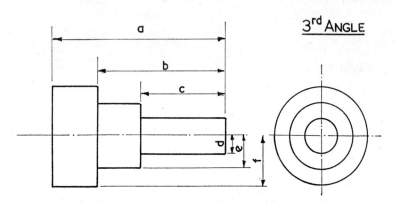

FIG. 8.19.—DIMENSIONS CONTROLLING AUTOMATIC TURNING

In addition, the following machine tools are now also available with numerical control:

(i) vertical milling machines;
(ii) horizontal milling machines;
(iii) drilling machines;
(iv) horizontal and vertical boring machines;
(v) jig boring machines.

The above list is by no means comprehensive, and much attention is now being applied to the use of numerical control for processes concerned with the manipulation of metals. Such processes include rolling, forging, forming and extrusion, all calculated to produce the shape or form required without resource to the more expensive method of metal removal as practised by the standard type of machine tool. In all cases the object is the complete elimination of the human element from the setting or positioning of the worktable or forming tool. Numerical control is readily applied also to the handling of materials or components; thus it is evident that complete automation of machined dimensions, with automatic handling from one stage of manufacture to another, is only a question of time, with numerical control providing the key to the complete sequence of operations involved in the efficient and economic manufacture of all types of component.

8.7. Spark machining

The working of metals by spark machining is now an established procedure. The importance of the spark-machining technique lies in its ability to erode extremely hard materials such as tungsten carbide and hardened die steels. An unusual feature of the process is that there is no physical contact between the eroding or cutting element, called the electrode, and the workpiece. Cutting stresses normally associated with orthodox machining are not present during spark machining, and this means that slender or delicate work may be spark machined with little risk of fracture. The scope of spark machining extends over a wide range of components, including:

(i) extrusion dies;
(ii) forging dies;
(iii) dies for plastic and rubber components;
(iv) dies for press tools;
(v) coining and embossing dies.

It can be seen that most of the operations given above consist in the production of a profile of relatively complex form in a hardened steel die, and in many cases the profile is three-dimensional.

Fig. 8.20 shows a typical three-dimensional form machined in an alloy-steel die, and it is clear that a considerable degree of skill is required from the craftsman if the cavity is to be machined to close limits of

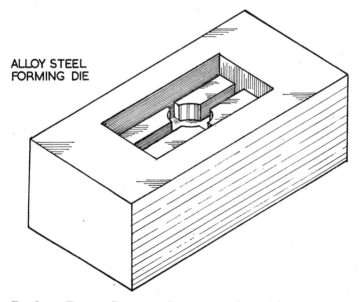

ALLOY STEEL
FORMING DIE

Fig. 8.20.—Typical Component Produced by Spark Machining

accuracy. Such work is more commonly known as die-sinking, essentially a time-consuming, highly skilled and therefore expensive method of manufacture. It is precisely this class of work that the spark-machining process replaces with great effectiveness, producing complex forms in the hardest of steels in a fraction of the time required by the more conventional method of die-sinking.

Spark machining is essentially a metal-removing process. This metal removal is achieved by the combined energy of the spark discharge from a shaped electrode. Firstly, the heat of the spark discharge causes fusion of small areas of the workpiece, and secondly, the large current density results in repulsion of the heated particles from the workpiece. Both the electrode and the workpiece to be spark machined must be electrical conductors. The spark-machining principle is illustrated at Fig. 8.21A, and the following notes will help to simplify the process.

1. *Workhead with Servomotor*

The purpose of the workhead is to provide a suitable location for the electrode, and any simple workholding device may be used. The purpose of the servomotor is to provide vertical feed of the electrode, and at the same time maintain the correct gap between the electrode and the workpiece. The greater the gap, the greater the spark intensity, with an increased rate of metal erosion; hence a gap of about 0·25 mm may be used for roughing or maximum metal removal and a gap of about 0·02 mm for finishing.

2. *Electrode*

The electrode must be made from an electrical conductor, and copper is an obvious choice. At Fig. 8.21B we see the two main functions of the electrode, namely forming and piercing. In forming, the shape or profile of the electrode is reproduced on the workpiece, and this technique is always used for the manufacture of moulds and dies. Copper and brass are most used for this class of work; a roughing electrode is used to give rapid metal erosion, and a series of finishing electrodes follow according to the degree of accuracy required. For a piercing operation, similar to that shown at Fig. 8.21B, a harder electrode is required, and a sintered material with about 70 per cent copper and 30 per cent tungsten is employed. This has excellent wearing properties and so can be used for dies and tools of high precision.

3. *Dielectric fluid*

It may be seen from the diagram at Fig. 8.21A that the whole operation takes place while both electrode and workpiece are immersed in a dielectric fluid. This fluid is essentially an insulator and provides the correct conditions for the spark discharge. In addition the dielectric fluid helps carry the eroded particles away from the spark discharge area.

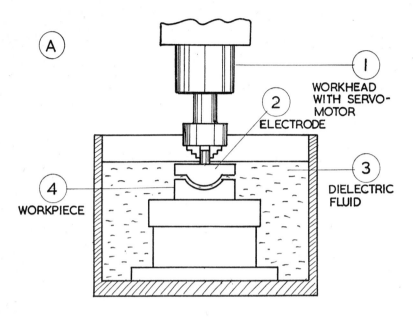

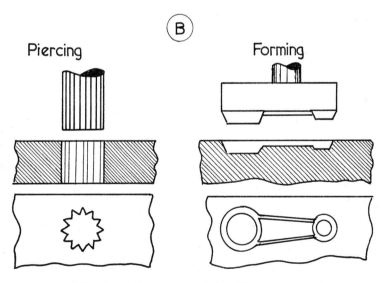

FIG. 8.21.—PRINCIPLE OF SPARK MACHINING

4. *Workpiece*

As stated, it is an essential condition that the workpiece be an electrical conductor. The hardness of the workpiece is of little importance, as a copper electrode will erode a tungsten-carbide die with little trouble, and as there is no actual contact between the electrode and the workpiece there is little risk of fracture or damage of the die during the spark-machining process.

8.7.2. Cutting rate and surface finish

The cutting rate depends on two main factors:
   (i) intensity of spark discharge;
   (ii) material to be spark machined.

Most spark-erosion machines are fitted with a simple selector switch, allowing immediate choice of a suitable spark intensity. The greater the spark intensity, the faster will be the rate of metal removal, but the surface finish will suffer as a result. It is therefore more economical to rough out first with a roughing electrode employing a relatively high spark intensity together with a fast cutting rate. This ensures rapid metal removal, although the surface finish will be poor. This roughing operation, however, may be followed by a finishing operation, where a more precise electrode is used with a reduced gap and spark intensity, resulting in a much better finish on the workpiece.

Material	*Machinability*
Tungsten carbide	1
Mild steel	$2-2\frac{1}{2}$
Hardened steel	$2\frac{1}{2}-3$
Nimonic	$2\frac{1}{2}-3$
Brass	4–6
Aluminium	4–6

TABLE 8.1. Metal-removal rates when spark machining.

Under suitable conditions, the surface finish obtained with a finishing cut can be as low as 0·2 micrometres on a tungsten-carbide die, the surface having a matt or non-reflective appearance. This type of surface, however, is easily brought to a highly polished finish by the application of suitable polishing powders or very fine diamond paste.

The non-ferrous metals such as brass and aluminium can be spark machined at much higher rates than mild or alloy steels, while tungsten carbide requires more time than any of the metals mentioned above.

If we take the machinability of tungsten carbide as unity or 1, using the spark-machining process, then Table 8.1 may be used to give an indication of the machining rates of the other metals.

For example, aluminium or brass may be spark machined about five times as fast as tungsten carbide, while a nimonic alloy could be spark machined about three times as fast. Nimonic alloys are much used for those parts of jet engines that are subject to considerable rise in temperature, for example the flame tubes, where it is of vital importance that the physical or mechanical properties of such components do not deteriorate as a result. Nimonic alloys are not easy to machine, especially if a relatively complicated form or profile is required; hence spark machining provides an alternative method of machining.

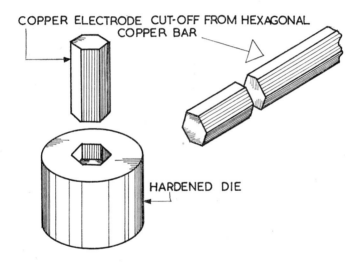

COPPER ELECTRODE CUT-OFF FROM HEXAGONAL COPPER BAR

HARDENED DIE

FIG. 8.22.—USE OF STANDARD SECTIONS FOR ELECTRODES

8.7.3. Examples of spark machining

1. *Heading die in hardened alloy tool steel*

This example shows how the electrode may be easily available from standard sections. In other words, the electrode is made from hexagonal copper bar, and thus practically no machining of the electrode is needed. Fig. 8.22 shows the heading die together with the copper electrode used to spark machine the cavity.

2. Pressure die casting insert in hardened alloy steel

While great accuracy is not needed in the previous example, as the limits on commercial nuts and bolts are generous, the die insert illustrated at Fig. 8.23 needs to be produced to fairly close limits of accuracy with a good sharp impression or cavity.

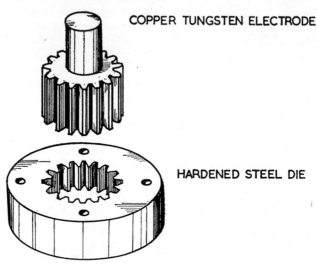

COPPER TUNGSTEN ELECTRODE

HARDENED STEEL DIE

FIG. 8.23.—SPARK MACHINING A PRECISION DIE

For spark machining this die three copper–tungsten electrodes are used, one rougher, one semi-finisher and one finisher. Copper–tungsten is preferred to copper because the relatively sharp nature of the profile calls for a hard-wearing electrode material. It must be appreciated that in this example the electrodes have to be machined to a considerable degree of accuracy.

In any event the machining of the die shown in Fig. 8.23 by the spark-machining process is infinitely superior to the more conventional technique of die-sinking, because the die can be spark machined while in the hardened state. This is not possible in die-sinking, where the die must be hardened afterwards, with the likelihood of shrinkage or distortion during the heat-treatment process.

In addition, renovation of the die profile is a fairly simple matter when spark machining, as it is necessary only to apply the finishing electrode for a short while to the worn die.

3. Press-tool die in alloy steel

In this example a dual purpose is served by spark machining. Firstly, the die aperture is spark machined, and secondly, this aperture mates with

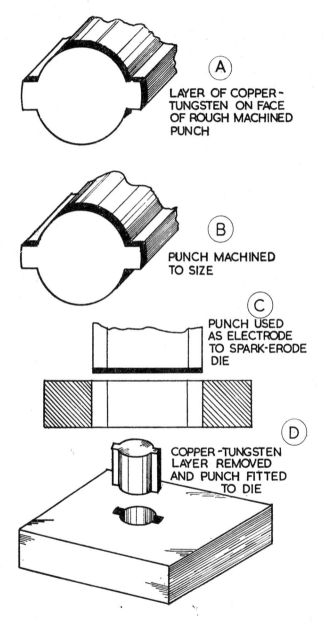

FIG. 8.24.—USE OF PUNCH TO SPARK MACHINE APERTURE IN DIE

the punch without any further fitting or machining. The technique is simply illustrated at Fig. 8.24, and the stages of manufacture are as follows:

A. Copper–tungsten is applied to the top of the punch block as a layer of brazed metal.
B. The punch is machined to size together with the layer of electrode.
C. The punch used as an electrode to spark machine the die.
D. The layer of copper–tungsten removed, the punch is hardened and tempered ready for assembly with the die.

All the above stages are simply illustrated at Fig. 8.24, showing once again the versatility of the spark-machining technique.

4. *Extruding die in tungsten carbide*

Fig. 8.25 shows a die used to produce a complicated extruded section in aluminium alloy. This section is produced by forcing a heated aluminium-alloy billet through the tungsten–carbide die, the die orifice being spark machined using copper–tungsten electrodes for both roughing and finishing.

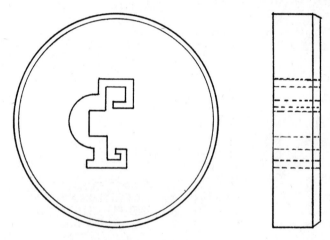

Fig. 8.25.—Spark Machined Extruding Die

8.7.4. Types of spark-erosion machine

There is a wide range of spark-erosion machines available, including small bench-type machines suitable for precision toolroom work. These machines are equipped with co-ordinate slides, allowing movement of the servo-head to within 0·02 mm by means of vernier scales. Here we see another example of the use of rectangular co-ordinates, for with a circular copper electrode it is an easy matter to spark machine holes to accurate centre distances in hardened die steels or tungsten carbide.

Fig. 8.26 shows a simple outline of the bench-type spark-erosion machine, and an interesting point is that this machine can be connected to an ordinary single-phase supply system using a 13-amp plug. This simple spark-erosion machine is most suitable for the average run of work in a small toolroom or die-making shop and is easily set up for spark machining holes, profiles and even removing broken taps from dies.

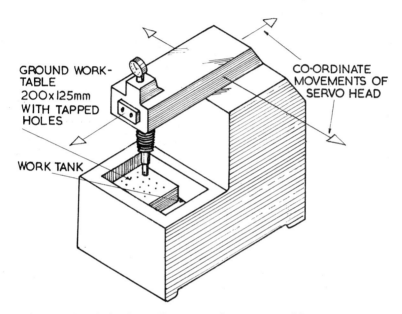

GROUND WORK-TABLE 200x125mm WITH TAPPED HOLES

CO-ORDINATE MOVEMENTS OF SERVO HEAD

WORK TANK

FIG. 8.26.—SMALL BENCH-TYPE SPARK-EROSION MACHINE

A medium-sized spark-erosion machine is simply illustrated at Fig. 8.27, and this type of machine is better suited as a production unit, although it may be used for the larger size of precision work associated with toolroom or diemaking practice.

The large work tank houses a worktable of about 450 mm by 380 mm, and seven different cutting rates are available to suit the particular spark-machining job to hand.

The largest-size spark-erosion machines are specially designed both to manufacture and to recondition large forging dies. Such a machine can accommodate a forging die of the following dimensions:

700 mm long, 500 mm wide, 380 mm deep.

In general, such machines are equipped with the minimum of controls, allowing easy operation. Once set up, the machine will spark-machine under automatic control and cease when a predetermined depth has been attained.

It may be appreciated at this stage that spark machining is now an accomplished method of metal removal, fast replacing the more conventional metal-removing techniques, and it is certain that spark erosion has a great part to play in the manufacture of dies required for plastic mouldings, pressure die castings, extrusions and forgings.

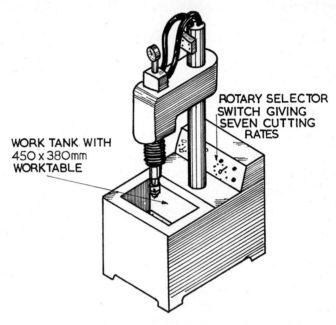

WORK TANK WITH
450 x 380mm
WORKTABLE

ROTARY SELECTOR
SWITCH GIVING
SEVEN CUTTING
RATES

FIG. 8.27.—LARGE CAPACITY SPARK-EROSION MACHINE

8.8. Crack detection

The behaviour of metal when cast in the molten state, hot forged, hot extruded and cold worked is difficult to predict, and the strictest checks need to be maintained to ensure that faulty components are not passed to the production line and hence to the customer.

Any crack which is present on the surface of a stressed component is likely to lead to subsequent failure, while a crack or void within the metal is certain to produce the same undesirable result. Hence two problems face the engineer:

(i) the detection of surface cracks;
(ii) the detection of internal cracks, faults or voids.

In both cases a non-destructive method is needed; that is to say, a crack detection technique which involves no deformation, damage or destruction of the component under test.

8.8.1. Detection of surface cracks

A popular method of detecting surface cracks was simply described in *T.3 Workshop Technology*, Chapter 1, the principle consisting in the use of magnetic particles, usually iron filings. An essential condition is that the material to be tested must be magnetic and this limits the application of this technique to the ferrous metals.

Dry magnetic crack detection

This technique is best suited for welds, large forgings and castings. Three types of magnetic powders are in common use as follows.

(i) *Grey powder.* This is the most widely used colour, and gives good results on most surfaces under normal lighting conditions.

(ii) *Black powder.* Suitable for use on shot-blasted or finish-machined components.

(iii) *Red powder.* Another general-purpose powder, suitable for most surfaces.

The powder is applied to the surface under test while the component is magnetised, excess powder being removed by blowing or tapping the component. Fig. 8.28A shows a typical flash-loop magnetic crack detector which is completely portable. With the cable looped around the specimen longitudinal magnetisation is induced, thus revealing cracks in the direction shown at Fig. 8.28B.

When circular magnetisation is required, as shown at Fig. 8.28c, a pair of electrodes is applied at both ends of the specimen as shown, revealing any surface cracks parallel with the work axis.

Wet magnetic crack detection

In this process a suitable bath is prepared in which the magnetic particles are highly mobile in an oil suspension. This technique is best suited to the detection of surface cracks on finished components. The surfaces to be tested must be free from grease, dirt or scale before immersion in the bath. On removal they are magnetised with the current passed first around and then along the shaft. In this way magnetic particles will collect in the vicinity of any surface cracks both parallel and at right angles to the shaft axis.

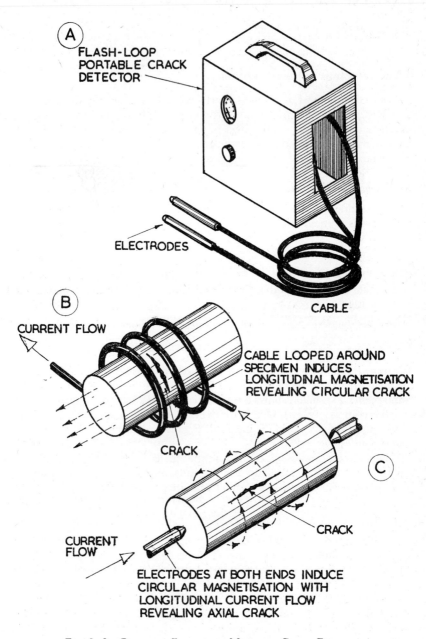

A FLASH-LOOP PORTABLE CRACK DETECTOR

ELECTRODES

CABLE

B CURRENT FLOW

CABLE LOOPED AROUND SPECIMEN INDUCES LONGITUDINAL MAGNETISATION REVEALING CIRCULAR CRACK

CRACK

C

CRACK

CURRENT FLOW

ELECTRODES AT BOTH ENDS INDUCE CIRCULAR MAGNETISATION WITH LONGITUDINAL CURRENT FLOW REVEALING AXIAL CRACK

Fig. 8.28.—Portable Flash-loop Magnetic Crack Detector

Crack detection by penetrant methods

This technique may be used for the detection of surface cracks on non-metallic materials such as plastics and also non-ferrous or non-magnetic metals such as aluminium alloy or zinc-based components produced by pressure die casting. Essentially the technique consists of

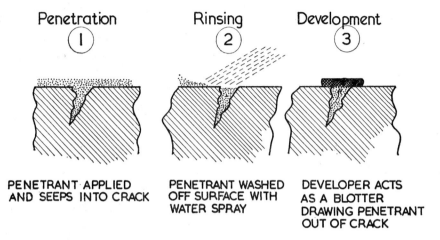

Penetration ①	Rinsing ②	Development ③
PENETRANT APPLIED AND SEEPS INTO CRACK	PENETRANT WASHED OFF SURFACE WITH WATER SPRAY	DEVELOPER ACTS AS A BLOTTER DRAWING PENETRANT OUT OF CRACK

FIG. 8.29.—PRINCIPLE OF CRACK DETECTION BY PENETRANT METHODS

the application of a suitable penetrant to the specimen and, after a suitable interval of time, applying a developer after washing away the excess penetrant. This principle is simply illustrated at Fig. 8.29 where we see the sequence of operations:

1. When the penetrant is applied it seeps into the surface crack.

2. The application of a fine water spray washes away the excess penetrant from the surface of the specimen, but residual penetrant remains in the crack.

3. The application of a developer acts like a blotter, drawing out the penetrant from the crack and thus revealing the presence of cracks that would not otherwise be visible to the naked eye.

Once again the specimen to be tested must be free from all grease or foreign matter, and after completion of the test it is necessary to rinse the specimen thoroughly. To assist in the detection of the surface cracks a bright red penetrant may be used, while the purpose of the developer is to draw out the penetrant from the very finest defects or hair cracks.

Fluorescent dyes may also be added to the penetrant and also to magnetic particles, the detection procedure being carried out in a specially constructed booth equipped with ultra-violet lighting; this technique greatly assists and speeds up the process of crack detection on mass-produced components.

8.8.2. Detection of internal cracks and defects

So far we have dealt with the techniques adopted to ensure that no surface cracks are present on components that may have been produced by extrusion, casting or forging. It must be appreciated that all the methods so far described are **non-destructive**; that is to say, it is not necessary to machine or otherwise cut up the component to discover any defects that may be present on the surface layers.

The detection of internal defects, such as piping, blowholes or porosity in forgings or castings by non-destructive methods is a highly specialised field, demanding the application of one of the following techniques:

(i) radiography;
(ii) ultrasonics.

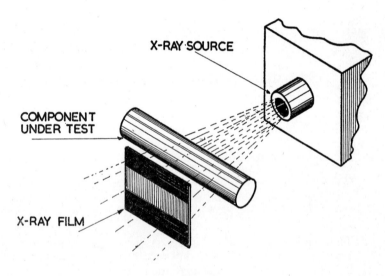

FIG. 8.30.—PRINCIPLE OF CRACK DETECTION BY X-RAYS

Radiography techniques in non-destructive testing

Probably the most widely used radiography technique is the application of X-rays. This technique is most suitable when a permanent record of the component quality is required, for by the X-ray technique a picture or record of the internal structure is made available. A simple diagram illustrating the X-ray technique may be seen at Fig. 8.30, and it may be appreciated that the following considerations apply to the detection of faults:

(i) An X-ray film must be positioned behind the component.
(ii) The component is subjected to radiation from an X-ray source.
(iii) The absence of any internal faults such as porosity, cracks, blow-holes, shrinkage or cavitation results in a picture of the component having uniform density of light when the negative is suitably processed or developed.

For example, Fig. 8.31A shows a simple casting, while at Fig. 8.31B we see two radiographs of such a casting resulting from X-ray treatment. On the left we see a radiograph of a sound casting free from any defect or fault. On the right, however, the radiograph reveals cavities caused by unequal cooling rates.

On the negative film the cavities appear as dark areas, caused by the fact that the X-rays have less metal to penetrate and strike the film with greater intensity than those rays which have passed those sections of the casting free from any internal defect. A developed picture of the negative would, of course, reveal the defects or cavities as lighter areas, as shown in the diagram at Fig. 8.31B.

X-ray equipment available covers fixed installations capable of detecting internal faults in components through 80 mm of steel, and greater thicknesses of less dense metals, while portable equipment is available which can be taken to castings or machinery requiring non-destructive testing.

Gamma radiography

This technique is similar in principle to X-ray radiography, except that a small pellet of radio-active material is used to emit the radiation. This radiation is directed through the component under test, and allowed to fall on X-ray film, any defects showing up on the developed film, which provides a permanent record of the inspection test.

This type of equipment is sturdy, compact and easily portable, and is ideally suited to the inspection of outside jobs such as welding on construction sites or pipe-lines. The use of gamma rays allows also the inspection of steel castings or forgings up to 250 mm in thickness, but the resulting picture lacks the sharpness or clarity of an X-ray exposure.

Ultrasonics

We have seen in the preceding notes that the application of radiography techniques requires that an X-ray film be placed behind the component or section under test. When this is not possible, as with some parts of forgings and castings, the ultrasonic test may be applied. The principle is essentially that of echo-sounding, in which high-frequency sound waves

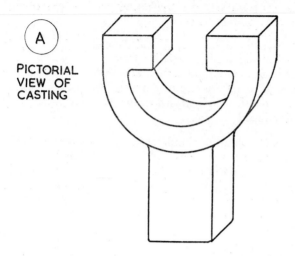

A

PICTORIAL
VIEW OF
CASTING

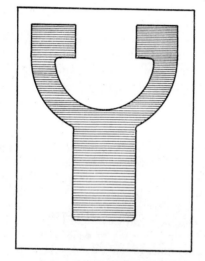

RADIOGRAPH OF CASTING
SHOWING NO INTERNAL
FAULTS

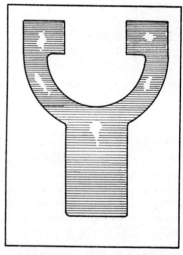

RADIOGRAPH OF FAULTY
CASTING SHOWING INTERNAL
CAVITIES CAUSED BY
UNEQUAL COOLING RATES

B

FIG. 8.31.—USE OF RADIOGRAPHS TO REVEAL FAULTS

are passed through the test piece and then transmitted back to a receiving device in the form of a cathode-ray tube.

A sound section of metal, free from any internal defect such as a cavity, blowhole or other fault, shows up as a regular pulse on the screen of the

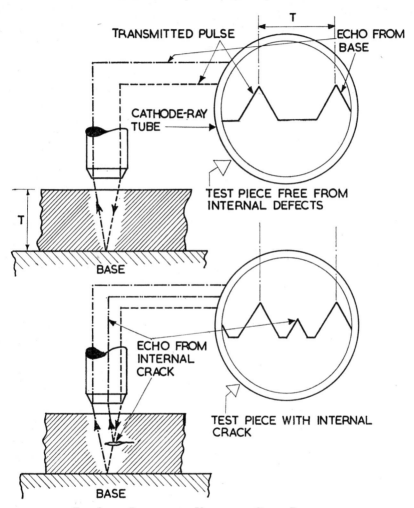

Fig. 8.32.—Principle of Ultrasonic Crack Detection

cathode-ray tube, as simply illustrated at Fig. 8.32, while any discontinuity in the section results in an additional pulse as the ultrasonic waves strike the bottom part of the fault. Thus the appearance of an intermediate pulse on the cathode-ray screen reveals an internal defect in the specimen under test. This technique may be readily applied in those cases where radiography is not possible, for example in the non-destructive testing of enclosed vessels such as large-diameter pipe welds, or for checking the soundness of boiler plates.

SUMMARY

It cannot be emphasised too often that it is the business of engineers to make things. The material needs of a modern society increase with each passing day, and if products are to sell in world markets it is essential that they are manufactured using every new technique or development available.

We have seen in this chapter, some of the newer technologies applied to engineering manufacture, and it is the ultimate responsibility of a mechanical engineering technician to ensure that the process or manufacturing sequence under his control is carried out with the minimum delay, and with immediate recognition of errors or faults, together with the application of proper remedial action.

It is clear that the complexity of the more modern production techniques such as chemical milling or electrochemical machining is such that the technician can hope only for a simple grasp of the basic principles underlying the engineering application of the process, and the main aim of this chapter is to present these newer production techniques in a simple and practical manner.

In this way, the technician will at least be familiar with the process and, what is more important, appreciate its purpose and the kind of work or finish expected. It is strongly urged that at all times the technician makes the fullest possible use of the excellent information and literature always made available by the manufacturers of the equipment described in this chapter. For unlike college lecturers, these are the people in real and live contact with the problems and difficulties associated with the economical manufacture of engineering products to high standards of accuracy and quality.

Nevertheless it is hoped, that not only this final chapter but also the three preceding volumes of the Technician Series have been of assistance in promoting and stimulating interest in the ever-fascinating art of engineering manufacture.

EXERCISE 8

1 Make a neat sketch of a component that can be produced by impact extrusion, outlining the economic advantages of this process.

2 Explain the difference between electro-chemical machining and chemical milling, giving in each case a typical application of the process.

3 Make neat sketches of the principles underlying the application of the following fine-finishing techniques:

(i) machine lapping;
(ii) machine honing.

Make neat sketches of simple engineering components that would require the application of the above processes, explaining the need for the fine finishes so produced.

4 With a neat sketch illustrate the application of a diamond-tipped tool for the superfinishing of an engineering component.

5 With neat sketches illustrate the essential movements of an open-front type of jig boring machine, and explain how the principle of rectangular co-ordinates may be applied to the precision machining of an engineering component.

6 In simple terms, explain the principle underlying the application of numerical control of machine tools.

7 With the aid of a neat diagram, outline the technique of spark machining, giving a practical example of the type of component for which the process is ideally suited.

8 Give a practical method of detecting any internal defects in a medium-sized steel forging without any destruction or damage to the forging under test.

9 Describe suitable non-destructive testing techniques calculated to detect surface cracks in the following products:

(i) mass-produced drop-arms for motor-car suspension units, produced as drop-forgings;
(ii) a large cast-iron casting of cylindrical shape.

10 Explain the essential difference between ultrasonic testing and X-ray testing for the detection of internal defects in engineering components, illustrating a typical application of each technique.

INDEX

Numbers in bold type refer to illustrations